FOUNDATIONS OF ENGINEERING
Series Editor: G.E. Drabble

Electric Circuits

Peter Silvester
Lecturer
Department of Engineering
Lancaster University

First published 1993 by
THE MACMILLAN PRESS LTD
Houndmills, Basingstoke, Hampshire RG21 2XS
and London
Companies and representatives
throughout the world

Printed in Hong Kong

ISBN 0–333–48077–5

A catalogue record for this book is
available from the British Library

To my Mother
who taught me the value of a good book

CONTENTS

SERIES EDITOR'S FOREWORD

This series of programmed texts has been written specifically for first year students on degree courses in engineering. Each book covers one of the core subjects required by electrical, mechanical, civil or general engineering students, and the contents have been designed to match the first year requirements of most universities and polytechnics.

The layout of the texts is based on that of the well-known text, *Engineering Mathematics* by K. Stroud (first published by Macmillan in 1970, and now in its third edition). The remarkable success of this book owes much to the skill of its author, but it also shows that students greatly appreciate a book which aims primarily to help them to learn their chosen subjects at their own pace. The authors of this present series acknowledge their debt to Mr Stroud, and hope that by adapting his style and methods to their own subjects they have produced equally helpful and popular texts.

Before publication of each text the comments of a class of first year students, of some recent engineering graduates and of some lecturers in the field have been obtained. These helped to identify any points which were particularly difficult or obscure to the average reader or which were technically inaccurate or misleading. Subsequent revisions have eliminated the difficulties which were highlighted at this stage, but it is likely that, despite these efforts, a few may have passed unnoticed. For this the authors and publishers apologise, and would welcome criticisms and suggestions from readers.

Readers should bear in mind that mastering any engineering subject requires considerable effort. The aim of these texts is to present the material as simply as possible and in a way which enables students to learn at their own pace, to gain confidence and to check their understanding. The responsibility for learning is, however, still very much their own.

G.E. DRABBLE

AUTHOR'S PREFACE

Engineers are interested in designing and making things which will work. To do this they must first understand the principles behind the operation of the things they are designing with and then put this knowledge to use in the construction of useful artefacts. The main tool they use in acquiring this understanding is Mathematics. The first step in trying to understand how something works is to try to build a 'mathematical model' of it. Physical principles are described in the language of mathematics and equations are written to represent the behaviour of devices which operate according to those principles. It is very important to develop a technique for writing correct equations so Programme 1 introduces you to a way of improving your chances of doing this first time. You should try to master the skills described in this programme and then apply them to all the remaining programmes in the text and, in fact, to all the equations you ever write in future!

Programmes 2 and 3 lay the foundations for all the remaining programmes. Energy sources which provide direct (that is, unchanging) voltages and currents are discussed and mathematical models to represent them introduced. Resistors (components which can conduct the flow of direct currents) are described and the basic rules introduced which allow designers to analyse circuits made up with resistors and direct current and voltage sources. Many examples of these 'resistive' circuits are analysed and many different techniques for analysing them introduced. In the revision questions throughout the programmes and in the tests at the ends you can practise the skills you acquire as you go along. The further questions provide more chances for you to practise these analytical techniques but also include a number of examples where you will have the opportunity to put the skills to use in a design context. In later programmes you will learn how to use very similar techniques to analyse the behaviour of a much wider range of circuits so it is vital that you understand these two programmes before proceeding.

In Programme 4 you will learn how to write mathematical models that describe the behaviour of time-varying electrical quantities. A particularly important group of time-varying quantities, steady-state sinusoidal 'signals', is introduced and phasor analysis, a kind of shorthand technique for analysing these signals, is explained. Two further circuit components, capacitors and inductors, are introduced and the steady-state behaviour of circuits containing them analysed.

Another extremely powerful method of circuit analysis known as j-notation is introduced in Programme 5. Complex numbers, when applied to phasor analysis, make the technique even more useful and allow circuits containing resistors, capacitors and inductors to be analysed as if they contained only resistors. All the analytical techniques used in Programmes 1 and 2 can therefore be employed and results which would otherwise be relatively difficult to obtain are produced quite easily.

Two important properties of circuits which process time-varying signals, their 'Frequency and Phase responses', are described in Programme 6. These properties are defined and ways of calculating them using the circuit techniques already learnt covered in detail. The frequency and phase responses of a range of circuits are then derived. The use of logarithmic graph paper to plot the responses is explained.

A more general method of circuit analysis is introduced in Programme 7. The use of differential equations allows any circuit with any kind of excitation to be analysed. The method is particularly useful in describing what happens to a circuit when the energy source which is used to excite it is subject to a sudden change. It can also, however, be used to derive the steady-state 'response' of a circuit and the way in which this technique links back to the methods used in Programmes 4 and 5 is illustrated.

PETER SILVESTER

HOW TO USE THIS BOOK

This book contains seven 'programmes'. Each programme is a self-contained unit of study which deals with one specific topic. However as the later programmes build on material studied in earlier parts of the book, you are advised to work systematically through the text studying the programmes in the given sequence.

You *must* start at the beginning of and work sequentially through each programme. Every programme is subdivided into a number of short 'frames', each of which contains a limited quantity of information. The frames are designed to enable you to learn at your own pace, and most of them end with a short question or problem for you to tackle. These enable you to test your understanding of the material that you have just studied. The correct answer to each problem is given at the top of the next frame.

To use the book most effectively you should use a piece of paper or card to conceal the next frame until you have answered the given question. You can use the paper for rough working if necessary. Only when you have made a response should you look at the answer. If you have given an incorrect answer you should not proceed until you have found out why you made a mistake. Usually a worked solution or some further explanation will be given immediately below each answer so that you should be able to find where and why you went wrong. If you still cannot understand how to get the correct answer, you should make a note to discuss it with another student or with your tutor.

At the end of and at intermediate stages throughout each programme you will find sets of problems for you to tackle. You must attempt as many of these problems as possible. They are graded in difficulty and will give practice in applying the techniques that you have learnt.

The most important thing to remember is that you should work systematically, sequentially and carefully through the book at whatever pace of learning you find comfortable. Do not miss out any part of any programme, don't 'cheat' by looking at the answers to questions before offering your own solution and do not proceed at any stage until you are satisfied that you have grasped the information in the frame that you have just studied.

Programme 1

THE DIMENSIONAL CONSISTENCY OF EQUATIONS

INTRODUCTION

When you are trying to solve a problem in science or engineering you will usually begin by setting up a mathematical model of the physical system you are dealing with. That is to say, you represent physical quantities by mathematical expressions and then try to set up an equation or set of equations which describes how they are interrelated.

Whenever you write down an equation you should get into the habit of quickly checking it for dimensional consistency. If you do this you will find that you are less likely to write down inaccurate or even impossible equations – something done by far too many students, especially under the pressure of examination conditions.

If you have never come across the concept of dimensions and the dimensional consistency of equations, do not worry. This programme is going to teach you about these concepts and show you how to use them. You should then try to apply them to all the programmes in this book and, in fact, to all the work you do in future. The programme begins with some examples using non-electrical results which will be familiar to most people embarking on tertiary education in engineering. Even if you are not familiar with them, you will be able to understand the principles behind the concept of simple dimensional analysis based solely on an understanding of the units of time, distance, velocity and acceleration.

You may find the idea of checking every equation you write a bit tedious to begin with but, once you have mastered the skill, you will find the small extra investment of time it involves well worth the effort. In examinations it may well, in fact, save you time by guiding you away from pages of incorrect algebra which can never lead to the correct solution to a problem. In your broader academic and professional life, regular use of the concept of dimensions will again save you time and will also give you a better understanding of the physical quantities you are dealing with.

1

THE CONCEPT OF DIMENSIONS

You are probably familiar with the equations of motion of a particle moving with constant acceleration a:

$$v = u + at \tag{1}$$

$$s = ut + \tfrac{1}{2}at^2 \tag{2}$$

$$v^2 = u^2 + 2as \tag{3}$$

In these equations, s represents the distance the particle has moved from its starting point after a time t. The symbol u represents the velocity it started with and v represents the velocity it has reached in time t. These are all very simple mathematical models – physical properties are being represented by mathematical symbols. The three equations are a mathematical model of the movement of the particle.

All the terms in all these equations are said to have 'dimensions' which are some combination of the 'fundamental dimensions' of length L and time T. That is, each term represents a property which can be characterised by some combination of the fundamental dimensions. Velocity, for example, is often measured in metres per second which is a length divided by a time. It could be measured in other units but all consist of a length divided by a time. It therefore has dimensions of L/T or LT^{-1}. What are the dimensions of acceleration?

2

Acceleration has dimensions LT^{-2}.

Acceleration is always measured as a length divided by time squared, metres per second squared for example. It therefore has dimensions LT^{-2}.

Now look at equation (1). The terms v and u are both velocities and so have dimensions LT^{-1}. The third term (at) is an acceleration a with dimensions LT^{-2} multiplied by a time t with dimension T. Using square brackets to denote dimensions (which is the usual convention) we can therefore write:

$$[at] = [a][t] = [LT^{-2}][T] = [LT^{-1}]$$

All terms in equation (1) thus have the same dimensions, LT^{-1}. What are the dimensions of the terms in equation (2)? Do not worry about the $\tfrac{1}{2}$. In this equation it is a 'pure' number and is therefore 'dimensionless'.

3

> All terms in equation (2) have the dimension of length L.

The equation is $s = ut + \frac{1}{2}at^2$

The term on the left-hand side of the equation is a length, so $[s] = [L]$.

$$[ut] = [u][t] = [LT^{-1}][T] = [L]$$

$$[at^2] = [a][t^2] = [LT^{-2}][T^2] = [L]$$

It was stated in frame 2 that the $\frac{1}{2}$ in this equation is a 'pure' number and so is 'dimensionless'. Whenever numbers appear in an expression you should evaluate the dimensions of the other terms first. If the term including the number has the same dimensions as all the others, then the equation is 'dimensionally consistent' and the number is dimensionless. If the term including the number does not have the same dimensions as all the others, then the number represents the numerical value of a physical quantity which has dimensions. Its dimensions must then combine with those of the other terms so that the equation is dimensionally consistent.

The crucial thing to notice about the dimensions of terms in an equation which represents a physical situation is that all terms which are separated by an = sign, a + sign or a − sign MUST HAVE THE SAME DIMENSIONS!

What are the dimensions of the terms in equation (3): $v^2 = u^2 + 2as$? Is the '2' dimensionless?

4

> All terms have dimensions L^2T^{-2}. The number 2 *is* dimensionless.

$$[v^2] = [u^2] = [LT^{-1}]^2 = [L^2T^{-2}]$$

$$[as] = [a][s] = [LT^{-2}][L] = [L^2T^{-2}]$$

Since v, u and (as) have the same dimensions, the '2' *must* be dimensionless.

The principle of dimensional consistency applies equally well to differential and integral relationships. We will investigate this in the next frame.

5

In the first few frames we looked at the equations of motion of a particle in terms which included a velocity v and an acceleration a. Such motion is often described using the methods of differential and integral calculus.

Using differential calculus, we may write:

$$v = ds/dt$$

Alternatively, when a is known, we can write:

$$v = \int a dt$$

The principle of dimensional consistency applies equally well to these relationships. The quantity ds/dt is the limit of a ratio $\delta s/\delta t$. Again this is a length divided by a time, so has dimensions LT^{-1}. The integral $\int a dt$ is the limit of a summation of terms of the form $a\delta t$ and so has dimensions $[a][\delta t] = [LT^{-2}][T] = [LT^{-1}]$. What are the dimensions of terms dv/dt and $\int v dt$?

6

$$\boxed{[dv/dt] = [LT^{-2}] \quad [\int v dt] = [L]}$$

Here is the reasoning: dv/dt is the limit of $\delta v/\delta t$, a velocity divided by a time, so:

$$[dv/dt] = [dv]/[dt] = [LT^{-1}]/[T] = [LT^{-2}]$$

$\int v dt$ is the limit of a summation of terms of the form $v\delta t$. That is, all terms are products of a velocity and a time, so:

$$[\int v dt] = [v][t] = [LT^{-1}][T] = [L]$$

To describe other properties of mechanical systems we need to recognise a further dimension, the dimension of mass $[M]$. This enables us to determine the dimensions of terms involving mass. If, for example, the particle whose motion we have been studying in the preceding frames was of mass m and was being acted on by a force F, we could write:

$$F = ma \quad \text{and hence} \quad [F] = [m][a] = [M][LT^{-2}] = [MLT^{-2}]$$

The kinetic energy of a particle of mass m moving with velocity v is given by the expression:

$$KE = \tfrac{1}{2} mv^2 \text{ (the } \tfrac{1}{2} \text{ is dimensionless)}$$

What are the dimensions of kinetic energy?

7

$$[KE] = [ML^2T^{-2}]$$

By the same kind of reasoning as we have had before:

$$[\tfrac{1}{2}mv^2] = [m][v^2] = [M][LT^{-1}]^2 = [M][L^2T^{-2}] = [ML^2T^{-2}]$$

The usefulness of dimensional checking lies in recognising that all equations which truly represent a physical situation MUST be dimensionally consistent. Checking the dimensions of every equation you write when you are working on a problem is a habit you should try to cultivate. If everything you write down is dimensionally consistent you are well on the way to obtaining a correct solution to your problem. On the other hand, if you spot a term in an equation which is not dimensionally consistent with all the other terms, you know there must be an error somewhere. It is the spotting and correcting of errors of this kind almost as soon as they are made that make dimensional checks of equations so worthwhile.

Here is an example for you to try to illustrate this point.

In estimating the change in energy experienced by a particle of mass m accelerating from a speed u to a speed v in falling through a distance h, a student wrote down the equation:

$$mv^2/2 = mu^2/2 + mh$$

Can you say from dimensional reasoning alone what is wrong with this equation and what, in dimensional terms, must be done to correct it?

8

The first two terms have dimensions ML^2T^{-2}.
The third term has dimensions ML.
The third term must be multiplied by a term of dimensions LT^{-2}.

The first two terms are kinetic energies and have dimensions ML^2T^{-2}. The third term must also, therefore, have the same dimensions and must also, therefore, be some kind of energy. It is, of course, a potential energy and the product of m and h must be further multiplied by an acceleration, in this case the acceleration due to gravity g. The correct term is mgh. Here, an analysis of the error in dimensional terms alone gives a very strong clue to the correct form of the equation.

9

An important corollary of the problem solved in the previous frame is the fact that all kinds of energy have the same dimensions – a point we shall examine further shortly. The equation we have just analysed also shows us how to use the concept of dimensions in a different, often more convenient form. Instead of breaking every term in an equation down into its fundamental dimensions, we can describe common physical properties in terms of their 'derived dimensions'. We could, for example, say that all terms in the equation just analysed have 'derived dimensions' of energy. To avoid writing this out in full every time, we will from now on use single inverted commas round the word 'dimensions' when describing something in terms of its derived dimensions, using the word dimensions on its own when we are referring to fundamental dimensions. Thus the term $\frac{1}{2}mv^2$ has 'dimensions' of energy and dimensions of $[ML^2T^{-2}]$.

What are the 'dimensions' of the terms in equations (1) and (3) in frame 1? The equations were:

$$v = u + at \dots (1) \quad \text{and} \quad v^2 = u^2 + 2as \dots (3)$$

10

The terms in equation (1) have 'dimensions' of velocity.
The terms in equation (3) have 'dimensions' of velocity squared.

This approach can often save a little extra time and is particularly useful when we look at electrical circuit equations in which the fundamental dimensions of the terms involved are less familiar. In order to link the idea of dimensions in electrical systems to the general concept of dimensions in mechanical systems discussed above, we need to introduce a new fundamental electrical dimension. Several electrical properties could be chosen. We shall take charge as the fundamental one. It is given the symbol $[Q]$. All electrical quantities can then be represented as being made up of the fundamental dimensions of M, L, T and Q. You may find it odd that electrical quantities can contain 'mechanical' dimensions M and L. This follows because energy is essentially the same physical property whatever kind of energy it is. Different kinds of energy can be converted into each other. Mechanical energy, for example, can be converted into electrical energy and vice versa. An equation which has electrical energy on one side and mechanical energy on the other must be dimensionally consistent so mechanical energy terms can be 'dimensionally equated' to electrical energy terms. Power, which is rate of change of energy, also often occurs in both systems. What are the dimensions of power?

11

The dimensions of power are ML^2T^{-3}

We know that the dimensions of energy are ML^2T^{-2} and power is rate of change of energy so the dimensions of power must be:

$$[\text{Power}] = [ML^2T^{-2}]/[T] = [ML^2T^{-3}]$$

You are probably familiar with the equations for the power P dissipated in a resistor R which has a current I flowing through it and a voltage V across it. (If you are not familiar with these concepts, you should still be able to follow the working in the next few frames just by looking at the dimensions of the terms involved and checking that the equations containing them are dimensionally consistent.) The equations are:

$$P = VI \quad \text{or} \quad P = I^2R \quad \text{or} \quad P = V^2/R$$

Power, too, just like energy, must have the same dimensions whether it is electrical power, mechanical power or any other kind of power. All the above equations, then, must have dimensions ML^2T^{-3}. Let us investigate this for the first of these expressions: $P = VI$.

Voltage in electrical systems can be expressed as energy per unit charge. A certain amount of energy is required to move a unit charge through a given voltage. The dimensions of voltage can thus be written as $ML^2T^{-2}Q^{-1}$.

Current in electrical systems can be expressed as a rate of flow of charge dq/dt. The amount of charge flowing past a given point in a circuit in unit time determines the current at that point. The dimensions of current can thus be written QT^{-1}.

Using these ideas, can you deduce the dimensions of power from the first equation, $P = VI$?

12

The dimensions of power are ML^2T^{-3}

Since $P = VI$ then $[P] = [V][I] = [ML^2T^{-2}Q^{-1}][QT^{-1}] = [ML^2T^{-3}]$

The dimensions are thus the same as those derived from consideration of a purely mechanical system as, of course, they must be.

Using the equation $P = I^2R$, can you obtain an expression for the dimensions of resistance?

13

> The dimensions of resistance are $ML^2T^{-1}Q^{-2}$

Since $P = I^2R$ then $R = P/I^2$, so $[R]$ is given by:

$$[R] = [ML^2T^{-3}]/[Q^2T^{-2}] = [ML^2T^{-3}Q^{-2}T^2] = [ML^2T^{-1}Q^{-2}]$$

Now check that the expression $P = V^2/R$ also has dimensions of power.

14

> $[P] = [V^2]/[R] = [M^2L^4T^{-4}Q^{-2}]/[ML^2T^{-1}Q^{-2}] = [ML^2T^{-3}]$

This equation, too, has the same dimensions as the other two – as, of course, it must.

We can see from the above equations that writing electrical quantities in terms of their fundamental dimensions can often lead to very cumbersome expressions. It is usually better, as mentioned in frame 9, to use the idea of derived dimensions.

We could, for example, say that, since all terms in frame 11 have 'dimensions' of power, we have:

'dimensions' of power = 'dimensions' of voltage times 'dimensions' of current
That is $[P] = [V][I]$ or

'dimensions' of power = 'dimensions' of current squared times
'dimensions' of resistance
That is $[P] = [I^2][R]$ or

'dimensions' of power = 'dimensions' of voltage squared divided by
'dimensions' of resistance
That is $[P] = [V^2]/[R]$.

We can use these ideas to check electrical equations for dimensional consistency just as we did for the mechanical equations considered in the earlier frames.

Here is an example to illustrate this point.

In writing down the total power in a complicated system of resistors, an engineer produced the following equation:

$$P_{\text{tot}} = V_1I_1 + \frac{I_2^2R_1R_2}{R_1 + R_2} + \frac{V_2^2(R_3R_4 + R_4R_5 + R_3R_5)}{R_3R_4R_5}$$

Is there any reason to doubt the validity of this equation?

15

> Not necessarily. All terms have dimensions of power.

Let us consider the answer to this question in two parts. Why do we say 'Not necessarily' rather than just 'No'? The reason for this element of caution is that a dimensional check is not a *guarantee* that an equation is correct. Incorrect quantities which have the same dimensions as correct quantities could be written down by mistake or dimensionless constants could be missed out, for example. It *can* be guaranteed, however, that an equation which is *not* dimensionally consistent *cannot* be correct.

Now let us consider each term in the expression for power. Here it is:

$$P_{\text{tot}} = V_1 I_1 + \frac{I_2^2 R_1 R_2}{R_1 + R_2} + \frac{V_2^2(R_3 R_4 + R_4 R_5 + R_3 R_5)}{R_3 R_4 R_5}$$

The first term is the product of a voltage and a current so is certainly of the correct form. In the second term the resistors make a contribution with 'dimensions' of resistance squared to the numerator and resistance alone to the denominator. The net 'dimensions' of the term are thus I^2R which can also be recognised as a power. Similarly, the third term reduces to 'dimensions' of V^2/R so again has 'dimensions' of power.

Now move on to the next frame where we will examine another important consequence of the concept of dimensions.

16

In the analysis of physical systems, whether structural, mechanical or electrical, we frequently find mathematical functions being involved. We often encounter sinusoidal voltages of the form $v = V \sin \omega t$, for example. The velocity of a particle may 'decay' exponentially as $u = u_0 e^{-kx}$ and so on. Notice that the dimensions of the quantity under consideration are contained in the symbol acting as a multiplying factor for the mathematical function. In the expression $V \sin \omega t$, the fact that this is a voltage is contained in the symbol V. The $\sin \omega t$ gives the variation of v with time. Similarly, in $u_0 e^{-kx}$, u_0 is the velocity, e^{-kx} is the functional dependence – this time on x. In solving the equations relating to these quantities, we sometimes make use of power series. This leads to a very important corollary.

When a physical quantity is modelled by a mathematical function which can be represented by a power series and the dimensions of the quantity are determined by a multiplying factor, then the mathematical function MUST BE DIMENSIONLESS and every term in the series representing it must be so too!

In particular, the argument of the function, that is, the variable from which the function is derived, must be dimensionless. Note that a dimensionless quantity can be obtained from the ratio of two quantities having the same dimensions or the product of two quantities having reciprocal dimensions. To justify the above assertion, let us suppose that a physical quantity can be represented by a function $Kf(x)$ where K has the dimensions of the quantity being modelled and

$$f(x) = a_0 + a_1x + a_2x^2 + a_3x^3 + a_4x^4 + \ldots \text{ etc.}$$

where all the a terms are pure numbers (that is, they are dimensionless). The only way in which this equation can be dimensionally consistent is if every term is dimensionless and $f(x)$ itself is dimensionless. If this were not so and x had dimension of L, for example, then successive terms in ascending powers of x would have dimensions of L, L^2, L^3, etc., which is not possible.

Functions you will meet frequently, especially in electrical and electronic engineering, which fall into this 'dimensionless' category include all the trigonometric functions, the exponential function and the hyperbolic functions. In all these cases both the argument of the function and the function itself must be dimensionless. In the functions $\sin x$, $\cos x$, e^x, $\sinh x$, $\tanh x$ etc., both the variable x and the function of that variable must be dimensionless. It may often happen that, where x is itself a function, you will know the dimensions of one or more terms which make up x. You may then be able to deduce the dimensions of the others. The function $\sin \omega t$ mentioned above, for example, is often met with in electric circuit theory, where t has its usual meaning of time.

Since ωt must be dimensionless and t has the dimension of time T, what are the dimensions of ω and what physical property does it represent?

17

$\boxed{\omega \text{ must have dimensions of } 1/T \text{ and must represent a frequency}}$

A voltage which varies sinusoidally with time (we shall meet these often in the body of this text) can then be represented, as above, as $V \sin \omega t$. The quantity $V \sin \omega t$ would then, of course, have dimensions of voltage.

Now turn over for a summary of this programme, some revision questions and a short test.

18

SUMMARY

1. All physical quantities can be spoken of as having 'dimensions' which are some combination of the 'fundamental dimensions' of mass M, length L, time T and charge Q.
2. In any equation involving physical quantities, all terms separated by an = sign, a + sign or a − sign must have the same dimensions. The equation is then said to be dimensionally consistent.
3. The dimensional consistency of an equation is not a guarantee of its correctness but an equation which is not dimensionally consistent *cannot* be correct.
4. Terms which all reduce to the same combination of dimensions, however they are made up, can often be dealt with more conveniently in terms of their 'derived dimensions'. The terms VI, I^2R and V^2/R can all be seen to have the 'dimensions' of power for example.
5. When a physical quantity is modelled by a mathematical function which can be represented by a power series and the dimensions of the quantity are determined by a multiplying factor, then the mathematical function MUST BE DIMENSIONLESS and every term in the series representing it must be so too.

19

REVISION QUESTIONS

Here are some questions to help you consolidate the ideas in this programme. Try to complete them all before looking at the next page for the answers.

1. Write down the dimensions of the following quantities in terms of the fundamental dimensions M, L, T, Q: pressure; torque; capacitance; inductance.
2. Is the following equation dimensionally consistent? If not, which term is in error and how could it be corrected?

$$\text{Total energy} = \tfrac{1}{2}m_1v_1^2 + m_2gh + m_3ds/dt + \int VIdt$$

(All symbols have the meanings used in this programme.)
3. What are the 'dimensions' of the terms in the following equation? Is it dimensionally consistent?

$$V_{\text{tot}} = I_1R_1 + V_2R_2/(R_2 + R_3) - I_2R_4R_5/(R_4 + R_5)$$

20

1. Pressure is force/area. It has dimensions $MLT^{-2}/L^2 = ML^{-1}T^{-2}$.
   Torque is force $\times$ distance. It has dimensions $MLT^{-2} \times L = ML^2T^{-2}$.
   Capacitance is charge/voltage. It has dimensions $Q/ML^2T^{-2}Q^{-1} = M^{-1}L^{-2}T^2Q^2$.
   Inductance is defined in the relationship $v = L\,di/dt$ so is determined mathematically as voltage $\times$ time/current. It has dimensions $ML^2T^{-2}Q^{-1} \times T/QT^{-1} = ML^2Q^{-2}$.

2. The equation is not dimensionally consistent. On the right-hand side the first term is a kinetic energy, the second a potential energy and the fourth an electrical energy (power $\times$ time) so all have dimensions ML^2T^{-2}. The third term has dimensions MLT^{-1}. It needs to be multiplied by a term of dimensions LT^{-1}, that is, a velocity.

3. All terms in this equation can be described as having the 'dimensions' of voltage. Ohm's law gives a relationship for voltage as $V = IR$. The first term on the right is of this form, the second is a voltage multiplied by a dimensionless ratio of resistors, the third is a current multiplied by a term having dimensions of $R^2/R = R$ so is also of the correct form. The equation is therefore dimensionally consistent.

POST-SCRIPT

If you have now correctly completed the three examples, you have completed the programme. You should now begin to see the value of dimensional reasoning in the checking of equations representing physical situations. You are now strongly recommended to carry out this process, not only throughout your study of the rest of this text but throughout the rest of your academic and professional career. You will find, if you do, that you will make fewer mistakes in setting down equations, that those mistakes you do make you will pick up before they have turned into hopeless problems and that you will therefore obtain solutions to the problems you tackle much more quickly and with much more confidence.

| TEST ON PROGRAMME 1 |

1. It is well-known that if a heavy weight is suspended from a fixing point by a piece of wire, the wire stretches because of the force exerted on it by the action of the weight under gravity. Three quantities which are important in analysing this situation are stress, strain and Young's modulus. Stress is force per unit area, strain is the ratio of the extension of the wire to its original length and Young's modulus is the ratio of stress to strain. What are the dimensions of stress, strain and Young's modulus?

2. A bicycle dynamo works by having a small wheel connected to it which is rotated by the action of the bicycle road wheel rubbing against it and thus driving it round. The rotation of the dynamo mechanism in a magnetic field created inside it produces a voltage V which allows the bicycle lights to draw a current I. A student is asked to estimate the efficiency of conversion of mechanical power into electrical power and suggests the formula:

$$\text{Efficiency} = \frac{VI}{Fr}$$

where F is the force exerted on the rim of the dynamo driving wheel by the bicycle road wheel under the action of friction and r is the radius of the dynamo driving wheel. Can you say, by dimensional reasoning alone, why this expression cannot be right? What, in dimensional terms must be done to correct it? Can you deduce the correct expression? (Think what happens to a bicycle light as you speed up and slow down.)

3. A portable tape recorder is powered by a battery of voltage V. The motor is driven by a special speed-stabilising circuit which derives from the battery voltage a voltage $V - V_1$ which supplies the motor with a current I_1. The special circuit can be represented by a resistance R_1 through which the current I_1 also flows. The sound reproduction circuitry offers an effective resistance R_2 to the battery. If a certain battery is known to have an energy storage capacity of K joules, a student calculates that it will last for a time given by the expression:

$$T = \frac{K}{(V - V_1)I_1 + I_1R_1 + V^2/R_2}$$

What is wrong with this suggestion and what is the most likely correction that must be made to it?

(All symbols have their usual meanings.)

1. In terms of the basic of dimensions M, L, T and Q, what are the dimensions of electric field strength E and magnetic field strength H?
2. What are the dimensions of the terms in the following equations, (a) in terms of M, L, T and Q and (b) in the less formal way referred to as 'dimensions' in this text?

   (i) $e = mc^2$
   (ii) $v^2 = u^2 + 2as$
   (iii) $R = \rho l/A$.

3. Which terms in the following equations are most likely to be wrong and what must be done to make them consistent with the others?

   (i) $\dfrac{p}{\rho} = \dfrac{p_0}{\rho} + \dfrac{v^2}{2} + h$

   (ii) $s = (v_1 - v_2)t + \dfrac{(v_1 - v_2)^2}{2a} - at_2$

   (iii) $\dfrac{V_1}{V_2} = \dfrac{I_1R_1 - I_2(R_1 + R_2)}{(I_1 - I_2)R_1 - (R_1R_2)/(R_1 + R_2)}$.

4. The following expression is derived for the ratio of output to input voltage for a certain reactive circuit. Could it be correct? If not, why not and what must be done to correct it?

$$\frac{V_0}{V_i} = \frac{\omega^2C^2R^2}{5R - \omega^2C^2R^2 - j/\omega C + 6j\omega CR^2}$$

j is the square root of -1 and is dimensionless. So are the 5 and the 6.

5. How many dimensionless combinations of terms can you make within each of the following groups of quantities? (For example, among F, m and a, F/ma is dimensionless.) This kind of manipulation is widely used in the skill of dimensional analysis.

   (i) F, m, a, v, s, t
   (ii) M, m, g, F
   (iii) V, I, R, P
   (iv) ω, L, C, R, ω_0.

6. The voltage in part of a certain circuit varies with time according to the expressions:

$$v_0 = \frac{VRC}{RC - \tau}(e^{-t/RC} - e^{-t/\tau}) \quad \text{if } RC \neq \tau \quad \text{and}$$

$$v_0 = \frac{Vt}{\tau} e^{-t/\tau} \quad \text{if} \quad RC = \tau$$

Can you re-write these expressions in terms only of the dimensionless ratios $A = v_0/V$, $x = t/\tau$ and $n = RC/\tau$? Then draw graphs of A on the vertical axis against x on the horizontal axis for values of n of $n = 100$, $n = 10$, $n = 1$ and $n = 0.1$. 'Dimensionless plots' like this are very useful in predicting the outputs of a wide range of circuits once results for one circuit of a given type have been established.

Programme 2

DIRECT CURRENT CIRCUITS

PART 1

INTRODUCTION

This programme and the next, in effect, lay the foundation for the rest of the book. It is therefore of paramount importance that you make sure you understand all the concepts in these two programmes. You will then be well set to tackle all the remaining programmes.

You are first introduced to the fundamental concepts of current, voltage and resistance around which much of the study of circuits is based. You will learn how the devices which supply currents and voltages to circuits can be modelled by 'current generators' and 'voltage generators' and will discover the differences between practical generators available in the laboratory and the 'ideal models' which are used to analyse them. You will then see how circuits can be built using these generators together with resistors, and will learn how to calculate the distribution of currents and voltages within such circuits.

When a current flows in a circuit, energy is needed to supply that current. The concept of energy in an electrical circuit will be studied together with power which is rate of change of energy. Calculations involving energy and power will be carried out.

The two concepts of series and parallel connection will be studied. You will learn how generators can be connected in series and in parallel and how they cannot! Several important formulae concerning resistors in series and in parallel will be derived.

To conclude the programme, two very important 'circuit configurations' – the potential divider and the current splitter – will be introduced and analysed. You will find, in later programmes, that these configurations will appear again and again. They are, in fact, possibly the most important two configurations in the whole of circuit theory. Using techniques which you will learn about in future programmes, many different kinds of circuit can be reduced to one of these two basic forms for the purposes of analysis.

1

ELECTRIC CURRENT, RESISTANCE AND VOLTAGE

The phenomenon we know as *electricity* is based on the concept of an *electric charge*. This charge is carried by *electrons* – fundamental particles which are capable of movement through substances. The movement of electrons and hence charge is called *electric current*. A closed path through which current can flow is called an *electric circuit*.

The unit of current is the *AMPERE*.

The process of current flow through a substance is called *conduction*. Substances which conduct current easily are called *conductors*, substances which conduct with difficulty are called *insulators*. The ability to conduct is usually measured in terms of *resistance* to current flow. Conductors have a *very low resistance*, insulators have a *very high resistance*. A circuit component specifically designed to have a *known* resistance is called a *resistor*. A circuit constructed only with resistors is called a *purely resistive circuit*.

The unit of resistance is the *OHM*.

Since current flows through a circuit and a resistor is part of a circuit, current flows . . . . . . a resistor. You complete the sentence.

2

Current flows *through* a resistor

When current flows through a resistor a *potential difference* is developed across it. Current flows through a resistor if a *source of electrical energy* is connected to it, thus causing a potential difference to be developed across it. A potential difference is often called simply a *voltage*.

The unit of potential difference or voltage is the *VOLT*.

The equation linking current flow *I* to resistance *R* in a resistor which has a voltage *V* developed across it is *OHM'S LAW*, the most fundamental law of electric circuits. Ohm's Law states that the voltage developed across the resistor is the product of the current flowing through it and the value of the resistance and is written:

$$V = IR$$

So we now have two facts about resistors. Current flows through a resistor. Voltage is developed . . . . . . a resistor. You complete the sentence again.

3

Voltage is developed *across* a resistor

It is important to remember these two ideas when describing the currents and voltages in a circuit. Current flows *through* a resistor. Voltage is developed *across* a resistor. It is even more important to remember this distinction between current and voltage when trying to measure the two quantities. In order to discuss these concepts more readily it is helpful to be able to refer to a *circuit diagram*. A real circuit is made up of a number of components or *circuit elements* connected together by pieces of copper wire or, more commonly nowadays, by copper *tracks* on a *printed circuit board*. In a circuit diagram, different components are represented by different symbols. The interconnecting wire or track is represented by thin lines. Here are two alternative symbols for a resistor:

Preferred British Standard   *Alternative symbol*

The preferred British standard should be used in all professional documents. The alternative symbol is still widely used by practising engineers when sketching rough diagrams for their own use.

4

THE VOLTMETER AND THE AMMETER

A voltmeter is an instrument for measuring voltage. An ammeter is an instrument for measuring current. Each instrument has two 'terminals' on it which allow it to be connected to a circuit. A terminal is simply some kind of screw or clamp fixing to which a piece of wire can be firmly attached. Here are the circuit symbols for a voltmeter and an ammeter (the small circles on the ends of the wires represent the terminals):

Voltmeter   *Ammeter*

If a certain resistor is known to have a given current flowing through it we know that a voltage will be developed *across* the resistor. Can you work out how the voltmeter should be connected to the resistor to measure the voltage across it? Draw a diagram to show how the connection should be made.

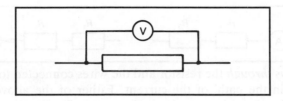

Since the voltage is developed *across* the resistor, the voltmeter is connected *across* the resistor. Notice that, if pieces of wire with 'clip-on' connectors were attached to the voltmeter terminals they could be clipped on to the wires coming from the ends of the resistor without otherwise disturbing the circuit. A further point of interest is that an ideal voltmeter has an infinite 'internal' resistance. Connecting it to a circuit has the same effect on the circuit as connecting a resistor 'of value infinity' instead of the voltmeter would have. We shall see in later analysis that this causes no disturbance to the electrical conditions in the circuit. That is, the voltage we are trying to measure is not affected by the measuring instrument if this instrument is ideal. This is not the case for real instruments, of course, and we shall also see later how to assess the effect of the measuring instruments we use on the circuit whose properties we are trying to measure.

Now let us suppose we wish to measure the current flowing through a resistor. There is an accepted convention for what is meant by the 'direction of flow' of a current which we shall learn about in later frames. When current is flowing in a circuit an arrow is drawn on the wire through which the current flows to indicate its presence. A resistor with a current flowing through it would thus be shown as follows:

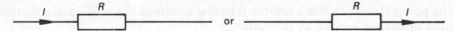

Current is a flow of charge and it is a property of resistive circuits that charge cannot 'build up' in them. If a certain amount of charge (and therefore a certain current) flows in at one end of a resistor then the same amount of charge (and therefore the same current) flows out of the other end. If we can measure the current in the wires joined on to a resistor therefore, we know the current in the resistor. Can you work out how to connect an ammeter to the (partial) circuit given here to measure the current in the resistor R_2? Draw a diagram to show a suitable connection.

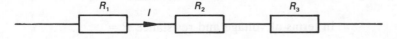

7

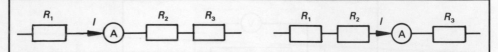

Since current flows *through* the resistor and the wires connected to it, the ammeter must be placed 'in the path' of the current. Either of the above connections is suitable. *Notice that, in order to measure the current flowing through it, the circuit has to be broken and the ammeter inserted into the break.* The situation is thus quite different from that of the voltmeter which we can simply attach to a circuit as it is. A further point of interest is that an ideal ammeter has zero 'internal' resistance. Connecting it to a circuit has the same effect on the circuit as would connecting a resistor 'of value zero' instead of the ammeter. We shall see in later analysis that this causes no disturbance to the electrical conditions in the circuit. That is, the current we are trying to measure is not affected by the measuring instrument if this instrument is ideal. As with the non-ideal voltmeter this is not the case for real instruments, of course, and we shall also see later what effect inserting a non-ideal ammeter into a circuit would have.

8

ELECTRIC POWER

The next basic quantity we shall study is electric power. A resistor is said to 'dissipate' power. That is, it converts electrical energy into heat energy. Electric power has the same dimensions as power derived from any other system – it is 'rate of change of energy'. Since energy is measured in Joules, power is measured in Joules per second which are called Watts.

The unit of power is the *WATT*.

The power P dissipated in a resistor R having a voltage V across it and a current I flowing through it is given by the equation:

$$P = VI$$

But Ohm's Law also applies to this resistor so we may solve the above equation simultaneously with Ohm's Law, first to eliminate the voltage and then to eliminate the current. This gives us two new expressions for power, one involving only current and resistance, the other involving only voltage and resistance. Can you derive these?

In terms of current and resistance $P = \ldots$

In terms of voltage and resistance $P = \ldots$

9

$$\boxed{P = I^2R \quad P = V^2R}$$

$P = VI$ and $V = IR$ so, substituting for V gives $P = I^2R$

$P = VI$ and $I = \dfrac{V}{R}$ so, substituting for I gives $P = \dfrac{V^2}{R}$

You may recall, for programme 1, that we can think of terms of the form I^2R and V^2/R as having 'dimensions' of power. It is worth recalling, for future reference, that *any* term of the form [current]^2 times a resistance or [voltage]^2 divided by a resistance must be a power. Let us now go back to the equation $P = VI$ and derive a relationship involving energy.

10

We started this section by saying that a movement of charge was called an electric current. More precisely, if a charge Q moves through a body in a time t, then the current I flowing is given by the equation:

$$I = Q/t$$

The unit of charge is the *COULOMB*.

You may also come across the relationship between current, charge and time in the form:

$$i = dq/dt$$

where i is the instantaneous value of a current which varies with time. The differential relationship shows that current can be expressed as a rate of change of charge. Such quantities will be studied in detail in later programmes. In general, small letters are used for quantities which vary with time, capital letters are used to represent 'direct' quantities, that is, quantities which are constant over long periods of time. All the currents and voltages considered in this programme are direct quantities. They will be encountered in practice in circuits consisting of resistors connected to batteries or laboratory power supplies.

Using the direct form of the expression and substituting for I in the equation for power $P = VI$, we can obtain an expression for V in terms of P, t and Q. Can you do this? Write an expression for V using only these terms.

11

$$V = Pt/Q$$

$P = VI$ so, substituting for I from $I = Q/t$ we get $P = VQ/t$. Rearranging this gives:

$$V = Pt/Q$$

Now, since Pt has 'dimensions' of energy we see that voltage has 'dimensions' of energy divided by charge and could be measured in Joules per coulomb. Thus voltage or electrical potential is not energy but energy per unit charge. In writing down electric circuit equations we shall often want to refer to terms which 'have the dimensions of voltage'. When doing this, it will be worth bearing the above relationship in mind.

What are the 'dimensions' of the term IR?

12

The term IR has 'dimensions' of voltage.

Since it comes directly from Ohm's Law $V = IR$, the term IR, which is on the right-hand side of the equation, has the same 'dimensions' as the term on the left-hand side. As emphasised in programme 1, you should, by now, be checking the 'dimensions' of every equation you write down.

Here is a problem for you to try. In a calculation for the total power dissipated in a set of resistors the following expression was obtained:

$$P = (V_1 - V_2) I_1 + (I_2 - I_1)^2 R_2 + \frac{V_3^2 (R_3 + R_4)}{R_3 R_4}$$

Could this equation be correct? Check each term carefully, then move on to the next frame.

13

Yes. All terms on the right have 'dimensions' of power.

Working term by term, we see that the term $(V_1 - V_2) I_1$ is the product of a voltage and a current (two terms added or subtracted still give a term having the same dimensions). This is one of the forms we recognise as having 'dimensions' of power. The term $(I_2 - I_3)^2 R_2$ is [current]^2 times resistance which is again recognisable as power. The term $V_3^2 (R_3 + R_4) /R_3R_4$ is [voltage]^2 divided by resistance. The [voltage]^2 is easy enough to see. The other terms comprise a resistance $(R_3 + R_4)$ in the numerator and a term R_3R_4 in the denominator. The denominator thus has dimensions of [resistance]^2. The net term involving resistance thus has dimensions of resistance divided by [resistance]^2 – in other words, 1/resistance. The complete third term thus has 'dimensions' of V^2/R which is also recognisable as power.

14

MULTIPLES AND SUB-MULTIPLES OF BASIC UNITS

It often happens in electric and electronic circuits that the quantities we are dealing with are so much larger or smaller than the basic units that it makes more sense to work in multiples or sub-multiples of the basic units. The multiples and sub-multiples commonly used are indicated by suitably prefixing the basic unit. The table below shows some of the internationally accepted prefixes in common use:

Power of ten	Prefix	Written
10^{12}	Tera	T
10^{9}	Giga	G
10^{6}	Mega	M
10^{3}	kilo	k
10^{-3}	milli	m
10^{-6}	micro	μ
10^{-9}	nano	n
10^{-12}	pico	p

In practice it often becomes convenient to use complementary pairs of these units. In Ohm's Law $V = IR$, for example, if V is measured in millivolts (mV) and I in milliamps (mA) then R is in ohms (Ω). If V is in volts (V) and I in milliamps (mA), them R is in kilohms (kΩ).

If V was measured in volts and R in Megohms, what would I be measured in? Give both the name of the unit and its symbol.

15

$$\boxed{\text{microamps } (\mu A)}$$

If $V = IR$ with V in volts and R in Megohms then the 10^6 associated with the R must be cancelled by 10^{-6} associated with the I. Thus I must be in μA.

These ideas extend more generally than just to Ohm's Law. If, in any circuit being analysed, all resistances are measured in kilohms and all voltages in volts, then all currents being calculated will automatically be given in milliamps. We shall meet examples of this kind in later frames. Making careful use of this kind of relationship can often simplify the numerical manipulation involved in solving a problem and can often help in ensuring that values obtained are 'sensible'. Dropped or added powers of 10 often produce answers which, in practical terms, are nonsense. Another practical consideration to be taken into account by circuit designers is the range of sizes of components available. We will look at this in the next frame.

16

PREFERRED VALUES

All practical components are available in only a limited range of different sizes. It would obviously be impossible for a manufacturer to provide 'off-the-shelf' devices in every size that a circuit designer might require and specially made devices, although available, are costly. The compromise made is to provide a range of components having 'preferred values'. The most widely used range is the 5% range. The full range of such components is the 'E24' range. The 'nominal' values of components in this range are:

10	11	12	13	15	16	18	20	22	24	27	30
33	36	39	43	47	51	56	62	68	75	82	91

These nominal values may be multiplied by a suitable positive or negative power of 10 to match the value nearest to that required in a particular design. The values in the range are so chosen that, if any nominal value varies by $\pm 5\%$, then the resulting values will overlap with those of the nearest components above and below if these too vary by $\pm 5\%$ as appropriate.

Try this with some of the values in the range. If the value of a resistor which was nominally 470 Ω varied by $\pm 5\%$, what values would it have? What would be the corresponding values of the next one up in the range if it were 5% lower and the next one down if it were 5% higher?

17

470 Ω + 5% = 493.5 Ω	470 Ω − 5% = 446.5 Ω
510 Ω − 5% = 484.5 Ω	430 Ω + 5% = 451.5 Ω

As may be seen from these values, the value of a 470 Ω resistor which is 5% too high is greater than the value of a 510 Ω resistor which is 5% too low. The rationale for these values is as follows: all components, when manufactured, are marked with a 'nominal value' plus or minus a 'manufacturing tolerance', usually quoted as a percentage. The component manufacturer guarantees only that the actual value of a component lies within the manufacturing tolerance of its nominal value. The actual value of a component may also change in use, owing to such factors as temperature and age. The percentage changes due to these factors will also be guaranteed by the component manufacturer. The total 'working tolerance' of a component during its lifetime of use can, in the worst case, be the sum of all these tolerances.

18

COMPONENT SELECTION AND THE EFFECT OF
TOLERANCES IN DESIGN

A circuit designer has to make allowance for these tolerances and particularly sensitive designs must be analysed very carefully for 'worst case performance'. When a design is made, the designer has to select components having an appropriate nominal value and then decide what tolerance components he intends to specify. He must then check that his design will still function satisfactorily even if the chosen components assume values at the limits of their ranges, and do this in the most disadvantageous way for the operation of the circuit. He does this to ensure that his design will work satisfactorily with components having the nominal values he has chosen, however these values may change during the working life of his design. This often results in a compromise being made – between ideal performance and cost, for example.

It frequently happens, too, that the ideal design value for a particular application lies between two preferred values. The designer then has to select one of these taking due account of the effects it may have on his circuit. Here is an example to illustrate the kinds of decision which need to be made.

In a certain circuit, an engineer requires a resistor which will have a voltage of 6.3 volts developed across it when a current of 2 milliamps flows through it. What values can he choose if selecting from the E24 range?

19

$$\boxed{3.0 \text{ k}\Omega \text{ or } 3.3 \text{ k}\Omega}$$

From Ohm's Law the calculated value required is given as:

$$R = \frac{V}{I} = \frac{6.3}{2} = 3.15 \text{ k}\Omega$$

The calculation is done with the current in mA so the answer is given directly in kΩ. The values given above are the nearest to this figure in the E24 range of preferred values.

If the current in the circuit is known to be exactly 2 mA, what are the largest and smallest values the actual voltage in the circuit could attain? The two 'worst cases' will occur if the components chosen in two different samples of the circuit, one with a 3.0 kΩ resistor and one with a 3.3 kΩ resistor, are at opposite limits of their range?

20

$$\boxed{\text{Largest value: } 6.93 \text{ V} \qquad \text{Smallest value: } 5.70 \text{ V}}$$

The largest value will occur when a 3.3 kΩ resistor is chosen and a sample is picked out which is 5% too large. We then have:

$$\text{Actual resistor value} = 3.3 \times 1.05 = 3.465 \text{ k}\Omega$$

So, by Ohm's Law, the voltage = 3.465 kΩ × 2 mA = 6.93 V.

The smallest value will occur when a 3.0 kΩ resistor is chosen and a sample is picked out which is 5% too small. We then have:

$$\text{Actual resistor value} = 3.0 \times 0.95 = 2.85 \text{ k}\Omega$$

So, by Ohm's Law, the voltage = 2.85 kΩ × 2 mA = 5.70 V.

For other samples of the circuit the actual circuit voltage will lie somewhere between these limits. The designer must decide whether a higher voltage than he wants will be acceptable or whether a lower one would be better, and must be aware of the limits on these values. If he has to have the voltage more precisely defined, he must budget for a more expensive component.

The next frame contains some more practical information followed by some revision examples, so you can practise using the ideas introduced so far.

PRACTICAL CONSIDERATIONS

While the E24 range is the complete range of 5% tolerance components you will frequently find, in both academic and industrial laboratories, that an E12 subset is used. That is, components with nominal values in the range:

$$10 \quad 12 \quad 15 \quad 18 \quad 22 \quad 27 \quad 33 \quad 39 \quad 47 \quad 56 \quad 68 \quad 82$$

This is strictly a 10% range. Furthermore, as manufacturing techniques improved in the 1980s, very cheap, good quality resistors with a manufacturing tolerance of 1% became widely available. In spite of this, it is still common practice to make most designs with components whose nominal values are in the E24 or E12 ranges. The result of this is that there will be quite large gaps in the range of actual values of resistors commonly met with in practice. You will find as you do more and more real designs that, limiting as this may sound, it presents few practical difficulties.

REVISION EXAMPLES

1. A 3.3 kΩ resistor has a current of 5 mA flowing through it. What is the potential difference across it?
2. A 130 kΩ resistor has a potential difference of 3.25 V across it. What is the current flowing through it?
3. The voltage across a resistor is measured as 14 V. The current through it is measured as 2 mA. What is the value of the resistor? If it has been selected from the E12 range, what is its nominal value? Assuming the value you decide on *is* its nominal value, what is its actual tolerance?
4. What is the power dissipation in each of the resistors in questions 1, 2 and 3? Use only the information *given* in each question to calculate the answers to this problem: the resistor value and current in question 1 and so on.
5. A designer wants a current of 20 mA to flow through a certain resistor in a circuit when a voltage of 2.8 volts occurs across it. (This kind of calculation is frequently met with in transistor circuit design. The voltage will be determined by properties of the transistors and other components.) What value (or values) of resistor can he select from the E24 range? What are the largest and smallest currents which could flow through the resistor in different samples of the circuit assuming that no samples of the resistor will ever exceed the rated tolerance of ±5%?

$$\boxed{\text{ANSWERS TO REVISION EXAMPLES}}$$

1. $V = IR$ so $V = 5 \times 10^{-3} \times 3.3 \times 10^3$ V $= 16.5$ V

or $V = 5$ mA $\times 3.3$ kΩ $= 16.5$ V

2. $I = \dfrac{V}{R}$ so $I = \dfrac{3.25}{130 \times 10^3}$ A $= 25 \times 10^{-3} \times 10^{-3}$ A $= 25 \times 10^{-6}$ A $= 25$ μA

or $I = \dfrac{3.25 \text{ V}}{130 \text{ kΩ}} = 25 \times 10^{-3}$ mA $= 25$μA

3. $R = \dfrac{V}{I}$ so $R = \dfrac{14}{2 \times 10^{-3}} = 7.0 \times 10^3$ Ω $= 7.0$ kΩ

or $R = \dfrac{14 \text{ V}}{2 \text{ mA}} = 7.0$ kΩ

The nearest preferred value in the E24 range is 6.8 kΩ so this must be the nominal value of the resistor. (The smallest value a 7.5 kΩ resistor can be, allowing for a −5% tolerance, is 7.125 kΩ.)

The actual tolerance is $\dfrac{7.0 - 6.8}{6.8} \times 100\% = 2.94\%$.

4. (1) $P = I^2R$ so $P = 25 \times 10^{-6} \times 3.3 \times 10^3$ W $= 82.5 \times 10^{-3}$ W $= 82.5$ mW

(2) $P = \dfrac{V^2}{R}$ so $P = \dfrac{10.5625}{130 \times 10^3}$ W $= 0.08125 \times 10^{-3}$ W $\times 81.25 \times 10^{-6}$ W

$= 81.25$ μW

Note: power calculations involving the expressions I²R and V²/R are best carried out as above. Because of the squared terms it is easy to make mistakes in calculating the power of 10 to be used with the basic unit of Watts.

(3) $P = VI$ so $P = 14 \times 2 \times 10^{-3}$ W $= 28 \times 10^{-3}$ W $= 28$ mW

or $P = 14$ V $\times 2$ mA $= 28$ mW

5. Design value of resistor $= \dfrac{2.8 \text{ V}}{20 \text{ mA}} = 0.14$ kΩ $= 140$ Ω.

Values of 130 Ω or 150 Ω can be selected from the E24 range.

Largest current would be $\dfrac{2.8}{(130 - 6.5)}$ A $= \dfrac{2.8}{123.5}$ A $= 22.7$ mA.

Smallest current would be $\dfrac{2.8}{(150 + 7.5)}$ A $= \dfrac{2.8}{157.5}$ A $= 17.8$ mA.

23

GENERATORS

In circuit terms, a generator is a circuit element which is capable of supplying electrical energy to a circuit. For circuit modelling purposes, we use the concept of an 'ideal' generator. This then allows us to produce models of practical generators like batteries and laboratory power supplies. There are two basic kinds of generators: voltage generators and current generators. We will look at voltage generators first.

> An ideal *voltage generator* is a circuit element which will supply a given voltage to a circuit regardless of the current drawn from it.

Such a generator will supply current only through a closed path or *closed circuit*. Such a path may be set up when a resistor is connected to the generator. Connection between the two devices (the generator and the resistor) is made via terminals. For circuit modelling purposes, we can imagine that any circuit element has terminals on it. In some cases these 'model terminals' may represent real terminals such as metal connectors which can be screwed or clamped together as mentioned earlier in frame 4. In other cases the model terminals may simply represent the ends of pieces of wire attached to the circuit element. These will be useful reference points when we connect many elements together.

24

We saw in frame 3 how circuit diagrams are used to help clarify theoretical concepts. In circuit diagrams, each circuit element is represented by a different symbol. Here is the symbol for a voltage generator:

Notice the pair of terminals. These are the small circles on the ends of the lines. When drawing a diagram to represent two or more circuit elements connected together, we often miss off the terminals.

How would you represent an ideal voltage generator connected to a resistor to form a closed circuit? Do not show any terminals.

25

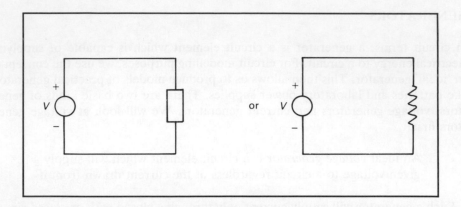

Here is the diagram with the terminals missed off. Unless you specifically want to refer to a particular point in the circuit, it usually makes the diagram tidier if you do miss them off. Notice that you can draw resistors vertically (as in the diagram above) or horizontally to make your diagram as neat as possible. There are certain conventions to be observed when large diagrams containing many elements are drawn but, as long as the interconnections truly represent those in the real circuit being modelled, they can be put on paper in many different ways. Sometimes, when analysing circuits, it is convenient to make use of this fact by re-drawing a circuit to make it more easy to understand.

26

Let us now analyse this simple circuit. The + and − signs on the symbol for the generator are there to indicate its 'polarity'. They determine in which direction a current will *flow* from the generator. It is necessary, before proceeding, to establish what we mean by the 'direction' of current flow. In the first frame of this section current was described as being produced by the movement of charged particles called electrons. An electron carries a *negative* charge, so moving electrons carry negative charges round a circuit in the direction of their movement. In the diagram above, electrons would move in an anticlockwise direction. In circuit analysis, however, we always work in terms of what is called *conventional current*. Conventional current flows in the opposite direction to *electron current*. This model has the advantage that, outside a generator, conventional current flows from the positive terminal to the negative terminal. That is, outside a generator conventional current flow is from a point of higher potential to a point of lower potential or, more simply, from a high voltage to a lower voltage.

Which way does conventional current flow in the diagram above?

27

Clockwise

Conventional current flows clockwise from the positive terminal of the generator down through the resistor and back into the generator at its negative terminal. Inside the generator it flows from the negative terminal to the positive terminal so completing the circuit. If the generator represents one which is designed to give a steady, unchanging voltage, we call it a direct voltage generator. The current is then called a direct current. Capital letters are used to represent direct quantities in mathematical equations. If the generator voltage is V and the resistor is of value R, we could re-draw the diagram to indicate the magnitude and direction of the current as shown here. We have added an ideal *voltmeter* to measure the voltage.

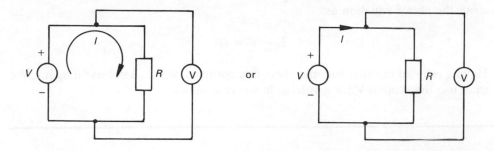

28

The two terminals on the voltmeter allow it to be connected to circuits so that the voltage between two points in the circuit can be measured. The reading on the voltmeter in this circuit can be interpreted in two ways. It can be regarded as telling us the *output voltage* of the voltage generator if we think of it as measuring the voltage across the left-hand side of the circuit. Alternatively, it can be regarded as telling us the voltage across the resistor if we think of it as measuring the voltage across the right-hand side of the circuit. Since there is, of course, only one reading, the two quantities must be the same. Notice that thin lines, such as those joining the generator and the resistor, are regarded as representing wires having zero resistance so, by Ohm's Law, there can be no voltage drop across them. It therefore does not matter where on the lines the connections are assumed to be made. For most practical purposes connecting wires in real circuits can be taken as having zero resistance.

Can you write down an equation showing the equivalence of the two quantities represented by the reading on the voltmeter?

29

$$V = IR$$

Notice that the equation we have written is Ohm's Law. When we wrote down Ohm's Law earlier, we talked of the voltage V developed across a resistor R when a current I flows through it. This circuit shows one of the ways we can make a current flow through a resistor. That is, we can connect a voltage generator across it. The output of a voltage generator is often called an 'electromotive force' or e.m.f. This acknowledges the fact that it can be thought of as a 'force that moves electrons'. (It does not, of course, have the dimensions of force but can, by means of electric field theory be associated with one. See, for example, *Electromagnetism* by R. Powell in the same series as this text.) Some authors like to use the symbol E for e.m.f., keeping the symbol V for the voltage across a resistor. With this notation we could write the above equation as:

$$E = V = IR$$

Having pointed out that you may meet this notation, we shall not use it again. We shall use the symbol V for a voltage however it arises.

30

We can re-draw the diagram again to show that the voltage across the resistor also has polarity associated with it. It is, of course, the same as that across the generator as is shown by the reading on the voltmeter.

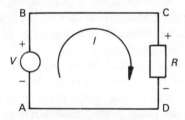

When related to the direction of conventional current flow in the circuit, notice that the two polarities are, in effect, 'equal and opposite'. There is an increase of voltage from A through the generator to B. There is no change in voltage from B to C because the connecting wire has zero resistance. There is a drop in voltage from C through the resistor to D. There is no change again from D via the other zero-resistance connecting wire to A which brings us back to the point we started at.

The result we have just established is, in fact, a very simple example of an important circuit law we shall look at in detail later. The generator produces a voltage or e.m.f. which, when connected to the resistor, causes a current to flow through it. As a result of this current flowing through the resistor, a voltage is developed across it. From consideration of this result, we can make a very import-ant statement about voltages across and currents through resistors.

When a conventional current flows through a resistor, a voltage is developed across it such that the end the current flows into is positive with respect to the end the current flows out of.

Now, remembering that an ideal voltage generator maintains the same voltage between its terminals regardless of the current drawn from it, can you say what total current would be drawn from the generator discussed in the last few frames if an additional resistor of value $R/2$ were connected between the generator ter-minals? Do the calculation by applying Ohm's Law to each resistor in turn then draw a diagram to illustrate the situation.

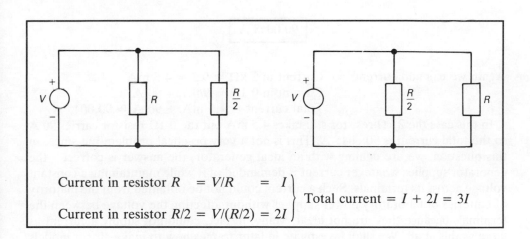

Current in resistor R $= V/R$ $= I$

Current in resistor $R/2 = V/(R/2) = 2I$

Total current $= I + 2I = 3I$

Either of the diagrams given above can be used to represent the connection of the additional resistor. To calculate the total current we note that both resistors have the generator voltage connected across them and this does not change what-ever the load, so the current in each can be calculated by applying Ohm's Law to each in turn. The total current draw from the generator must then be the sum of the two individual currents.

Suppose the generator voltage was 9 V and the resistors were respectively 2 kΩ and 1 kΩ, what would the currents be?

33

> 4.5 mA, 9.0 mA and 13.5 mA

From the last frame we have: Current in $R = V/R = 9/2 = 4.5$ mA

Current in $R/2 = 2V/R = 18/2 = 9.0$ mA

Total current $= 4.5 + 9.0 = 13.5$ mA

Currents in a very wide range of electronic circuits from radio and television sets to computers are in the milliamp or microamp range, so you should get used to dealing with quantities of this order.

Suppose, instead of 1 kΩ and 2kΩ resistors in the above circuit, resistors of value 0.1Ω and 2 kΩ had been used. What then would be the total current drawn from the generator?

34

> 90.0045 A

Again we can add currents so: Current in 2 k$\Omega = 9/2 = 4.5$ mA

Current in 0.1$\Omega = 9/0.1 = 90$ A

Total current $= 4.5$ mA $+ 90$ A $= 90.0045$ A

In this case the 2 kΩ resistor still takes 4.5 mA but the 0.1Ω resistor carries 90 A so the total current is 90.0045 A. This is not a very practical problem but since, in this question, we are dealing with an ideal generator, the answer is correct – the generator supplies whatever current is demanded of it while maintaining a constant voltage across its terminals. Such a current could not be obtained from the majority of batteries or laboratory power supplies without affecting the voltage between the terminals because they are not ideal. Many, in fact, could not supply a current as large as this at all. We shall investigate in later frames how to make circuit models which take account of the imperfections of non-ideal generators.

In the last few frames we have analysed circuits consisting of resistors connected to voltage generators. Another circuit element which is very useful in modelling circuit behaviour is the current generator. We will look at this in the next few frames.

CURRENT GENERATORS

An ideal current generator is a circuit element which will supply a given current to a circuit regardless of the voltage developed across it.

The definition is similar in form to that for the ideal voltage generator. To understand it we must first examine how a voltage is developed across a current generator when it supplies current. The following diagram represents a current generator connected to a resistor. The arrow shows the direction in which conventional current flows.

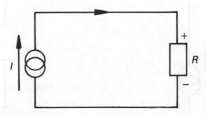

As current I flows from the generator and round the circuit it passes through the resistor R. A voltage V is therefore developed across the resistor where, as before:

$$V = IR$$

The polarity of the voltage across the resistor is indicated by the plus and minus signs. As before, the end of the resistor that the current flows into is at a higher potential than the end it flows out of. Here, just like the circuit in frame 30 where we had a voltage generator connected to a resistor, there must be a voltage across the current generator which is equal and opposite to that across the resistor. If the current is 25 mA and the resistor is 1.2 kΩ, what is the magnitude of the voltage?

36

> The voltage is of magnitude 3 V

The voltage is $2.5 \times 10^{-3} \times 1.2 \times 10^3 = 3$ volts

So, connecting the current generator to a resistor produces a voltage of 3 V across the resistor. This voltage also appears across the terminals of the generator. We could confirm this by connecting a voltmeter between these terminals. Now let us investigate the effect of changing the resistor.

37

ANALYSING A CURRENT GENERATOR CIRCUIT

If the circuit is broken and a second resistor of value 2.4 kΩ is added in so that the new circuit is as shown here, what will be the new voltage across the current generator? You may make use of the following facts which are contained in another fundamental circuit law which we shall study more fully later: the same current flows through both resistors; the voltages across them are in the same sense so they simply add together.

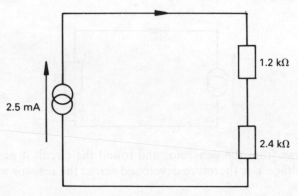

38

> The new voltage will be 9 volts.

Here we have the opposite situation to the voltage generator. This time the current is maintained constant by the generator. Since the current flows through both components we can again calculate the voltage across each using Ohm's Law. Now, however, the two voltages across the resistors add together to give the total voltage across the generator. Hence we have:

$$\text{Voltage across 1.2 k}\Omega \text{ resistor} = 2.5 \times 10^{-3} \times 1.2 \times 10^3 = 3 \text{ V}$$

$$\text{Voltage across 2.4 k}\Omega \text{ resistor} = 2.5 \times 10^{-3} \times 2.4 \times 10^3 = 6 \text{ V}$$

$$\text{Total voltage} = 3 \text{ V} + 6 \text{ V} = 9 \text{ V}$$

What would be the voltage across the current generator if, instead of the 2.4 kΩ resistor, a 2.4 MΩ resistor was inserted into the circuit?

39

> The voltage would be 6.003 kV

Here we have: Voltage across 1.2 kΩ = 2.5 × 1.2 = 3 V

Voltage across 2.4 MΩ = 2.5 × 10^{-3} × 2.4 × 10^6 = 6000 V

Total voltage = 3 V + 6000 V = 6003 V

As before, this voltage is also developed across the terminals of the current generator.

This is another example which is not very realistic in practice but which serves to illustrate that, if perfect current generators are assumed, very large voltages can be generated. An ideal current generator will continue to supply a fixed current whatever voltage is developed across its terminals. Circuits can be designed which approximate quite closely to perfect current generators under certain conditions but, in general, they will not support voltages in the kilovolt range across their terminals.

40

We have discovered in the last few frames that current flow, which is the basic phenomenon on which the science of electric circuit theory depends, can be produced in resistors by connecting voltage or current generators to them. We have seen too that, when a current flows through a resistor, a voltage is developed across it. We saw in earlier frames that a resistor with a current flowing through it and a voltage across it dissipates power. As power is dissipated over a period of time energy is 'consumed'. This energy must be supplied from somewhere. It is, of course, the generators which supply it.

In the next few frames we will look at power and energy considerations associated with generators.

41

POWER AND ENERGY IN GENERATOR CIRCUITS

A resistor which is connected to a generator to form a closed circuit so that current is drawn from the generator is often referred to as a *load resistor* or just a *load*. If an ideal voltage generator of output V is connected to a load resistor of resistance R so that a current I flows from the generator through the load we can represent this situation, as we have seen, by the following diagram:

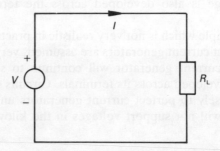

The voltage shown on the diagram can be interpreted either as the voltage across the load or as the voltage across the generator. The current flows through both. The power P dissipated in the load is given by the expression $P = VI$ so the energy W absorbed by the load in time T is VIT.

By the conservation of energy, this must also be the energy supplied by the generator in the same time T. Thus the product VI of the voltage across the generator and the current through the generator also gives the amount of power being supplied by the generator at any instant.

How much energy would a perfect 12 volt battery supply to a 3 Ω resistor in half an hour?

42

> 86.4 kilojoules

Here are the calculations:

I = V/R_L so the current in the load is 12/3 = 4 A
P = VI so the power dissipated in the resistor is 12 × 4 = 48 W
W = VIT so the energy absorbed in half an hour is 48 × 30 × 60 joules
$$= 86.4 \text{ kJ}$$

So the energy supplied by the battery is also 86.4 kJ.

The same kind of calculations can be carried out when an ideal current generator is connected to a load resistor. Now draw a diagram of an ideal current generator of output I connected to a load resistor R_L so that a voltage V is developed across the load. Show on your diagram the polarities of both the voltage across the load and the voltage across the generator.

43

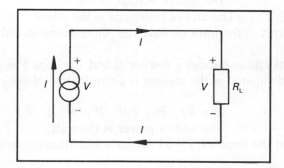

As is the case with the voltage generator, the voltage shown on this diagram can be interpreted either as the voltage across the load or the voltage across the generator. The current again flows through both.

What is the power dissipated in the load and what is the energy supplied by the generator in time T?

44

> The power dissipated in the load is VI.
> The energy supplied by the generator is VIT.

The power dissipated in the load is given by the product of the current through it and the voltage across it. The energy absorbed by the load is the product of this power and the time for which it is dissipated. As before this must be the energy supplied by the generator over the same period.

Now turn the page for a summary of the work we have done so far and then try to complete the revision examples which follow it.

45

SUMMARY

1. Ohm's Law states that, when a current I is flowing through a resistor R, the voltage V developed across the resistor is given by the equation:

$$V = IR$$

The unit of current is the ampere.
The unit of voltage is the volt.
The unit of resistance is the ohm.
Terms of the form IR have the 'dimensions' of voltage.

2. When a current I flows through a resistor R and a voltage V is developed across it, the power dissipated in the resistor is given by one of the expressions:

$$P = VI \quad P = I^2R \quad P = V^2/R$$

The unit of power is the watt.
Terms of the form VI, I^2R, V^2/R have the 'dimensions' of power.

3. Cheap, readily available, practical components come in a limited range of sizes known as 'preferred values'. The 5% range consists of the values:

$$10 \quad 11 \quad 12 \quad 13 \quad 15 \quad 16 \quad 18 \quad 20 \quad 22 \quad 24 \quad 27 \quad 30$$
$$33 \quad 36 \quad 39 \quad 43 \quad 47 \quad 51 \quad 56 \quad 62 \quad 68 \quad 75 \quad 82 \quad 91$$

These 'nominal' values may be multiplied by an appropriate positive or negative power of ten to match the value nearest to that required in a particular design.

4. An ideal voltage generator is a circuit element which will supply a given voltage to a circuit regardless of the current drawn from it.

5. An ideal current generator is a circuit element which will supply a given current to a circuit regardless of the voltage developed across it.

6. When a generator supplies energy that is absorbed by a load, the power delivered at any instant can be calculated either as the product of the voltage across the generator and the current drawn from the generator or as the product of the voltage across the load and the current through the load. The energy supplied is the product of the power and the time for which it is supplied.

REVISION QUESTIONS

1. Here is a diagram of an ideal voltage generator connected to a resistor:

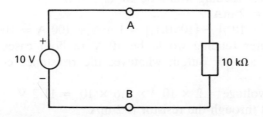

(a) What is the current drawn from the generator?

(b) What would be the reading on a voltmeter connected between the terminals A and B?

(c) If an additional resistor of value 10 kΩ were connected between the terminals A and B, what now would be the current drawn from the generator? What would be the reading on the voltmeter, assuming it were still left connected?

(d) If, instead of the resistor in (c), a resistor of value 0.1 Ω were connected between the terminals A and B, what would be the current drawn from the generator? What would be the reading on the voltmeter?

2. Here is a diagram of an ideal current generator connected to a resistor:

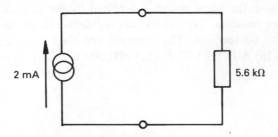

(a) What is the voltage across the generator?

(b) What is the current through the resistor?

(c) What would be the voltage across the terminals A and B if a 560 Ω resistor were substituted for the one in the diagram?

(d) What would be the voltage across the terminals A and B if a 56 MΩ resistor were substituted for the one in the diagram?

(e) What are the currents through the resistors in (c) and (d)?

3. What is the power dissipated in each of the resistors in questions 1 and 2? What energy would be delivered by the generators in a period of 10 minutes?

47

ANSWERS TO REVISION QUESTIONS

1. (a) $I = V/R$ so current $= 10/(10 \times 10^3) = 1$ mA.

(b) The voltmeter reading would be 10 V.

(c) $I = 2(V/R) = 2$ mA.

(d) $I = [10/(10 \times 10^3)] + [10/(0.1)] = 1$ mA $+ 100$ A $= 100.001$ A.

(e) The voltmeter reading would be 10 V in both cases. Being ideal, the generator gives a 10 V output whatever the resistance connected across its terminals.

2. (a) $V = IR$ so voltage $= 2 \times 10^{-3} \times 5.6 \times 10^3 = 11.2$ V.

(b) The current through the resistor is 2 mA.

(c) With 560 Ω in circuit, the new voltage would be $2 \times 10^{-3} \times 560 = 1.12$ V.

(d) With 56 MΩ in circuit, the new voltage would be $2 \times 10^{-3} \times 56 \times 10^6 = 112 \times 10^3 = 112$ kV!

(e) The current in each case would still be 2 mA. Being ideal, the generator gives a 2 mA output whatever the resistance connected between its terminals.

3. In case 1a, power $= 1$ mA $\times 10$ V $= 10$ mW.

In case 1b, power $= 2$ ma $\times 10$ V $= 20$ mW.

In case 1c, power $= 100.001$ A $\times 10$ V $= 1000.01$ W $= 1.00001$ kW.

In case 2a, power $= 2$ mA $\times 11.2$ V $= 22.4$ mW.

In case 2b, power $= 2$ mA $\times 1.12$ V $= 2.24$ mW.

In case 2c, power $= 2$ mA $\times 112$ kV $= 224$ W.

In each case above the same power is supplied by the generator as is dissipated in the resistor or resistors. To find the energy delivered we multiply each power in turn by 10×60 seconds. The answers are then in Joules. So we get for the six cases: (1a) 6 J; (1b) 12 J; (1c) 600.006 kJ; (2a) 13.44 J; (2b) 1.344 J; (2c) 134.4 kJ.

48

NON-IDEAL GENERATORS

So far, we have looked only at ideal generators. Practical generators cannot sustain the voltages and currents, regardless of loads, that ideal generators can. The reason for this is that practical generators have internal resistances. For most purposes a practical generator can, however, be modelled by an ideal generator and a resistor. In reality there may be no single identifiable resistor inside the generator corresponding to the one in the model but, for all practical purposes, it will appear to users of the generator that there is one. A practical voltage generator may be represented by the model in the left-hand diagram below:

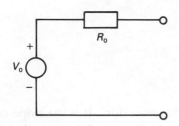 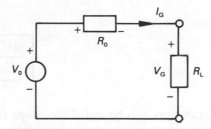

The right-hand diagram above shows a load resistor R_L connected to the generator so that a current I_G is drawn from it. The terminals shown on these diagrams represent the connections to the practical generator that are available to the 'outside world'. The voltage V which could be measured at these terminals is given by the equation:

$$V_G = V_0 - I_G R_0$$

This is the voltage across the load resistor R_L and is, effectively, the ideal generator voltage minus the voltage 'dropped' across the internal resistance R_0 due to the current I_G taken from the generator. Notice how the expression for this voltage is derived. It takes account of the 'sense' of the terms involved depending on their polarities as indicated by the plus and minus signs on the diagram. Starting from the bottom of the load resistor, we move clockwise round the circuit. There is no voltage across the line at the bottom of the diagram. Across the generator the voltage increases by an amount V because the polarity is from negative to positive. Across the resistor, R_0, the voltage decreases by an amount $I_G R_0$ because the polarity is from positive to negative.

Which terms in this equation are constants of the generator and which will change for different values of load resistor?

49

V_0 and R_0 are constants; V_G and R_G are variables.

V_0 and R_0 are constants of the generator. V_0 is called the 'generator open circuit voltage' and R_0 is called the 'generator output resistance'. We will examine the reasons for these names later. V_G and I_G are variables which depend on the value of R_L connected to the generator. They are the observable or measurable generator voltage and current at its terminals.

Can you differentiate the equation $V_G = V_0 - I_G R_0$ by I_G? What is the result?

50

$$\frac{dV_G}{dI_G} = - R_0$$

R_0 can thus also be called the 'slope resistance of the generator'. It is the slope or gradient of a graph of generator voltage against generator current. Now, you sketch this graph, choosing arbitrary scales for V_G and I_G. All you need do at this stage is show the general shape of the graph and the direction of its slope.

51

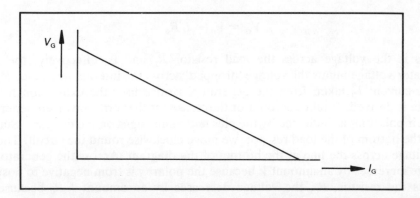

The slope of the graph is negative which is consistent with the result in frame 46. What is the intercept on the V_G axis?

52

| The intercept is V_0 |

From the graph and the equation in frame 49, this is the value of V_G when I_G is equal to zero. But, if $V_G = V_0$, the ideal generator voltage then, looking at the diagram (reproduced below), we can see that there is no potential difference across R_0. This also, in fact follows from applying Ohm's Law to R_0, since I_G flows through R_0 and I_G is zero. But I_G flows through R_L too and the voltage across R_L is V_G which, in this case, equals V_0.

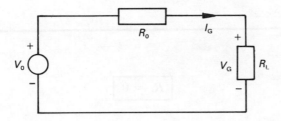

So, if we apply Ohm's Law to R_L we shall be able to deduce the value of R_L. You do this and say what the value of R_L is. Be careful how you answer this question!

53

| $R_L = \infty$ |

Applying Ohm's Law to R_L, we have $V_G = I_G R_L$ and so $R_L = V_G/I_G$.
But $I_G = 0$ and V_G is equal to V_0, a constant, so R_L must be infinite.

R_L thus has such a high resistance that no current at all flows through it. It is the same as if there was no connection at all between the two terminals and so no closed path through which current could flow. This is what is called an 'open-circuit' and explains why the voltage V_0 is called the generator open-circuit voltage. It is the voltage which can be measured at the terminals of the generator when these terminals are open-circuit.

Looking again at the graph, what is the intercept on the I_G axis?

54

> The intercept on the I_G axis is V_0/R_0

From the graph and the equation $V_G = V_0 - I_G R_0$, this is the value of I_G when V_G is zero. When this is so we have:

$$0 = V_0 - I_G R_0 \quad \text{so} \quad V_0 = I_G R_0 \quad \text{and} \quad I_G = V_0/R_0$$

Once again, by applying Ohm's Law to R_L, we should be able to deduce the value of R_L which brings about these conditions. You do that and say what the value of R_L is.

55

> $R_L = 0$

Again $R_L = V_G/I_G$ but now $V_G = 0$ while I_G is finite and non-zero so R_L must be zero. Since R_L has no resistance it follows that, even though a current I_G flows through it, no voltage is developed across it. A connection such as this which offers no resistance is called a short-circuit. Under these conditions, when the value of $I_G = V_0/R_0$, it is called the 'short-circuit current'. It is the current which flows through a short-circuit connected across the output of the (non-ideal) generator.

Now look back over the last few frames and answer the following question. What is the ratio of the open-circuit voltage to the short-circuit current in the circuit we have just studied?

56

> The ratio is R_0

This is a simple example of a very important theorem we shall return to later. The ratio of the open-circuit voltage to the short-circuit current is the output resistance of the generator. This relationship, in fact, *defines* the output resistance of the generator. For any practical generator, measurements of these two quantities could be made and their ratio calculated to give the output resistance. Special equipment could, however, be necessary in cases where this resistance was known to be very small!

PRACTICAL CURRENT GENERATORS

As we have seen, a practical voltage generator can be modelled by an ideal voltage generator and a resistor. In just the same way, a practical current generator can be modelled by an ideal current generator and a resistor. This time, however, the resistor is connected across the generator as is shown in the following diagram (the reason for the different resistor connection in the two models will become clear shortly):

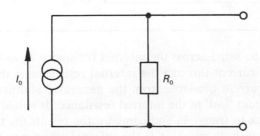

How would you show a load resistor R_L connected to this generator so that current could flow through the load?

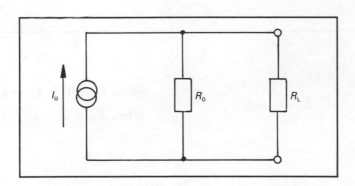

If current is to flow through the load resistor R_L, it must be connected to both output terminals of the generator so that current can flow in at one end of the resistor and out at the other end. As we did in frame 56 for the voltage generator, we can again call the voltage observable at the generator terminals V_G and the current drawn from the generator I_G. Can you re-draw the diagram with these quantities marked on it and then write an equation for I_G in terms of V_G and the generator constants I_0 and R_0?

59

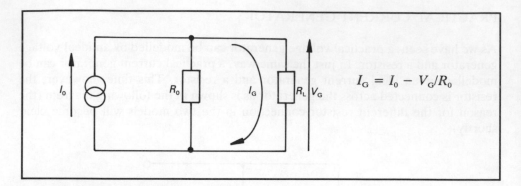

$$I_G = I_0 - V_G/R_0$$

The voltage V_G is the same across the internal resistance R_0 as it is across the load resistance R_L. The current through the internal resistance is therefore, by Ohm's Law, V_G/R_0. The current available from the generator is thus less than the ideal amount by the amount 'lost' in the internal resistance. It would now be instructive for you to turn back to frame 48 and compare the results for the two generators. You will see that, in both cases, it is the internal resistance that represents the non-ideal aspect of the generators and its presence results in the available outputs of either voltage or current being less than the ideal amount.

Can you now draw a graph of V_G against I_G for this circuit, marking the values of the intercepts on the V_G and I_G axes?

60

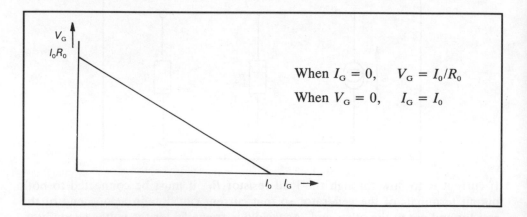

When $I_G = 0$, $V_G = I_0/R_0$

When $V_G = 0$, $I_G = I_0$

Rearranging the equation in frame 59 gives $V_G = I_0R_0 - I_GR_0$. The intercepts can be found by setting first $I_G = 0$ and then $V_G = 0$ in this equation. What values of R_L correspond to these intercepts?

> The intercept on the V_G axis is obtained when R_L is infinite.
> The intercept on the I_G axis is obtained when R_L is zero.

It will be useful to have the diagram again to help understand the situations that result in the intercepts on the axes of the graph. Here it is:

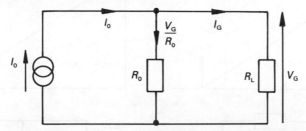

We have drawn it this time with the currents shown as arrows on the lines through which they flow. This is the preferred British Standard way of showing currents and gives a clearer picture in this example.

The equation of the graph is $V_G = I_0 R_0 - I_G R_0$.

The intercept on the V_G axis is obtained when $I_G = 0$.

Hence, substituting this value in the equation, we have $V_G = I_0 R_0$.

From the diagram we can see that, if there is no current in R_L, then all the current I_0 must flow in R_0. There must therefore be a non-zero voltage $I_0 R_0$ across this resistor. But this voltage is also across R_L.

So, by Ohm's Law, the value of R_L is therefore $I_0 R_0 / I_G = I_0 R_0 / 0 = \infty$.

The intercept on the I_G axis is obtained when $V_G = 0$.

Hence $0 = I_0 R_0 - I_G R_0$ and so $I_G = I_0$.

This means that all the generator current I_0 must flow through R_L. From the diagram we can see that this means there is no generator current left to flow through R_0 so the current in R_0 must be zero. But we have started with the condition that there is no voltage across R_L.

So, again by Ohm's Law, the value of R_L is therefore $V_G / I_0 = 0 / I_0 = 0$.

Some very interesting and useful results can be obtained by comparing the graphs derived when a non-ideal voltage generator and a non-ideal current generator are connected to a load resistor. We will investigate this in the next frame.

62

Here are the two graphs we have been studying in the last few frames together with the circuits whose operation they represent.

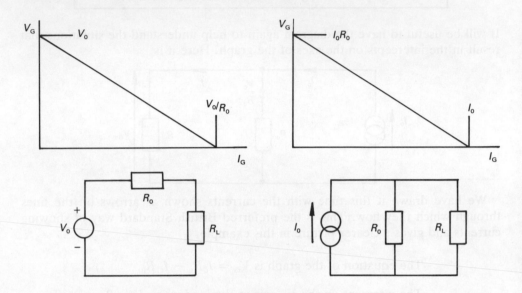

Now suppose we had a generator concealed inside a 'black box' on which there was just a pair of terminals showing. By connecting a range of resistors of different values to the terminals and measuring the voltage V_G across each resistor and the current I_G flowing through it, we could produce a graph of V_G against I_G just like those above.

By comparing the two graphs above, can you answer the following question? Under what conditions would it be impossible for us to say that one model rather than the other represented what was in the box?

63

$$V_0 = I_0 R_0$$

With this condition the two graphs would be identical, the intercepts on both axes being the same. It would thus be impossible, simply from measurements made from outside the box, to say exactly what was in the box. We could say only that the generator inside the box could be represented by one of the two models shown above.

This discovery gives us a very important result:

Any practical generator can be modelled either as a voltage generator V_0 and a resistor R_0 connected as shown in the left-hand diagram in frame 62, or as a current generator I_0 and a resistor R_0 connected as shown in the right-hand diagram in frame 62. As long as $V_0 = I_0 R_0$ the two different models will give identical results for all measurements of V_G and I_G made at the terminals of the generator.

We shall see in later frames that it is more appropriate to use the voltage generator model when all load resistors used are much greater than the internal resistance R_0. When load resistors much less than the internal resistance R_0 are used, the current generator model is more appropriate.

64

SERIES AND PARALLEL CONNECTIONS

In the preceding frames we have been analysing circuits containing only a few components. Many practical circuits contain large numbers of components interconnected in many different ways. Many interconnection patterns, however, can be described as combinations of two basic configurations: series and parallel. Using these two basic configurations, it is then often possible, for analytical purposes, to reduce a circuit to a simpler form. We will examine these two configurations in the next few frames and see how they can be used for circuit reduction.

The series connection

Components which are connected end-to-end in a chain formation are said to be 'in series'. Adjacent components share only one common terminal. When they are part of a circuit, the *same* current flows through both components. A diagram shows the configuration most clearly.

Here is a diagram of two resistors connected in series:

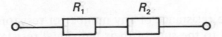

We can calculate the effective resistance of these two components taken together by connecting them to a voltage generator to form a closed circuit and then finding the current drawn from the generator. Can you draw a suitable circuit diagram? Remember that you can draw components any way you like to give a convenient picture.

65

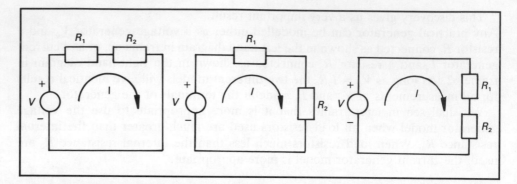

Any of the three diagrams above is suitable as, in fact, would be any diagram which represented the same connections. The right-hand ones appear more balanced and are the kind which would be more likely to be used in professional reports. You should cultivate the habit of sketching diagrams like those on the right.

Analysing the circuit, we have:

The voltage across $R_1 = IR_1$ The voltage across $R_2 = IR_2$

Now, voltages can be added so the total voltage $= IR_1 + IR_2$

But the total voltage $= V$, the generator voltage

So $V = IR_1 + IR_2 = I(R_1 + R_2)$

Letting the combined resistance of the two resistors be R, we also have:

$$V = IR$$

hence $IR = I(R_1 + R_2)$ and so $R = R_1 + R_2$

The result extends to any number of resistors in series and, in general:

The effective resistance of any number of resistors in series is
equal to the sum of their individual resistances.

It follows that the effective resistance of any number of resistors in series is greater than the resistance of any of the individual resistors.

What would be the effective resistance of:

(a) A 4.7 kΩ resistor in series with a 6.8 kΩ resistor?
(b) Three resistors in series, one of 200 Ω, one of 1.2 kΩ and one of 620 kΩ?

(a) 11.5 kΩ   (b) 621.4 kΩ

In both cases the values of the resistances are simply added together. In the second case we have to convert all values into kΩ before adding them.

The parallel connection

Components which are connected between the same pair of terminals are said to be 'in parallel'. All components share the same two terminals and thus have the same voltage across them. Again a diagram helps to illustrate the situation.
   This diagram shows two resistors connected in parallel:

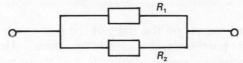

Here is a voltage generator connected across the resistors. We can now determine the current I and hence their effective combined resistance:

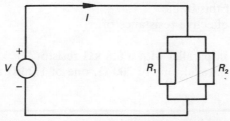

The generator voltage V appears across both components, so:

$$\text{Current in } R_1 = \frac{V}{R_1} \quad \text{Current in } R_2 = \frac{V}{R_2} \quad \text{so} \quad \text{Total current} = \frac{V}{R_1} + \frac{V}{R_2}$$

But total current = I, the generator current so, letting the combined resistance of the two resistors be R, we also have

$$I = \frac{V}{R} = \frac{V}{R_1} + \frac{V}{R_2} \quad \text{and so} \quad \frac{1}{R} = \frac{1}{R_1} + \frac{1}{R_2}$$

A reciprocal resistance is called a conductance and is given the symbol G. Hence $G = G_1 + G_2$. The unit of conductance is the *siemens*. This result, too, can be extended and we find that the effective conductance of any number of resistors in parallel is greater than the conductance of any individual resistor. Can you deduce a statement linking the effective *resistance* of any number of resistors in parallel to their individual resistances?

67

> The effective resistance of any number of resistors in parallel is less than the resistance of any of the individual resistors.

This result follows if the defining relationship is written in reciprocal form. Since $1/R$ is the *sum* of all the individual $1/R_n$ terms, it *must* be greater than any individual $1/R_n$. It follows that R must be *smaller* than any individual R_n. The result can be appreciated another way if only two resistors are involved as in the example in frame 66:

$$\text{If} \quad \frac{1}{R} = \frac{1}{R_1} + \frac{1}{R_2} \quad \text{then} \quad R = \frac{R_1 R_2}{R_1 + R_2} \quad \text{or} \quad R = R_1 \left(\frac{R_2}{R_1 + R_2} \right)$$

Since the last term in brackets on the right of the line above has a denominator which is larger than its numerator, it is clearly less than 1. Hence R must be less than R_1. But the expression is symmetrical in R_1 and R_2, so we can write a similar expression for R_2 to show that R is also less than R_2. If we had more resistors in parallel we could continue this line of argument for each additional resistor to give the result at the top of this frame.

What would be the effective resistance of:

(a) A 4.7 kΩ resistor in parallel with a 6.8 kΩ resistor?
(b) Three resistors in parallel, one of 200 Ω, one of 1.2 kΩ and one of 620 kΩ?

68

> (a) 2.78 Ω
> (a) 171.38 Ω

For only two resistors we can use $\quad R = \dfrac{R_1 R_2}{R_1 + R_2} = \dfrac{4.7 \times 6.8}{4.7 + 6.8} = 2.78$ kΩ.

With more than two resistors it is easier to use the reciprocal rule:

$$\frac{1}{R} = \frac{1}{R_1} + \frac{1}{R_2} + \frac{1}{R_3} = \frac{1}{200} + \frac{1}{1200} + \frac{1}{620,000} = 0.005835$$

So $R = 171.38$ Ω.

69

GENERATORS IN SERIES AND PARALLEL

Generators can be connected in series and in parallel, just as resistors can. Some connections, however, are meaningless if postulated with ideal generators since they make the generators try to do impossible things. Diagrams (a) and (b) below show respectively two voltage generators and two current generators in series. Diagrams (c) and (d) show two voltage generators and two current generators in parallel. Checking, if necessary, the definitions of ideal voltage and current generators in frame 45, can you say which of the connections below are meaningful and which are not?

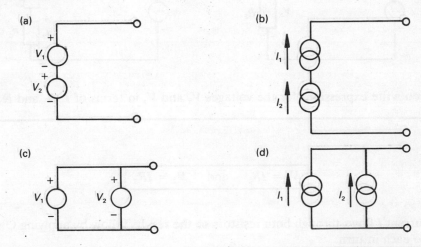

70

> (a) and (d) are meaningful; (b) and (c) are not.

Considering (a) and (d) first, we see that, in case (a) the two voltages simply add together so the total voltage that is developed across a resistor connected between the terminals is the sum of the two individual voltages. In case (d) the two currents add together so the total current that flows in a resistor connected between the terminals is the sum of the two individual currents. In both cases (b) and (c) the two generators 'fight each other for supremacy'. In case (b) the two current generators each try to force a different current through the same piece of wire, which cannot happen. In case (c) the two voltage generators each try to maintain a different voltage across the same pair of terminals which also cannot happen. (We will examine the effect of these connections with practical generators in a later programme.)

71

THE POTENTIAL DIVIDER

The configuration we first analysed in frame 48 and shown again here is often called a potential divider. Either diagram may be used. Both are equally good representations of the connections made.

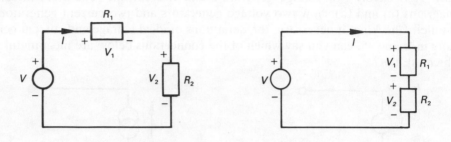

Can you write expressions for the voltages V_1 and V_2 in terms of I, R_1 and R_2?

72

$$V_1 = IR_1 \quad \text{and} \quad V_2 = IR_2$$

The current I flows through both resistors so the results follow by applying Ohm's Law to each in turn.

Now, since the combined resistance of the two resistors is $R_1 + R_2$ we know also that $I = V/(R_1 + R_2)$. We may therefore express V_1 and V_2 in terms only of V, R_1 and R_2 as follows:

$$V_1 = \frac{VR_1}{R_1 + R_2} \quad V_2 = \frac{VR_2}{R_1 + R_2} \quad \text{giving} \quad V_1 + V_2 = \frac{VR_1}{R_1 + R_2} + \frac{VR_2}{R_1 + R_2} = V$$

We see that V_1 is proportional to R_1 and V_2 is proportional to R_2. The voltage V is divided between the two resistors such that the potential or voltage across each resistor is proportional to the value of that resistor, hence the name potential divider.

Now, if we relate the above expressions back to the work we did on the non-ideal voltage generator in frames 48 to 56, and let $V = V_0$, $R_1 = R_0$ and $R_2 = R_L$ we see that the diagrams above represent the same circuit that we analysed earlier.

If R_L is very much greater than R_0, what can you say about the relative sizes of the voltages across the two resistors?

73

> The voltage across R_L is very much greater than the voltage across R_0

$$V_{R_L} = \frac{V_0 R_L}{R_0 + R_L} \qquad V_{R_0} = \frac{V_0 R_0}{R_0 + R_L}$$

The two expressions for the voltages are obtained simply by substituting the new symbols in the expressions derived in frame 72. Since the voltages are proportional to the resistors across which they are developed, the condition given above follows. We can write for the voltage across R_L:

$$V_{R_L} = \frac{V_0 R_L}{R_0 + R_L} \approx V_0 \text{ because } R_0 << R_L$$

Because $R_0 << R_L$, nearly all the generator voltage appears across R_L and, as seen at its terminals, the generator appears to be very close to the ideal model. We discovered in frame 63 that any practical generator can be modelled either as a voltage generator or as a current generator with an appropriately connected internal resistor. The above analysis shows why the voltage generator model is more appropriate when the generator is to be used with loads which are much greater than its internal resistance. Under these conditions, as we see, the observed output voltage across the load is very close to the full voltage available from the ideal generator.

74

THE CURRENT SPLITTER OR CURRENT DIVIDER

The configuration we first analysed in frame 58 and shown again here is often called a current splitter or current divider:

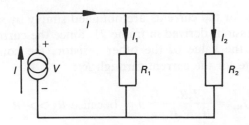

Can you write expressions for the currents I_1 and I_2 in terms of V, R_1 and R_2?

75

$$I_1 = \frac{V}{R_1} \quad \text{and} \quad I_2 = \frac{V}{R_2}$$

The voltage V appears across both resistors so the results follow from applying Ohm's Law to each in turn.

Now, since the combined resistance of the two resistors in parallel is $R_1R_2/(R_1 + R_2)$, we know also that $V = IR_1R_2/(R_1 + R_2)$. We may therefore express I_1 and I_2 in terms only of I, R_1 and R_2 as follows:

$$I_1 = \frac{IR_2}{R_1 + R_2} \quad I_2 = \frac{IR_1}{R_1 + R_2} \quad \text{giving} \quad I_1 + I_2 = \frac{IR_2}{R_1 + R_2} + \frac{IR_1}{R_1 + R_2} = I$$

In this case I_1 is proportional to R_2 and I_2 is proportional to R_1. The current is split between the two resistors such that the current in one resistor is proportional to the value of the other resistor and vice versa.

Now, if we relate the above expressions back to the work we did in frames 53 to 57, and let $I = I_0$, $R_1 = R_0$ and $R_2 = R_L$, we see that the two circuits are the same.

If R_L is very much less than R_0, what could you say about the relative sizes of the currents through the two resistors?

76

The current through R_L is very much greater than the current through R_0

$$I_{R_L} = \frac{I_0R_0}{R_0 + R_L} \quad I_{R_0} = \frac{I_0R_L}{R_0 + R_L}$$

The two expressions for the currents are obtained simply by substituting the new symbols in the expressions derived in frame 71. Since the currents in each resistor are proportional to the value of the other resistor, the condition given above follows. We can write for the current through R_L:

$$I_{R_L} = \frac{I_0R_0}{R_0 + R_L} \approx I \quad \text{because } R_0 >> R_L$$

Because $R_0 >> R_L$, nearly all the generator current flows through R_L and, as seen at its terminals, the generator appears to be very close to the ideal model.

We discovered in frame 59 that any practical generator can be modelled either as a voltage generator or as a current generator with an appropriately connected internal resistor. The above analysis shows why the current generator model is more appropriate when the generator is to be used with loads which are much less than its internal resistance. Under these conditions, as we see, the observed output current through the load is very close to the full current available from the ideal current generator.

77

A COMPARISON OF THE VOLTAGE GENERATOR AND THE CURRENT GENERATOR

Here are the two basic generator configurations again, with the voltage and current distributions in the circuits when a load is connected:

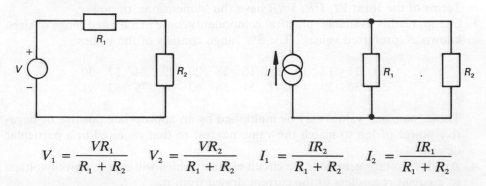

$$V_1 = \frac{VR_1}{R_1 + R_2} \qquad V_2 = \frac{VR_2}{R_1 + R_2} \qquad I_1 = \frac{IR_2}{R_1 + R_2} \qquad I_2 = \frac{IR_1}{R_1 + R_2}$$

Comparing the two cases we see that, if two resistors are connected in series across an ideal voltage generator, the generator voltage is divided between the two in such a way that the *greater voltage* is developed across the component with the *larger resistance*. If the circuit is a model of a load connected to a non-ideal generator and the load is much larger than the internal resistance of the generator, then the voltage across the load is very close to the full voltage available from the ideal voltage generator.

If two resistors are connected in parallel across an ideal current generator, the generator current is split between the two in such a way that the *greater current* flows through the component with the *smaller resistance*. This could also be stated as saying that the greater current flows through the component with the larger conductance. If the circuit is a model of a load connected to a non-ideal generator and the load is much smaller than the internal resistance of the generator, then the current through the load is very close to the full current available from the ideal current generator.

78

SUMMARY OF PROGRAMME 2

1. Ohm's Law states that, when a current I is flowing through a resistor R, the voltage V developed across the resistor is given by the equation:

$$V = IR$$

The unit of current is the ampere. The unit of voltage is the volt. The unit of resistance is the ohm. Terms of the form IR have the 'dimensions' of voltage.

2. When a current I flows through a resistor R and a voltage V is developed across it, the power dissipated in the resistor is given by one of the expressions:

$$P = VI \quad P = I^2R \quad P = V^2/R$$

The unit of power is the watt.

Terms of the form VI, I^2R, V^2/R have the 'dimensions' of power.

3. Cheap, readily available, practical components come in a limited range of sizes known as 'preferred values'. The 5% range consists of the values:

10	11	12	13	15	16	18	20	22	24	27	30
33	36	39	43	47	51	56	62	68	75	82	91

These 'nominal' values may be multiplied by an appropriate positive or negative power of ten to match the value nearest to that required in a particular design.

4. An ideal voltage generator is a circuit element which will supply a given voltage to a circuit regardless of the current drawn from it.

5. An ideal current generator is a circuit element which will supply a given current to a circuit regardless of the voltage developed across it.

6. When a generator supplies energy that is absorbed by a load the power delivered at any instant can be calculated either as the product of the voltage across the generator and the current drawn from the generator, or as the product of the voltage across the load and the current through the load. The energy supplied is the product of the power and the time for which it is supplied.

7. Components connected end-to-end in a chain formation so that adjacent components share only a single terminal are said to be connected in series. Components connected in series have the same current flowing through them.

8. Components connected between the same two terminals so that all components share these terminals are said to be connected in parallel. Components connected in parallel have the same voltage across them.

9. A practical, non-ideal generator may be modelled either by an ideal voltage generator in series with a resistor or by an ideal current generator in parallel with a resistor. The value of the resistor is called the internal resistance of the generator. The following diagrams represent a non-ideal voltage generator and a non-ideal current generator connected to a load resistor of resistance R_L. The voltage across the load V_G and the current through the load I_G are designated the generator voltage and current and are related to each other by the equations given below the diagrams. The two diagrams represent the same generator if $V_0 = I_0 R_0$.

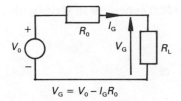

$$V_G = V_0 - I_G R_0$$

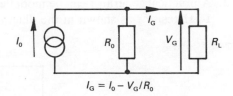

$$I_G = I_0 - V_G / R_0$$

The voltage generator model is most appropriate when using the generator with loads which are much greater than its internal resistance since, under these circumstances, it behaves nearly like an ideal voltage generator.

   The current generator model is most appropriate when using the generator with loads which are much less than its internal resistance since, under these circumstances, it behaves nearly like an ideal current generator.

10. The circuit configuration consisting of two resistors in series with a voltage generator is called a potential divider. The circuit configuration consisting of two resistors in parallel with a current generator is called a current splitter. Here are diagrams and equations describing them:

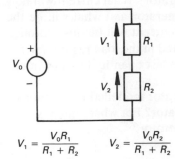

$$V_1 = \frac{V_0 R_1}{R_1 + R_2} \qquad V_2 = \frac{V_0 R_2}{R_1 + R_2}$$

The greater voltage is developed across the resistor with the largest resistance

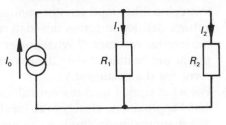

$$I_1 = \frac{I_0 R_2}{R_1 + R_2} \qquad I_2 = \frac{I_0 R_1}{R_1 + R_2}$$

The greater current flows through the resistor with the smallest resistance

REVISION QUESTIONS

1. What is the effective resistance of three resistors in series whose individual values are 1.6 MΩ, 510 kΩ and 750 Ω? What single preferred value resistor from the E24 range could be used instead of these three?

2. What is the effective resistance of three resistors in parallel whose individual resistances are 1.6 MΩ, 510 kΩ and 750 Ω? What single preferred value resistor from the E24 range could be used instead of these three?

3. A practical generator can be modelled by a 9 volt ideal generator in series with a 1 kΩ resistor as shown in the diagram below:

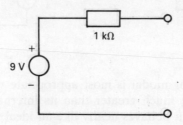

What voltage will be developed across a 2 kΩ load resistor connected to this generator and what will be the current through this load resistor? What voltage will be 'lost' across the internal resistance? What power will be dissipated in the load resistor? What power will be delivered by the generator? (Find this last quantity by calculations involving the generator.)

4. What component values should be used and how should they be connected to model the generator in question 3 as a current generator? What current will flow through a 2 kΩ load resistor connected to this generator and what will be the voltage developed across this load resistor? What current will be 'lost' through the internal resistance? What power will be dissipated in the load resistor? What power will be delivered by the generator? (Find this last quantity by calculations involving the generator.)

5. For what kind of load resistor values will the generator modelled in questions 3 and 4 approximate closely to an ideal voltage generator? For what kind of values will it approximate closely to an ideal current generator?

6. Which of the following generator/resistor circuits represent meaningless configurations? Explain why the connections are meaningless. For each of the allowable circuits, work out the voltages across and currents through all the resistors in the circuit.

(a)

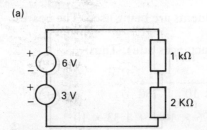

(b)

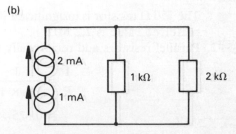

(c)

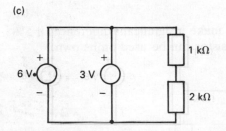

(d)

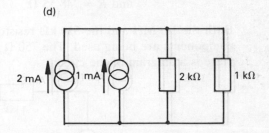

$$\boxed{\text{SOLUTIONS TO REVISION QUESTIONS}}$$

1. Series resistors add so total resistance is

$$1,600,000 + 510,000 + 750 = 2,110,750 = 2.11075 \text{ M}\Omega$$

The 750 Ω resistor is insignificant if 5% components are being used. The nearest preferred value is 2.2 MΩ.

2. Parallel resistors add reciprocally (their conductances add). Thus:

$$\frac{1}{R} = \frac{1}{1.6 \times 10^6} + \frac{1}{510 \times 10^3} + \frac{1}{750}$$

$$= 0.625 \times 10^{-6} + 1.96 \times 10^{-6} + 1.33 \times 10^{-3}$$

$$= 1.336 \times 10^{-3}$$

$$\text{and } R = 748.55 \ \Omega$$

Both the 1.6 MΩ and the 510 kΩ resistors make insignificant differences if 5% components are being used. The 750 Ω resistor can be used on its own.

3. Here is a diagram of the circuit:

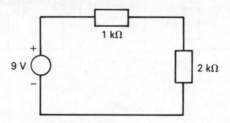

Voltage across 2 kΩ load $= \dfrac{2 \times 9}{2 + 1} = 6 \text{ V}$

Current through 2 kΩ load $= 6/2 = 3 \text{ mA}$

Voltage across 1 kΩ resistor $= \dfrac{1 \times 9}{1 + 2} = 3 \text{ V}$

Power in load resistor $= 6 \text{ V} \times 3 \text{ mA} = 18 \text{ mW}$

Power delivered by generator = Power in ideal generator
$\qquad\qquad\qquad\qquad\qquad - \text{power in 1 k}\Omega \text{ resistor}$
$\qquad\qquad\qquad\qquad = 9 \text{ V} \times 3 \text{ mA} - 3 \text{ V} \times 3 \text{ mA}$
$\qquad\qquad\qquad\qquad = 27 - 9 = 18 \text{ mW}$

Notice that the net power delivered by the non-ideal generator must equal the power dissipated in the load.

4. The series resistor/voltage generator combination can be replaced by a parallel resistor/current generator combination as shown to the left below:

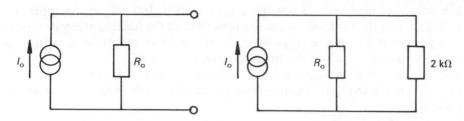

For both generators the short-circuit current and open-circuit voltage must be the same. Thus we have:

s/c currents the same $\Rightarrow I_o = 9 \text{ V}/1 \text{ k}\Omega = 9 \text{ mA}$

o/c voltages the same $\Rightarrow 9 \text{ V} = I_oR_o, \quad R_o = 9 \text{ V}/9 \text{ mA} = 1 \text{ k}\Omega$

When a 2 kΩ load is connected, the circuit becomes as shown to the right. The current in the load can be found using the current splitter rule. Hence:

$$I_{\text{load}} = \frac{1 \times 9}{1 + 2} = 3 \text{ mA so voltage across load} = 3 \text{ mA} \times 2 \text{ k}\Omega = 6 \text{ V}$$

Applying the current splitter rule again for the other resistor gives:

$$I = \frac{2 \times 9}{2 + 1} = 6 \text{ mA}$$

Power in load resistor $= I^2R = (3 \text{ mA})^2 \times 2 \text{ k}\Omega = 18 \text{ mW}$

Power delivered = power in ideal generator $-$ power in 1 kΩ resistor

$$= 9 \text{ mA} \times 6 \text{ V} - 6 \text{ mA} \times 6 \text{ V} = 54 - 36 = 18 \text{ mW}$$

All answers, as they must be, are the same as for question 3.

Notice that the two power calculations, although they yield the same result for the power delivered, give different values for the power distribution inside the generator. In the voltage model the power in the ideal voltage generator is 27 mW while 9 mW is 'lost' in the internal resistor. In the current model the power in the ideal current generator is 54 mW while 36 mW is 'lost' in the internal resistor. The net power delivered is 18 mW in both cases. The reason for this apparent discrepancy is that the two models are equivalent only insofar as they represent the generator 'as seen looking into its terminals from outside'. They do not purport to model the internal operation of the generator.

5. The generator modelled in questions 3 and 4 will approximate most closely to an ideal voltage generator for load resistor values which are large compared with 1 kΩ, the internal resistance.

For values of load resistor which are greater than 100 kΩ, for example, the voltage across the load will be greater than 99% of the ideal generator voltage.

The generator will approximate most closely to an ideal current generator for load resistor values which are small compared with 1 kΩ.

For values of load resistor which are smaller than 10 kΩ, for example, the current through the load resistor will be greater than 99% of the ideal generator current.

6.

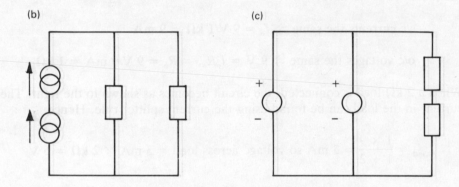

(b)   (c)

Diagrams (b) and (c) both represent unallowable configurations. The two current generators in diagram (b) are each trying to drive different currents through the same piece of wire, which is impossible. The two voltage generators in diagram (c) are each trying to maintain different voltages across the same two points in the circuit, which is also impossible.

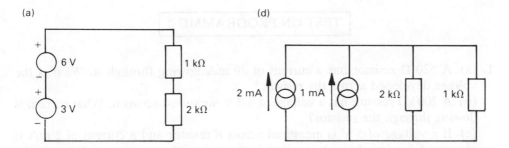

Voltage generators in series add so the two generators in diagram (a) are equivalent to a single 9 V generator. The total resistance 'seen' by this generator is given by the two resistors in series, that is 3 kΩ.

The current through both resistors is thus 9 V/3 kΩ = 3 mA.

The voltages across the two resistors are thus respectively:

$$1 \text{ k}\Omega \times 3 \text{ mA} = 3 \text{ V} \quad \text{and} \quad 2 \text{ k}\Omega \times 3 \text{ mA} = 6 \text{ V}$$

These voltages can alternatively be calculated using the potential divider rule thus:

$$V_2 = \frac{6}{9} \times 9 = 6 \text{ V} \qquad V_1 = \frac{3}{9} \times 9 = 3 \text{ V}$$

Current generators in parallel add so the two generators in diagram (d) are equivalent to a single 3 mA generator. The total resistance 'seen' by this generator is given by the two resistors in parallel, that is $(1 \times 2)/(1 + 2) = 2/3$ kΩ.

The voltage across the two resistors is therefore 3 mA $\times \frac{2}{3}$ kΩ = 2 V.

The currents through the two resistors are thus respectively:

$$2 \text{ V}/2 \text{ k}\Omega = 1 \text{ mA through the 2 k}\Omega \text{ resistor}$$

and

$$2 \text{ V}/1 \text{ k}\Omega = 2 \text{ mA through the 1 k}\Omega \text{ resistor}$$

These currents can alternatively be calculated using the current splitter rule thus:

$$V_2 = \frac{2}{3} \times 3 = 2 \text{ mA} \qquad V_1 = \frac{1}{3} \times 3 = 1 \text{ mA}$$

| TEST ON PROGRAMME 2 |

1. (a) A 520 Ω resistor has a current of 20 mA flowing through it. What is the voltage developed across the resistor?

(b) A 200 kΩ resistor has a voltage of 9.3 V measured across it. What current is flowing through the resistor?

(c) If a voltage of 5 V is measured across a resistor and a current of 2 mA is measured flowing through it, what is the value of the resistor? What is the nearest preferred value to this actual value and by what percentage does the actual value differ from the nominal value?

What is the power dissipated in each of these resistors? Compute the power in each part of the question by using only the information given in that part: the resistor value and current in part (a) and so on.

2. A circuit designer wishes to introduce a resistor into a circuit so that a current of 20 mA will flow through it when a voltage of 9.0 V is applied across it. Using 5% components, what value resistor should he choose? If the voltage is fixed at 9.0 V, what will be the largest and smallest currents which may flow through the resistor if, for any reason, the component selected for the circuit takes on values at the extremes of the range?

3. An ideal 10 V generator is connected in series with a 1 kΩ resistor and a load resistor R_L to form a closed circuit.

(a) Draw the circuit diagram.

(b) Draw a graph of the voltage across the load against the current through the load for different values of R_L.

(c) Write down the equation of the graph.

(d) With what two components connected in what way could the generator and 1 kΩ resistor be replaced to produce the same graph?

4. A non-ideal generator can be represented either as an ideal 5 V generator in series with a certain resistor, or as an ideal 5 mA current generator in parallel with the same resistor. What is the value of the resistor? Does the generator act more nearly like an ideal current generator or an ideal voltage generator when loads of 1 Ω, 2 Ω, 1 MΩ, 2 MΩ are connected to it? Calculate the currents through and voltages across each of these loads.

5. A non-ideal voltage generator of open-circuit output voltage V_0 has an internal resistance R_0. It is connected to a load resistor R_L. For what value of R_L will the power dissipated in R_L be a maximum? This result is called the maximum power theorem. (*Hint*: express P in terms of V, R_0 and R_L, and differentiate with respect to R_L.)

FURTHER QUESTIONS ON PROGRAMME 2

1. A non-ideal generator produces the following characteristic for a range of load resistors:

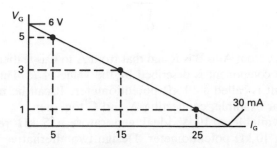

   Draw models of it (a) as a voltage generator and (b) as a current generator. What values of load resistor produce the points marked on the characteristic? For which points does the generator 'look most like' a voltage generator and for which most like a current generator.

2. Three resistors R_1, R_2 and R_3 are connected in series. The current through R_1 is 1 mA. The voltage across R_2 is 5 V. The power dissipated in R_3 is 10 mW. If these effects are the result of an ideal voltage generator of output 30 V being connected in series with the resistors to form a closed circuit, what are the values of the resistors?

3. Three resistors R_1, R_2 and R_3 are connected in parallel. The current through R_1 is 1 mA. The voltage across R_2 is 5 V. The power dissipated in R_3 is 50 mW. If these effects are the result of connecting an ideal current generator of output 15 mA in parallel with the resistors, what are their values?

4. A potential divider is made from a 10 V ideal generator, a 6.8 kΩ resistor (nearer the positive terminal of the generator) and a 4.7 kΩ resistor. What are the largest and smallest possible output voltages across the 4.7 kΩ resistor if the components can take on extreme values in their range:
   (a) when they are 5% components
   (b) when they are 1% components?

5. A current divider is made from a 50 mA ideal generator, a 1.5 kΩ resistor and a 3.3 kΩ resistor. What are the largest and smallest possible currents through the 3.3 kΩ resistor if the components can take on extreme values in their range:
   (a) when they are 5% components
   (b) when they are 1% components?

6. A potentiometer is a resistive circuit element having three terminals. Two are connected to the ends of the resistor. The third is connected to a 'slider' which may be positioned anywhere between the two ends of the resistor. It may be shown by the following symbol:

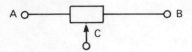

If the resistance from A to B is R and that from A to C is r, then that from C to B is $R - r$. The component is described by the value of R. Thus, if $R = 10$ kΩ, the component is called a 10 kΩ potentiometer. It can be used as a variable resistor by, for example, connecting A and C together.

You have available a 10 V ideal generator, a 5 kΩ resistor, a 10 kΩ resistor and a 10 kΩ potentiometer. Design two alternative circuits using the potentiometer as a variable resistor which can give an output between zero and 5 volts but which must not exceed 5 volts. Compare the potentiometer settings for your two designs when the outputs are 4 volts and 1 volt.

7. Are the following circuit configurations meaningful? Calculate the voltages across and currents through the loads of any that are. Calculate also the voltages across the current generators and the currents through the voltage generators.

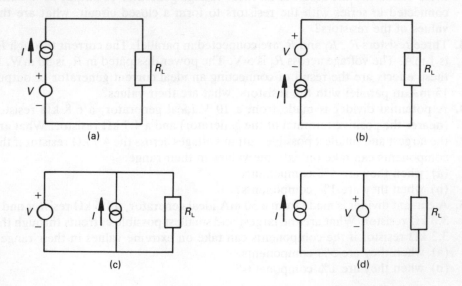

(a)

(b)

(c)

(d)

8. The potential divider circuit configuration is also known as an 'attenuator':

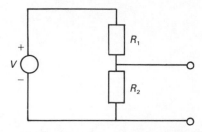

The voltage across R_2 is said to be an 'attenuated' version of V – that is, it is a smaller version of V. The 'attenuation ratio' is $(R_1 + R_2)/R_2{:}1$. Attenuators are used, for example, to reduce the size of a voltage to a value which is within the compass of an instrument designed to measure it or some property with which it is associated. If R_2 represents the resistance of an instrument and is 10 kΩ, design 2:1, 5:1 and 10:1 attenuators for the instrument.

9. An instrument offers a resistance of 1 MΩ to anything connected to it. Design 2:1, 5:1 and 10:1 attenuators for the instrument which still offer a resistance of 1 MΩ to anything connected to them.

10. The circuit in this diagram is to be used as a 'two-position attenuator':

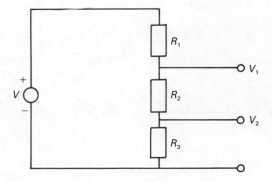

Voltages V_1 and V_2 can be 'tapped off' from the resistor chain. If $V = 1$ volt, design such an attentuator which offers a total resistance of 50 kΩ to the generator V and gives $V_1 = 0.5$ V and $V_2 = 0.2$ V.

Programme 3

DIRECT CURRENT CIRCUITS

PART 2

INTRODUCTION

In the last programme we introduced the ideas of current, voltage and resistance on which the theory of direct current and voltage circuits depends. We found that simple circuits could be modelled using idealised current and voltage generators and saw how these idealisations needed to be modified in practice. Two important circuit configurations, the potential divider and the current splitter, were introduced. In this programme we shall extend these ideas to more complicated circuits and develop methods of analysis and design which will enable us to deal with them.

The programme begins with a description of the terms used to describe complicated circuits and introduces two important circuit laws, Kirchhoff's voltage and current laws, which enable us to write down sufficient equations to calculate all the voltages and currents in a circuit. Two kinds of analysis in particular, mesh and nodal analysis, are used to help set up the equations needed to describe a circuit, and matrix methods are introduced as a method of solving them.

When only a limited amount of information about a circuit is required, powerful circuit reduction techniques can be used. Two especially useful and important theorems, Thevenin's and Norton's, are introduced and the way in which they can be used to simplify circuit calculations demonstrated.

The principle of duality is shown to be a way of obtaining 'two circuit theorems for the price of one' and the Superposition theorem is introduced as a useful method of simplifying the calculations when analysing the effect of more than one generator in a circuit.

The usefulness of these methods in analysing several widely used circuit configurations is demonstrated.

1

BRANCHES, NODES, LOOPS AND MESHES

Most electric circuits are more complicated than those we have looked at in programme 2. They often contain many components interconnected to form a '*circuit network*', usually just called a *network*. There are many ways of analysing such networks. First, however, we need to define some terms.

The four terms at the top of this frame are conventionally used to describe the topology of a circuit network. That is, they define the parts of which a network is made up and how they are interconnected. There is some variation between different circuit designers concerning exactly what each term means. The definitions given here are those most commonly accepted but readers should look out for variations and, in discussing circuits with others, should make sure they are clear what is intended.

A *branch* is part of a network made up of one or more components connected between two terminals so that the same current can flow into the branch via one of the terminals and out of it via the other. The terminals may be real or may be 'notional' – that is, just used as reference points. Associated with the flow of current there will be a voltage between the two terminals. In a network consisting of many branches there are thus two 'unknowns' associated with the branch: the current flow through the branch and the voltage across the branch.

Can a single resistor constitute a branch?

2

Yes, a single resistor is the simplest possible form of branch.

If a resistor R_n forms part of a complicated network then there will be a current I_n flowing through the resistor and a voltage V_n across the resistor. V_n and I_n are the two unknowns which need to be determined by circuit analysis. They are, of course, linked by Ohm's Law $V_n = I_n R_n$.

We saw, in programme 1, that an effective 'combined resistance' could be calculated for two or more resistors in series. Such combinations of resistors could thus, for purposes of analysis, be combined into a single 'equivalent resistance' and could thus form a branch. In most practical problems it is usually most convenient to consider branches which consist of one or more resistors (and other components) connected in series. A point at which such branches meet also has a special name to define it. We will discuss this in the next frame.

3

A *node* is a single point in a network which is the junction of two or more branches. Currents can flow into or out of nodes from or to the branches connected to them. The junction of three or more branches is called a *principal node*. The junction of only two branches is called a *secondary node*.

Here is a circuit diagram. Using the definitions given above, how would you describe the paths efab, eb, edcb and the points b and c?

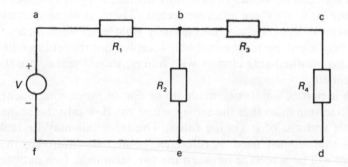

4

> Using the definition in frame 2, efab, eb and edcb are all branches
> Using the definition above, b is a principal node, c is a secondary node

The path efab contains a voltage generator in series with a resistor R_1, eb contains just a resistor R_2 and edcb contains two resistors R_3 and R_4 in series so each path satisfies the description of a branch given in frame 2. The three branches meet at the point b so this is a principal node. The resistors R_3 and R_4 could each be regarded separately as branches which meet in the secondary node c. It is seldom necessary in practice to pay particular concern to secondary nodes since, if the current in the branch edcb can be determined then the voltages across R_3 and R_4 can be calculated by applying Ohm's Law to each resistor in turn. Notice that ef and ed are parts of branches across which there is no potential difference because they have no resistance. They are, in fact spread out and given separate letters purely for convenience and because the normal convention in circuit diagrams is, if possible, to draw all components either horizontally or vertically and to join them by lines which are also horizontal or vertical. In a real network all three points d, e and f would be the same point on the circuit.

How would you describe this point?

5

> The 'point' def is a principal node

The branch efab consists essentially of the voltage generator, the resistor R_1 between a and b and the wires connected to them. The path ef is really only *part* of the wire from the negative terminal of the generator to the point e. Similarly the branch edcb consists essentially of the two resistors R_3 and R_4 and the wires connected to them. Again de is only part of one of these wires. The points f and d can therefore be 'shrunk' into e and, since three branches meet at e, it is a principal node.

We need one final piece of terminology to describe the topology of a network. It is given in the next frame.

6

DEFINITION: LOOPS AND MESHES

A *loop* is a closed path in a network made up by the interconnection of two or more branches. A *mesh* is a loop in a '*planar*' network – that is, a network which can be drawn on a plane piece of paper without any two lines crossing over each other. Since real circuits are essentially three-dimensional structures which can be represented on paper in many different ways, the distinction between the two terms applies primarily to their representation. Furthermore, since the great majority of useful electronic circuits can be represented as planar circuits, the two terms are often used interchangeably.

To illustrate the difference, however, here is a problem for you to consider. Twelve equal pieces of resistance wire are made up into the shape of a cube. A voltage generator is connected first across a diagonal of one side and then across a diagonal of the cube. Are either of these configurations planar? Here is an isometric diagram to help you:

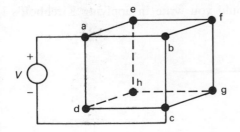 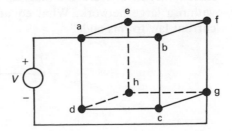

7

> With the generator across a diagonal of one side the circuit is planar.
> With the generator across a diagonal of the cube it is not.

The two statements are most easily verified by re-drawing the two circuits. As can be seen from the diagrams below, when the generator is across a diagonal of one side the circuit can be represented on a plane piece of paper without crossovers. When the generator is across a diagonal of the cube it cannot:

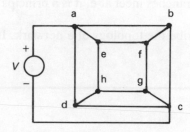 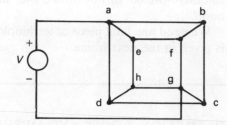

You will be able to use these two configurations later to calculate the effective resistance of the cube in these two cases. First, however, now that we have all the necessary terminology, we shall study two very important circuit laws: Kirchhoff's Current and Voltage Laws.

8

KIRCHHOFF'S FIRST LAW – THE CURRENT LAW

> In any electric circuit in which currents are flowing, the algebraic sum
> of currents entering and leaving a node is always zero.

In using this law, the currents referred to are always taken to be conventional currents as defined in frame 26 of programme 2. Currents entering a node are usually taken as being algebraically positive, those leaving a node as being algebraically negative. Here is a diagram of a node such as may be found somewhere within a large network. What equation could you write in applying Kirchhoff's current law to this node?

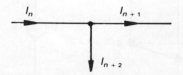

$$I_n - I_{n+1} - I_{n+2} = 0$$

Since I_n enters the node it is positive. I_{n+1} and I_{n-1} both leave the node so they are negative. In a large network similar equations can be written for every node in the network.

KIRCHHOFF'S SECOND LAW – THE VOLTAGE LAW

In any electric circuit containing components across which voltages are developed, the algebraic sum of the voltages around any loop is always zero.

In using this law the algebraic sign of a voltage across a component is associated with the current through it according to the convention given in frame 31 of programme 2. That is, when a conventional current flows through a resistor, the end that the current flows in at is positive with respect to the end that the current flows out of. The algebraic sign of the voltage across a voltage generator is an inherent property of the generator. The algebraic sign of the voltage across a current generator will depend on the components connected to the generator and can be determined when the equations describing the operation of the circuit have been solved.

Here is a diagram of a loop such as may be found somewhere within a large network. When applying Kirchhoff's voltage law to a loop, it is common practice to start from the bottom left-hand corner of the loop and work your way clockwise round the loop until you return to the point you started from. If there is an increase in voltage as you 'pass through' a component you should record this as a positive quantity. A decrease is recorded as a negative quantity. Can you write down the equation which would be obtained by applying Kirchhoff's voltage law to this loop? Take care that you give all the voltages their correct sign.

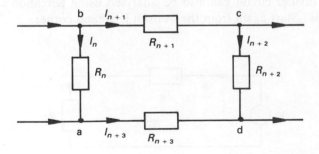

$$I_nR_n - I_{n+1}R_{n+1} - I_{n+2}R_{n+2} + I_{n+3}R_{n+3} = 0$$

Here is the diagram again to help you see how the above equation was obtained. The polarities of the voltages across the resistors are related to the directions of the currents flowing through them.

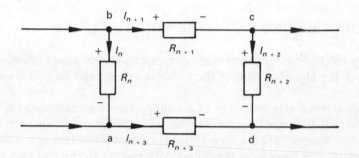

Starting from point a and setting off clockwise round the loop we move 'up' through R_n to point b. Since a current I_n flows down through R_n the voltage is greater at the top of it so, in 'passing through' R_n, we see an increase in voltage. We therefore record this as a positive quantity whose value, by Ohm's Law, is I_nR_n.

Continuing clockwise from b to c we pass through R_{n+1}. Related to I_{n+1} the voltage at b is greater than that at c so, in passing through R_{n+1}, we see a drop in potential. We therefore record this as a negative quantity whose value, again by Ohm's Law, is $I_{n+1}R_{n+1}$.

There is a similar drop in potential of $I_{n+2}R_{n+2}$ across R_{n+2} as we go from c to d, and a further increase in potential of $I_{n+3}R_{n+3}$ across R_{n+3} as we go from d to a. This brings us back to the point we started from so the sum of all these voltages is zero.

A potential divider circuit can also be analysed using Kirchhoff's voltage law. Can you do this? Start again from the bottom left-hand corner.

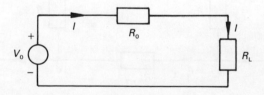

$$\boxed{V_0 - IR_0 - IR_L = 0}$$

Starting from the bottom left-hand corner and moving clockwise we first pass through the voltage generator and thus see an increase in voltage of V_0. There is then a drop in voltage of IR_0 across R_0 and a further drop of IR_L across R_L. Since there is no voltage across the (zero-resistance) wire at the bottom of the diagram, the three terms above are the sum of the voltages round the loop and are thus equal to zero.

Writing $I = I_G$, the observable generator current, and replacing IR_L by V_G, the observable generator voltage, we can rearrange the above equation into the form:

$$V_G = V_0 - I_G R_0$$

This is the same equation as we had before which, of course, it must be.

It is also worth reviewing the non-ideal current generator and recognising that it can be analysed by a simple application of Kirchhoff's Current Law.

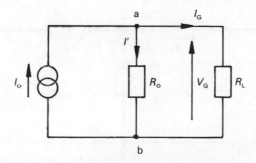

Using the terminology of the earlier frames in this programme, both a and b are principal nodes. Applying Kirchhoff's Current Law to node a we have:

$$I_0 - I' - I_G = 0$$

But, since we can write the voltage across R_L (and therefore across R_0 too) as V_G, we can replace I' by V_G/R_0 to give:

$$I_0 - \frac{V_G}{R_0} - I_G = 0 \quad \text{and therefore} \quad I_G = I_0 - \frac{V_G}{R_0}$$

This, too, is the same equation as we had before which, again, it must be.

We can now go on to see how to set up and solve the equations which describe the operation of more complicated circuits. The first thing to establish is how to know when we have enough information for a solution.

12

SETTING UP AND SOLVING CIRCUIT EQUATIONS

The purpose of circuit analysis is to determine the currents through and voltages across components in a circuit which is excited by some kind of energy source. It is usually the case that the characteristics of the energy source are known (that it is a voltage generator with an output of 10 volts, for example) and that the values of the components making up the circuit are known. A circuit analysis attempts to construct a set of equations in which the unknown currents and voltages appear as variables and then to solve the equations. If a circuit contains n components then the total unknown information about that circuit consists of $2n$ variables – the values of the current through and voltage across every component. It is one of the fundamental rules of algebra that $2n$ equations are needed to determine $2n$ unknowns so the task for large circuits seems a formidable one. Fortunately, however, techniques exist for reducing the amount of information which has to be determined by 'difficult' calculations and then deducing the rest by much simpler manipulation of the intermediate results.

We will start with a simple problem. Suppose we wish to determine the currents through and voltages across all the resistors in this circuit:

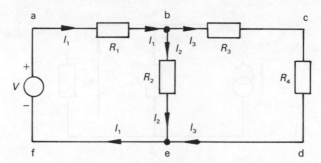

As a first attempt at a solution we have postulated that a current I_1 will be taken from the generator and that it divides into two currents I_2 and I_3 at node b. How many equations do we need to determine all the unknown information about the circuit?

13

We need three equations

Since there are three unknowns, the three currents, three equations are sufficient to find them. Applying Ohm's Law to each resistor in turn then gives us the unknown voltages across them.

We can now apply Kirchhoff's Laws to set up the necessary equations. Applying the Voltage Law to the mesh fabef (starting from the bottom left-hand corner f, just as we did in frame 10) gives one equation. Repeating this process for the mesh ebcde starting from e gives a second equation. Can you write down these equations?

14

$$V - I_1R_1 - I_2R_2 = 0$$

$$I_2R_2 - I_3R_3 - I_3R_4 = 0$$

In setting up these equations the polarities of the voltages across the components are associated with the directions of the postulated currents. In this particular problem it is plain that the currents must flow in the directions given by the arrows. This is not always the case, however, and, in many problems, arbitrary directions may have to be given to some currents. The voltages used in writing down the circuit equations are then related to these *assumed* directions. If any of the assumptions proves to be wrong then the answers for those currents whose directions have been incorrectly guessed will be negative, indicating that the current flows in the opposite direction from that shown on the diagram. Provided you manipulate the algebra correctly when solving the equations, the correct answers will 'come out in the wash'.

A further equation is required before enough information is available for a solution and this is provided by applying Kirchhoff's Current Law to node b (or node e). What is the equation which results from doing this?

15

$$I_1 - I_2 - I_3 = 0$$

If the equation was obtained from node e, all the signs given above would be reversed according to the normal convention but the equation would still be essentially the same. If $V = 10$ volts and R_1, R_2, R_3 and R_4 are respectively 1, 2, 3 and 4 kilohms, can you now solve these three equations to obtain the values of the three currents? Give your answers as fractions.

$$I_1 = \frac{90}{23} \text{ mA}, \quad I_2 = \frac{70}{23} \text{ mA}, \quad I_3 = \frac{20}{23} \text{ mA}$$

Substituting values in the equations and rearranging them a little we have:

$$I_1 + 2I_2 = 10$$

$$2I_2 - 7I_3 = 0$$

$$I_1 - I_2 - I_3 = 0$$

There are many ways of solving sets of simultaneous equations of this kind. One of the most reliable is the technique known as *Gaussian elimination* so we will demonstrate that one here. We will consider it first as it would apply to a general problem of this kind, and then see how it applies to this particular set of equations.

A general set of simultaneous equations in three variables x_1, x_2 and x_3 can be written as follows:

$$a_{11}x_1 + a_{12}x_2 + a_{13}x_3 = b_1$$

$$a_{21}x_1 + a_{22}x_2 + a_{23}x_3 = b_2$$

$$a_{31}x_1 + a_{32}x_2 + a_{33}x_3 = b_3$$

These equations can be expressed more compactly in *matrix form* thus:

$$\begin{bmatrix} a_{11} & a_{12} & a_{13} \\ a_{21} & a_{22} & a_{23} \\ a_{31} & a_{32} & a_{33} \end{bmatrix} \begin{bmatrix} x_1 \\ x_2 \\ x_3 \end{bmatrix} = \begin{bmatrix} b_1 \\ b_2 \\ b_3 \end{bmatrix}$$

Comparing the two forms shows how they are related. The 'square matrix' of coefficients $[a_{ij}]$ is multiplied into the 'column vector' of variables $[x_j]$ to give the column vector of constants $[b_j]$ as follows:

Row 1 of the $[a_{ij}]$ matrix times column vector $[x_j]$ equals b_1

Row 2 of the $[a_{ij}]$ matrix times column vector $[x_j]$ equals b_2

Row 3 of the $[a_{ij}]$ matrix times column vector $[x_j]$ equals b_3

In setting the equations out in matrix notation we have, in effect, separated out the information we need to use to solve for the three variables from the symbols for the variables. The variables are contained in the column vector $[x_j]$. The information from which their values can be determined is contained in the square matrix $[a_{ij}]$ and the column vector $[b_j]$.

The method of Gaussian elimination consists of reducing the matrix of coefficients $[a_{ij}]$ to an *'upper triangular'* form which has zeros in every position below the *'leading diagonal'* a_{11}, a_{22}, a_{33}. The equations will then appear in matrix form as follows:

$$\begin{bmatrix} a_{11} & a_{12} & a_{13} \\ 0 & c_{22} & c_{23} \\ 0 & 0 & e_{33} \end{bmatrix} \begin{bmatrix} x_1 \\ x_2 \\ x_3 \end{bmatrix} = \begin{bmatrix} b_1 \\ d_2 \\ f_3 \end{bmatrix} \begin{array}{c} = \\ = \\ = \end{array}$$

Several points should be noted. (1) The first row is unchanged. (2) The second row now begins with a zero. The two remaining terms in the row have both been altered and, most importantly, *so has the b_2 term*. (3) The third row is reduced to a single non-zero term which again has been altered and again *so has the b_3 term*.

To make the necessary alterations we first construct an *'augmented matrix'* by placing the column vector $[b_j]$ next to the $[a_{ij}]$ terms thus:

$$\begin{bmatrix} a_{11} & a_{12} & a_{13} & b_1 \\ a_{21} & a_{22} & a_{23} & b_2 \\ a_{31} & a_{32} & a_{33} & b_3 \end{bmatrix}$$

We then subtract a_{21}/a_{11} times the first row from the second and a_{31}/a_{11} times the first row from the third. This reduces the matrix to the form:

$$\begin{bmatrix} a_{11} & a_{12} & a_{13} & b \\ 0 & c_{22} & c_{23} & d_2 \\ 0 & c_{32} & c_{33} & d_3 \end{bmatrix}$$

where $c_{22} = a_{22} - a_{12} \times \dfrac{(a_{21})}{(a_{11})}$

$d_2 = b_2 - b_1 \times \dfrac{(a_{21})}{(a_{11})}$

and so on.

Finally we subtract c_{32}/c_{22} times the new second row from the new third row to give:

$$\begin{bmatrix} a_{11} & a_{12} & a_{13} & b_1 \\ 0 & c_{22} & c_{23} & d_2 \\ 0 & 0 & e_{33} & f_3 \end{bmatrix}$$

where $e_{33} = c_{33} - c_{23} \times \dfrac{(c_{32})}{(c_{22})}$

and $f_3 = d_3 - d_2 \times \dfrac{(c_{32})}{(c_{11})}$

This new augmented matrix can now be turned back into the matrix form of the equations as shown at the top of the page. Although you will not find the following procedure necessary when you are familiar with the technique, it will be instructive at this stage to write out in full the equations represented by this new matrix form. Do this now.

17

$$\begin{array}{r} a_{11}x_1 + a_{12}x_2 + a_{13}x_3 = b_1 \\ c_{22}x_2 + c_{23}x_3 = d_2 \\ e_{33}x_3 = f_3 \end{array}$$

The equations are obtained by multiplying the rows of the matrix into the column vector as indicated previously in frame 16. The solution for the three variables x_1, x_2 and x_3 is now found by '*back-substitution*' starting with the equation for x_3. From this equation we see that $x_3 = f_3/e_{33}$. This value for x_3 can now be 'substituted back' into the second equation which can then be solved to give the value of x_2. The values of x_2 and x_3 can then be 'substituted back' into the first equation to give the solution for x_1.

Gaussian elimination is a very systematic method of solving simultaneous equations and, if a solution to the equations exists, is one of the most reliable methods of solving them. It can be extended to solve equations containing any number of variables. In current practice, large matrices are most often solved with the aid of computers software packages. The algorithms on which these packages are based often employ some form of Gaussian elimination.

If you did not use this method to obtain the answers at the beginning of frame 16, you should now write out the original equations in matrix form and obtain the solution by this method. Do this before reading the rest of this frame. If you are already familiar with the technique, check your working with that given here.

Here are first the equations in matrix form and then the augmented matrix:

$$\begin{bmatrix} 1 & 2 & 0 \\ 0 & 2 & -7 \\ 1 & -1 & -1 \end{bmatrix} \begin{bmatrix} I_1 \\ I_2 \\ I_3 \end{bmatrix} = \begin{bmatrix} 10 \\ 0 \\ 0 \end{bmatrix} \qquad \begin{bmatrix} 1 & 2 & 0 & 10 \\ 0 & 2 & -7 & 0 \\ 1 & -1 & -1 & 0 \end{bmatrix}$$

The first term in row 2 is already zero, so nothing needs to be done to this row. The coefficients in rows 1 and 3 are the same, so we simply subtract row 1 from row 3 to give:

$$\begin{bmatrix} 1 & 2 & 0 & 10 \\ 0 & 2 & -7 & 0 \\ 0 & -3 & -1 & -10 \end{bmatrix}$$

We now wish to reduce the minus 3 in row 3 to zero so we subtract $(-3/2)$ times row 2 from the new row 3 to give:

$$\begin{bmatrix} 1 & 2 & 0 & 10 \\ 0 & 2 & -7 & 0 \\ 0 & 0 & -\dfrac{23}{2} & -10 \end{bmatrix}$$

The last row of this new augmented matrix represents the equation:

$$-\frac{23I_3}{2} = -10 \quad \text{so} \quad I_3 = \frac{20}{23}$$

The second row of the new augmented matrix represents the equation:

$$2I_2 - 7I_3 = 0 \quad \text{so} \quad I_2 = \frac{7I_3}{2} \quad \text{and hence} \quad I_2 = \frac{70}{23}$$

Finally, the first row of the new augmented matrix represents the equation:

$$I_1 + 2I_2 = 10 \quad \text{so} \quad I_1 = 10 - 2I_2 = 10 - \frac{140}{23} = \frac{230 - 140}{23}$$

$$\text{and hence } I_1 = \frac{90}{23}$$

So the full solution is $I_1 = \dfrac{90}{23}$, $\quad I_2 = \dfrac{70}{23}$, $\quad I_3 = \dfrac{20}{23}$

The remaining part of the task we set out on in frame 12 was to find the voltages across all the resistors in the circuit. What are these voltages?

18

> R_1 has $\dfrac{90}{23}$ volts across it, R_2 has $\dfrac{140}{23}$ volts across it
>
> R_3 has $\dfrac{60}{23}$ volts across it, R_4 has $\dfrac{80}{23}$ volts across it

Having solved for all the unknown currents, the voltages across the four resistors can be calculated by simply applying Ohm's Law to each resistor in turn, which gives the above results. We will now examine some alternative strategies for solving the same kind of problem in the next few frames.

19

Here is another circuit similar to the one we have just analysed. It differs from the previous circuit, however, in that it has an additional mesh which contains a second voltage generator. We will first see what happens if we try to analyse it using the approach outlined in frame 12.

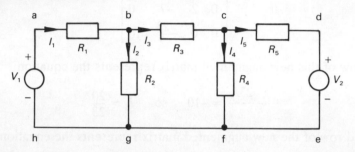

Just as before, we have postulated branch currents with an algebraic numeration starting from the left-hand side of the diagram. Notice that the current I_5 is shown flowing *into* the positive terminal of the generator V_2. It does not matter if this is an incorrect assumption. If it is, in fact, incorrect for certain values of the resistors and generators then I_5 will have a negative value in the solution.

How many equations are needed to determine all the currents? Use Kirchhoff's voltage and current laws to write down a suitable set of equations.

20

> Five equations are needed. A suitable set is given below.
>
> For the mesh habgh we have $V_1 - I_1R_1 - I_2R_2 = 0$ (1)
>
> For the mesh gbcfg we have $I_2R_2 - I_3R_3 - I_4R_4 = 0$ (2)
>
> For the mesh fcdef we have $I_4R_4 - I_5R_5 - V_2 = 0$ (3)
>
> At node b we have $I_1 - I_2 - I_3 = 0$ (4)
>
> At node c we have $I_3 - I_4 - I_5 = 0$ (5)

The first three equations are obtained by applying Kirchhoff's Voltage Law to the three meshes in turn starting, in each case, from the bottom left-hand corner of each mesh. The last two equations are obtained by applying Kirchhoff's Current Law at the two principal nodes b and c.

Can you now put these equations into matrix form?

21

$$\begin{bmatrix} R_1 & R_2 & 0 & 0 & 0 \\ 0 & R_2 & -R_3 & -R_4 & 0 \\ 0 & 0 & 0 & R_4 & -R_5 \\ 1 & -1 & -1 & 0 & 0 \\ 0 & 0 & 1 & -1 & -1 \end{bmatrix} \begin{bmatrix} I_1 \\ I_2 \\ I_3 \\ I_4 \\ I_5 \end{bmatrix} = \begin{bmatrix} V_1 \\ 0 \\ -V_2 \\ 0 \\ 0 \end{bmatrix}$$

As before, the equations have been rearranged so that the generator terms are included as a column vector on the right-hand side of the equation.

Several points are worth noting about this matrix equation. (1) The circuit has only three meshes but we need five equations for a solution. (2) The terms in the first three rows of the matrix have dimensions of resistance, those in the last two rows are dimensionless. (3) Some terms are negative and some positive, but there seems to be no particular pattern to them.

We could go on to solve the problem by Gaussian elimination as before but, instead, will examine a more efficient solving strategy.

22

MAXWELL'S CYCLIC CURRENTS

As may be guessed from its name, this method is due to the eminent 19th century scientist James Clerk Maxwell. Maxwell's idea was to postulate a 'cyclic' or circulating current in each adjacent mesh of the circuit as shown in this diagram. All currents are conventionally assumed to be flowing in the same sense – usually clockwise. If this proves to be a wrong assumption it will be taken care of by the algebra and negative answers for some currents may result.

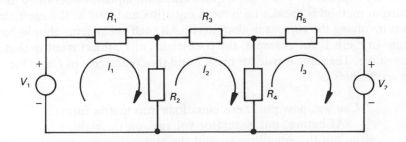

How many equations are required to find a solution?

23

| Three equations are needed |

Since there are now only three unknowns, the three mesh currents, only three equations are needed to determine them. The equations can be found by applying Kirchhoff's Voltage Law to each mesh in turn. Kirchhoff's Current Law is automatically satisfied by recognising that the current in a component common to two meshes is the difference between the two mesh currents flowing through that component.

Can you write down an equation for each of the three meshes using Kirchhoff's Voltage Law? Start from the bottom left-hand corner of each mesh and define the sense of potentials across resistors in the mesh in terms of the cyclic current *in that mesh*. The sense of generator potentials is defined by the orientation of the generator in the mesh.

24

$$
\begin{array}{c}
V_1 \quad - \quad I_1 R_1 \quad - \quad (I_1 - I_2) R_2 = 0 \\
- (I_2 - I_1) R_2 \quad - \quad I_2 R_3 \quad - \quad (I_2 - I_3) R_4 = 0 \\
- (I_3 - I_2) R_4 \quad - \quad I_3 R_5 \quad - \quad V_2 = 0
\end{array}
$$

You may not have all the equations written down exactly as they are shown above. If you have chosen to subtract the terms inside the brackets the other way round, some of your terms may be positive where those above are negative. Check your equations to see that the signs of all terms would be the same as those above if the brackets were expanded. A very good quick check for equations obtained using the cyclic current method is to take each mesh equation and look at the coefficients of the terms involving the current in that mesh. All such coefficients should have the same sign. In mesh 1, for example, the coefficients of I_1, the current in that mesh, are all negative. The same is true for mesh 2 and the coefficients of I_2 and for mesh 3 and the coefficients of I_3.

Can you now put these equations into matrix form?
As before, put generator voltages on the right.
Write out the equations so that the matrix is symmetrical.

25

$$
\begin{bmatrix}
R_1 + R_2 & -R_2 & 0 \\
-R_2 & R_2 + R_3 + R_4 & -R_4 \\
0 & -R_4 & R_4 + R_5
\end{bmatrix}
\begin{bmatrix}
I_1 \\
I_2 \\
I_3
\end{bmatrix}
=
\begin{bmatrix}
V_1 \\
0 \\
-V_2
\end{bmatrix}
$$

How would you describe the resistance values on the leading diagonal in rows 1, 2 and 3 in terms of the resistors in meshes 1, 2 and 3? Use one of the terms to define combinations of resistors defined earlier.

26

> Each term has a value equal to the resistance of all the resistors in the mesh connected in series.

More generally, we could say that each term on the leading diagonal was made up of the sum of the resistances in all the individual branches making up the mesh.

How would you describe the resistance values of the off-diagonal elements of the matrix? Try to relate row and column positions to corresponding meshes. Define the element in row i, column j of the matrix as r_{ij}.

27

> All off-diagonal elements of the form r_{ij} or r_{ji} are minus the resistance common to meshes i and j.

Because of the symmetry of the matrix, each pair of adjacent meshes i and j produce two terms r_{ij} and r_{ji}. Notice, in particular, that zero terms appear in the matrix where two meshes have no common branches. In this example there are no connections between meshes 1 and 3 so matrix elements r_{13} and r_{31} are both zero.

How would you describe the values in the column vector on the right-hand side of the matrix equation? Again relate the rows of the column vector to the corresponding meshes. Also try to relate the sign of the voltage term to the current direction in that mesh and the orientation of the generator in the mesh with respect to that current.

28

> Row i contains the value of the generator in mesh i.
> If the current in mesh i flows out of the positive terminal
> of the generator, the sign of the term is positive.
> If the current in mesh i flows into the positive terminal
> of the generator, the sign of the term is negative.

Do not worry about the possibility of current flowing into the positive terminal of a generator. This is quite alright and can happen in practice when, for example, a battery charger is used to re-charge a car battery.

Having observed how the values of all terms in the matrix and the column vector are arrived at, we can formulate some general rules for analysing circuits using Maxwell's Cyclic Current technique for a circuit containing only voltage generators and resistors. Once you are familiar with this method, you will find that you can, if you wish, set up the matrix equation using only these rules and without having to worry about applying Kirchhoff's Laws to the circuit at all. If you prefer to set up the equations first using Kirchhoff's Laws, then these rules form an excellent basis for checking that you have not made any algebraic errors.

1. First set up a square matrix with as many rows and columns as there are independent meshes in the circuit. (Since a mesh is, by definition, a closed path round which current can flow, other meshes than those we have considered above can be found in the circuit. The path right round the outside can be taken as a mesh, for example, but the information gained from this mesh would not be independent of that contained in the equations for the other three. We will discuss criteria for deciding how many independent meshes a circuit contains shortly. Confusion is avoided and a sufficient set of equations obtained, however, if only adjacent meshes are chosen.)
2. Fill the matrix with terms r_{ij} where, if $i = j$ then r_{ij} is the sum of all the resistances in mesh i but, if $i \neq j$ then r_{ij} is minus the value of the resistance common to meshes i and j. If meshes i and j have no common branches, enter a zero for element r_{ij}.
3. Set up a column vector with as many rows as the circuit has independent meshes. The element in row i is the value of the independent voltage generator (if any) in mesh i. If the current in mesh i flows out of the positive terminal of the generator, the sign of the term is positive. If the current in mesh i flows into the positive terminal of the generator, the sign of the term is negative.

Here is the circuit again and the matrix equation which describes it so that you can check the way that the two are related.

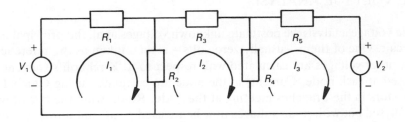

$$\begin{bmatrix} R_1 + R_2 & -R_2 & 0 \\ -R_2 & R_2 + R_3 + R_3 & -R_4 \\ 0 & -R_4 & R_4 + R_5 \end{bmatrix} \begin{bmatrix} I_1 \\ I_2 \\ I_3 \end{bmatrix} = \begin{bmatrix} V_1 \\ 0 \\ -V_2 \end{bmatrix}$$

We will now assign values to the circuit components and use this example for revision. Taking $V_1 = V_2 = 4$ V with $R_3 = 1$ kΩ and $R_1 = R_2 = R_4 = R_5 = 2$ kΩ, the equation becomes:

$$\begin{bmatrix} 4 & -2 & 0 \\ -2 & 5 & -2 \\ 0 & -2 & 4 \end{bmatrix} \begin{bmatrix} I_1 \\ I_2 \\ I_3 \end{bmatrix} = \begin{bmatrix} 4 \\ 0 \\ -4 \end{bmatrix}$$

Can you now use Gaussian elimination to find the currents? What are the voltages at the two principal nodes at the top of the diagram?

30

Using Gaussian elimination as before, the matrix reduces successively to:

$$\begin{bmatrix} 4 & -2 & 0 \\ 0 & 4 & -2 \\ 0 & -2 & 4 \end{bmatrix} \begin{bmatrix} I_1 \\ I_2 \\ I_3 \end{bmatrix} = \begin{bmatrix} 4 \\ 2 \\ -4 \end{bmatrix} \quad \text{and} \quad \begin{bmatrix} 4 & -2 & -0 \\ 0 & 4 & -2 \\ 0 & 0 & 3 \end{bmatrix} \begin{bmatrix} I_1 \\ I_2 \\ I_3 \end{bmatrix} = \begin{bmatrix} 4 \\ 2 \\ -3 \end{bmatrix}$$

$I_1 = 1$ mA; $I_2 = 0$ mA; $I_3 = -1$ mA. Both node voltages are 2 V.

The currents are obtained by back substitution starting with I_3. Since I_1 flows through R_1 and R_2 and I_2 is zero, the voltage at the node at the junction of R_1, R_2 and R_3 is $I_1 R_2$ above zero; that is 2 V. Since I_3 is negative, its direction is in the opposite sense to that shown on the diagram. It flows through R_4 and R_5 so the voltage at the other node is obtained by a similar calculation to the one just performed.

31

NODE VOLTAGE ANALYSIS

In node voltage analysis we postulate unknown voltages at all the principal nodes in the circuit. One of them – usually zero volts – is then taken as the reference node and all other voltages are calculated with respect to it. Kirchhoff's Current Law is then used at each node. Currents at the node are calculated using Ohm's Law for the resistors in the branches meeting at the node. Re-drawing the circuit we have just analysed but with node voltages now being used as the unknown variables, we have the following diagram:

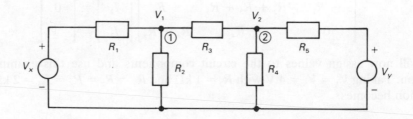

How many equations are needed for a solution using this method?

32

> Two equations are needed

Since there are now only two unknown variables, only two equations are needed to solve for them. Once the two node voltages are known, the currents in all the branches can be deduced from Ohm's Law and hence the voltages across all components calculated.

Can you now apply Kirchhoff's Current Law to the two principal nodes at the top of the diagram? Write the equations as if all currents were leaving the nodes. Although this must be a wrong assumption, it allows you to write the equations in a consistent manner in all problems. The algebra of the problem will take care of the apparent discrepancy and your answer will allow you to decide which currents are actually leaving and which are entering any given node. Write the equations in terms of the conductances of the resistors in the circuit this time. Let a resistor whose resistance is R_i have a conductance of G_i and so on. Why is this a good idea?

> At node 1 we have: $(V_1 - V_x)G_1 + V_1G_2 + (V_1 - V_2)G_3 = 0$
>
> At node 2 we have: $(V_2 - V_1)G_3 + V_2G_4 + (V_2 - V_y)G_5 = 0$
>
> Using conductances avoids writing reciprocal relationships.

Since we are working as if all currents leave their nodes, when we analyse node 1 it is as if V_1 was greater than any neighbouring voltage used to calculate currents. This explains the sense of all voltage terms in the first equation above. Notice that the effect, if we expand all the brackets, is to ensure that all coefficients of V_1 are positive in this equation. Similarly, in deriving the second equation, we work as if V_2 was greater than any neighbouring voltage so all coefficients of V_2 in the second equation are positive.

Can you now re-write these equations in matrix form? Remember that V_1 and V_2 are the unknown variables. Put terms involving the known independent generators on the right-hand side of the equation.

$$\begin{bmatrix} G_1 + G_2 + G_3 & -G_3 \\ -G_3 & G_3 + G_4 + G_5 \end{bmatrix} \begin{bmatrix} V_1 \\ V_2 \end{bmatrix} = \begin{bmatrix} V_xG_1 \\ V_yG_5 \end{bmatrix}$$

It is worth remarking that, in using this form of analysis, we have reduced a problem which, on our first attempt, required five equations down to one which can be solved with only two.

Notice that all terms in the matrix are conductances and that this matrix has the same kind of symmetry as the matrix we obtained when using mesh analysis on a previous circuit. Can you write the rules for constructing such a matrix for any circuit using nodal analysis? Consider the number of equations needed to solve a circuit with n nodes which will determine the size of the matrix and let a general element in the matrix be called g_{ij}. Think in terms of conductances in branches connected to and between nodes.

35

> 1. The number of rows and columns in the matrix is one less than the number of principal nodes in the circuit.
> 2. If $i = j$ then g_{ij} is the sum of all conductances in the branches connected to node i.
> 3. If $i \neq j$ then g_{ij} is minus the conductance in the branch between nodes i and j.

As was the case with the matrix equation obtained using Maxwell's cyclic currents, you can use these rules either to construct the matrix directly or to check it once you have constructed it from the circuit equations.

36

Now let us turn our attention to the column vector on the right-hand side of the matrix equation. Here is the equation again:

$$\begin{bmatrix} G_1 + G_2 + G_3 & -G_3 \\ -G_3 & G_3 + G_4 + G_5 \end{bmatrix} \begin{bmatrix} V_1 \\ V_2 \end{bmatrix} = \begin{bmatrix} V_x G_1 \\ V_y G_5 \end{bmatrix}$$

The first term, $V_x G_1$, has the dimensions of current. The value of this current is the same as that which would flow in a short-circuit connected across the ends of the branch containing the generator V_x. If there were a generator in the branch containing R_2, this would lead to another current term involving the value of the generator and the conductance G_2 in the first equation in frame 33 and thus in the first element of the column vector. In general, then, the first term of the column vector is made up of a sum of currents whose value is determined by any generators in the branches connected to node 1. Each current is equal in magnitude to the current that would flow in a short-circuit connected across the ends of the branch. If there is a current generator in a branch, its value is simply added in. (There is a problem if a branch contains only a voltage generator but no series resistor. We will deal with that situation later.)

The second term is similarly related to generators in branches connected to node 2. In this case only one of these branches contains a generator (the one containing R_5) so there is again just a single term.

How would you relate the sign of the term to the orientation of the generator in the branch and the assumed direction of the current leaving the node?

37

> If the current, which is assumed to be leaving the node, flows into the
> positive terminal of the generator then the term is positive.

This may seem strange but results from the assumption that all currents are assumed to leave the node and will, as stated earlier, be taken care of by the algebra of the problem.

Let us now solve the problem using the same component values as we did in frame 29. These are $V_x = V_y = 4$ V with $R_3 = 1$ kΩ and $R_1 = R_2 = R_4 = R_5 = 2$ kΩ.

Can you now write the nodal equation in matrix form? Remember that the elements of the matrix are conductances which are measured in siemens!

38

$$\begin{bmatrix} 2 & -1 \\ -1 & 2 \end{bmatrix} \begin{bmatrix} V_1 \\ V_2 \end{bmatrix} = \begin{bmatrix} 2 \\ 2 \end{bmatrix}$$

Conductances G_1, G_2, G_4 and G_5 are all 0.5 mS (millisiemens) and G_3 is 1 mS, giving the above terms in the matrix. The terms in the column vector on the right hand side are in mA.

Now solve this equation for V_1 and V_2 and then calculate
the currents corresponding to I_1, I_2 and I_3 in the mesh analysis.

39

> $V_1 = V_2 = 2$ V, $I_1 = 1$ mA, $I_2 = 0$ mA, $I_3 = -1$ mA

Voltages and currents are, of course, all the same as before. The matrix is very simple to reduce this time: just add half the first row to the second. Once the node voltages are known, the currents in all branches can be calculated from the voltage differences across the resistors and the application of Ohm's Law to each resistor. Notice how the algebra has given the right results. The relative sizes of the voltage generators and the node voltages lead to the positive sign for I_1 and the negative sign for I_3 which indicate that they actually flow *into* the nodes.

40

SOME DIFFICULTIES AND HOW TO COPE WITH THEM

Before leaving the methods of mesh and node analysis we will examine a few problems which can arise in these sorts of analysis and see how to deal with them. Apart from the simple circuit analysed in frame 11, all the examples we have considered so far have had voltage generators as their energy sources. Let us see how current generators can be handled using these methods.

Here is a circuit which appears to have three adjacent meshes, one of which contains a current generator. If we assign three unknown cyclic currents to the meshes we obtain the picture given here:

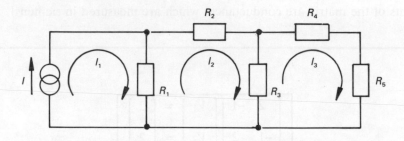

What problem arises if we try to apply Kirchhoff's Voltage Law to the mesh containing the current generator?

41

There is no simple way of directly writing an expression for the voltage across the current generator.

In previous examples using Kirchhoff's Voltage Law, we started from the bottom left-hand corner of each mesh and worked round the mesh, writing down the voltage across each component in the mesh. We cannot do this for the current generator in this example. How do we cope with this problem? If you look carefully at the mesh containing the current generator you will see that the 'unknown' current I_1 must be equal to I, the current supplied by the generator. I_1 flows through the generator and, by definition, the current through the generator is I, so the above assertion must be true. Using this information we can now apply Kirchhoff's Voltage Law to the other two meshes.

You do this and write down the equations.

42

$$-(I_2 - I)R_1 - I_2R_2 - (I_2 - I_3)R = 0$$

$$-(I_3 - I_2)R_3 - I_3(R_4 + R_5) = 0$$

Once again, a quick check to see that the equations are likely to be correct is to look at the coefficients of all terms involving the current in a given mesh. All such coefficients should be negative in the equation for that mesh. Thus, in the first equation, all coefficients of I_2 are negative and in the second equation, all coefficients of I_3 are negative. Now put these equations into matrix form. As usual, the matrix and the column vector of unknowns should be on the left and the column vector of known terms on the right. Signs should be adjusted so that terms on the leading diagonal of the matrix are positive.

43

$$\begin{bmatrix} R_1 + R_2 + R_3 & -R_3 \\ -R_3 & R_3 + R_4 + R_5 \end{bmatrix} \begin{bmatrix} I_2 \\ I_3 \end{bmatrix} = \begin{bmatrix} IR_1 \\ 0 \end{bmatrix}$$

We see that the problem has, in effect, reduced to one with only two unknowns and, since we have two equations (and thus a two-by-two matrix), a solution must exist. We will not work out the full solution yet. Instead, we will recall that, in programme 2, frame 63, we established that any non-ideal generator could be represented either as a current generator in parallel with a resistor or a voltage generator in series with a resistor. The current generator and the resistor R_1 in the diagram in frame 40 can be regarded as a non-ideal generator represented in the current generator form. We can therefore replace it with an equivalent voltage generator of value IR_1 (this term has dimensions of voltage and so is of the correct form) in series with a resistor of value R_1. The checks that the two representations of the non-ideal generator are the same are that the open-circuit voltage and short-circuit currents of both are the same.

Using this information can you now re-draw the circuit with the current generator replaced by a voltage generator, and then write the equations which allow a solution for the currents flowing to be found? Put the equations in matrix form. You can construct the matrix directly if you wish.

44

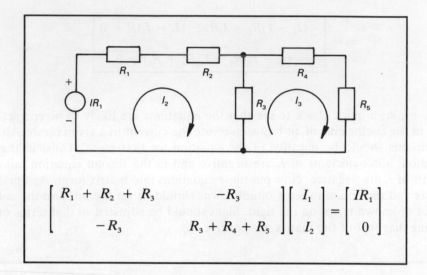

$$\begin{bmatrix} R_1 + R_2 + R_3 & -R_3 \\ -R_3 & R_3 + R_4 + R_5 \end{bmatrix} \begin{bmatrix} I_1 \\ I_2 \end{bmatrix} = \begin{bmatrix} IR_1 \\ 0 \end{bmatrix}$$

With the voltage generator representation of the first two components we can see how the circuit reduces to what is, in effect, only a two-mesh circuit and hence leads to equations in only two unknowns. The equations are, in fact, exactly the same as those obtained from the original circuit. The full solution of the problem will be left as an exercise for you to do later. The answer will then be given at the end of the text.

Suppose we were to tackle the same problem using nodal analysis. Here is the original diagram again:

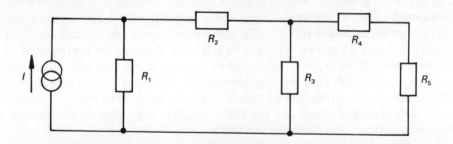

How many principal nodes has the circuit got in this form?
Which would you use as a reference node for analytical purposes?

45

> The circuit has three principal nodes. The line at the bottom of the diagram is one of these and would be the best to choose as a reference.

The other two nodes are: (1) the junction of the current generator with resistors R_1 and R_2 and (2) the junction of resistors R_2, R_3 and R_4. Calling the voltages at these nodes with respect to the reference node V_1 and V_2 respectively, can you write the nodal equations for this circuit? Take care with the last term in the second equation.

46

> For node 1 $-I \;\; + V_1 G_1 + \;\;\; (V_1 - V_2)G_2 \;\;\; = 0$
>
> For node 2 $(V_2 - V_1)G_2 + V_2 G_3 + V_2(G_4 G_5/(G_4 + G_5)) = 0$

The quantity multiplying the voltage in the last term is the series combination of two conductances. Notice that the algebraic 'shape' of this expression is the same as that for the parallel combination of two resistances. Notice, too, that it has the dimensions of conductance (the product of two conductances divided by a sum of conductances). Now write these equations in matrix form.

47

$$\begin{bmatrix} G_1 + G_2 & -G_2 \\ -G_2 & G_2 + G_3 + (G_4 G_5/(G_4 + G_5)) \end{bmatrix} \begin{bmatrix} V_1 \\ V_2 \end{bmatrix} = \begin{bmatrix} I \\ 0 \end{bmatrix}$$

Let us examine the terms in this matrix to see how well they obey the rules we produced in frames 35 to 37. The matrix has two rows and columns and there are three principal nodes so the first rule still holds. The first term in the top row is the sum of conductances in branches connected to node 1. Note that the branch containing the current generator does not affect this sum. This is because the generator term is an independent variable and so contributes to the terms on the right-hand side of the matrix equation. Note that, even if the branch containing the generator included a resistor in series with it, the conductance of this resistor would *not* be included in the sum of conductances for the node. Can you say why this is?

48

> A resistor in series with a current generator does
> not affect the current drawn from that generator.

The current entering node 1 would be the output current of the generator whatever value of resistor was included in series with it. Since the current is constant, the voltage developed across the resistor would depend on the resistor value but this would not affect the rest of the circuit.

Do the off-diagonal elements of the matrix obey the third rule in frame 35? Check back to see what this rule is if you have forgotten it.

49

> Yes. Off-diagonal elements are given as
> minus the conductances between nodes.

Does the sign of the current in the column vector on the right conform with the rule for current signs given in frame 37?

50

> Yes. The sign for the current is positive in the column vector because
> the assumed current flows in the opposite direction to the actual current.

In the previous rule a positive sign resulted from an assumed current which flowed into the positive terminal of a voltage generator. The positive sign for the current here results from the fact that, in writing the equation down initially, we knew that the actual current flowed into the node, but the convention for writing down the equations required us to set down the current as if it were leaving the node.

What would be the contribution to the matrix equation of a current generator between two nodes neither of which was the reference node? This situation could arise if R_2 was replaced by a current generator, for example.

51

> The generator would contribute terms in two rows on the
> right-hand side. One would be positive and the other negative,
> depending on the way the generator was connected between the nodes.

In writing down the simultaneous equations from which the matrix equation is derived, components between nodes appear in two equations. This leads to the condition above. The current must flow into one node and out of the other, so one sign must be positive and the other negative. Once again the full solution to this problem will be left for you to complete later. The answer will be given at the end of the text. The intention in these frames is to demonstrate the methods of solution.

A similar problem to the one we have just examined occurs when a voltage generator is connected directly between two nodes. We will look at this in the next frame.

52

Here is another circuit with three adjacent meshes in one of which there is a voltage generator. There are three principal nodes. Using the one at the bottom as a reference and putting in node voltage values with reference to this node, we obtain the following picture:

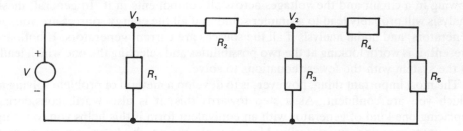

What problem arises if we try to apply Kirchhoff's
Current Law to the node nearest the voltage generator?

53

> There is no simple way of directly writing an expression
> for the node current through the voltage generator.

Here we have a very similar problem to the one we had in frame 40 with a current generator. In this case the 'unknown' voltage at node 1 is given directly as the value of the generator voltage V. V_2 is, in fact, the only truly unknown node voltage so this problem really reduces to a two-node system with just one equation. The current through resistor R_1 can be calculated directly from Ohm's Law and the generator current deduced when the system equation has been solved. What is the system equation?

54

$$(V_2 - V)G_2 + V_2 G_3 + V_2(G_4 G_5/(G_4 + G_5)) = 0$$

Terms in this equation can be rearranged so that the known voltage V is on the right-hand side and the solution for V_2 is then straightforward.

We have so far developed, in this programme, two methods of circuit analysis: mesh analysis and nodal analysis. Both methods enable us to find all the currents flowing in a circuit and the voltages across all components in it. In general, mesh analysis will probably lead to a simpler solution if all the energy sources are voltage generators, and nodal analysis if all the sources are current generators. If both are present, it is worth looking at the two possibilities and selecting the one which leads to the system with the fewest equations to solve.

The most important thing, however, is to develop a method of problem solving in which you are confident. As a step towards this, it is also worth considering replacing one kind of generator with an equivalent form if this helps you to set up the system equations more easily. Many people seem to be happier working with voltage generators than with current generators. If you can remember how to transform a current generator into a voltage generator, you can then perform analyses on any circuit by treating it solely as a system of voltage generators and resistors.

The next frame contains a summary of results.

55

SUMMARY

1. The topology of an electric circuit (that is, the way in which the various components which comprise it are interconnected) can be described in terms of its branches, loops or meshes and nodes.

2. *Kirchhoff's First Law (the Current Law)*: In any electric circuit in which currents are flowing, the algebraic sum of currents entering and leaving a node is always zero.

3. *Kirchhoff's Second Law (the Voltage Law)*: In any electric circuit containing components with voltages across them, the algebraic sum of the voltages around any mesh in the circuit is zero.

4. *Maxwell's cyclic currents in mesh analysis*: A clockwise cyclic or circulating current is postulated in each adjacent mesh of the circuit being analysed. A matrix equation can then be set up to solve for the unknown currents. The full rules for setting up the matrix are given in frames 12 to 18. The matrix has as many rows and columns as there are meshes in the circuit. All diagonal elements of the matrix contain terms which are positive and formed by the sums of resistances in the meshes of the circuit. All off-diagonal elements contain terms which are either negative or zero and are formed by the values of resistances common to two meshes in the circuit. Each term in the column vector on the right-hand side contains terms related to the values of generators in a given mesh.

5. *Nodal analysis*: One of the principal nodes of the circuit is taken as a reference node. Unknown voltages referred to this node are postulated at all other principal nodes of the circuit. A matrix equation can then be set up to solve for the unknown voltages. The full rules for setting up the matrix are given in frames 31 to 39. The number of rows and columns in the matrix is one less than the number of principal nodes in the circuit. All diagonal elements of the matrix contain terms which are positive and formed by the sums of conductances in the branches connected to a given node of the circuit. All off-diagonal elements contain terms which are either negative or zero and are formed by the values of conductances between two nodes in the circuit. Each term of the column vector on the right-hand side contains terms related to the values of generators in the branches connected to a given node.

Now turn to the next frame for some revision questions
on the material covered so far in this programme.

56

Note: *all numerical resistor values are given in kilohms; all voltages in volts and all currents in milliamps.*

1. How many meshes has the circuit in the diagram below left? How many principal nodes has it? Which node would be best as a reference node? How many branches are connected to each node? How many mesh or nodal equations are needed for a solution?

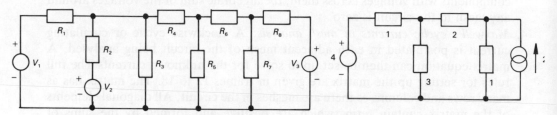

2. Draw up the matrix equations for both a mesh analysis and a nodal analysis of the circuit in the diagram above right. Use the circuit equations again as a first step if you need to. Solve one of these sets of equations to find the currents through and voltages across all the resistors in the circuit.

3. Draw up the matrix equations for a mesh analysis of the left-hand diagram below and a nodal analysis of the right-hand diagram. (If you cannot draw up the matrices directly, write down the circuit equations using Kirchhoff's Laws and then put them into matrix form.) Find the currents through and voltages across all the resistors in the two circuits.

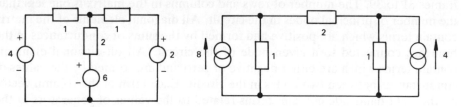

4. Find the currents through and voltages across all the resistors in this circuit. Compare the circuit with the one in question 2 above!

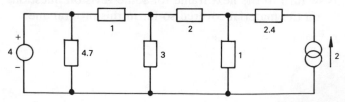

SOLUTIONS TO REVISION QUESTIONS

1. The circuit has five meshes and four principal nodes. The node at the bottom of the diagram would be the best reference node. There are six branches connected to this node. They are those containing V_1 and R_1, V_2 and R_2, R_3, R_5, R_7, and V_3 and R_8. The following branches also join at a node: V_1 and R_1, V_2 and R_2, R_3 and R_4. The following branches join at a third node: R_4, R_5 and R_6. The following branches join at the fourth node: R_6, R_7 and R_8 and V_3. Five mesh equations or three nodal equations are needed for a solution.

2.

With currents and voltages marked as above the circuit equations are:

$$V \quad - I_1R_1 - (I_1 - I_2)R_2 = 0 \qquad (V_1 - V)G_1 + V_1G_2 + (V_1 - V_2)G_3 = 0$$

$$- (I_2 - I_1)R_2 - I_2R_3 - (I_2 - I_3)R_4 = 0 \qquad (V_2 - V_1)G_3 + V_2G_4 \quad - I \quad = 0$$

$$I_3 = I$$

The third equation can be substituted directly into the second equation. The matrix equations are then:

Here there are only two equations which is all that are needed.

$$\begin{bmatrix} R_1 + R_2 & -R_2 \\ -R_2 & R_2 + R_3 + R_4 \end{bmatrix} \begin{bmatrix} I_1 \\ I_2 \end{bmatrix} = \begin{bmatrix} V \\ -IR_4 \end{bmatrix} \qquad \begin{bmatrix} G_1 + G_2 + G_3 & -G_3 \\ -G_3 & G_3 + G_4 \end{bmatrix} \begin{bmatrix} V_1 \\ V_2 \end{bmatrix} = \begin{bmatrix} VG_1 \\ I \end{bmatrix}$$

Putting in numerical values and reducing the matrices we obtain:

$$\begin{bmatrix} 4 & -3 \\ 0 & 15/4 \end{bmatrix} \begin{bmatrix} I_1 \\ I_2 \end{bmatrix} = \begin{bmatrix} 4 \\ 1 \end{bmatrix} \qquad \begin{bmatrix} 11/6 & -1/2 \\ 0 & 30/22 \end{bmatrix} \begin{bmatrix} V_1 \\ V_2 \end{bmatrix} = \begin{bmatrix} 4 \\ 34/11 \end{bmatrix}$$

Hence $I_1 = 18/15$ mA, $I_2 = 4/15$ mA and $V_1 = 42/15$ V, $V_2 = 34/15$ V. Circuit currents and voltages are:

18/15 mA L to R through R_1 18/15 V across R_1 LHS more positive
14/15 mA down through R_2 42/15 V across R_2 top more positive
4/15 mA L to R through R_3 8/15 V across R_3 LHS more positive
34/15 mA down through R_4 34/15 V across R_4 top more positive

3. Putting in mesh currents and node voltages for the two circuits, the diagrams become:

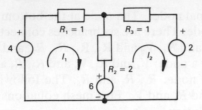 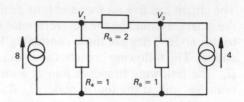

The circuit equations are:

$$4 - I_1 - 2(I_1 - I_2) - 6 = 0 \qquad -8 + V + (1/2)(V - V_2) = 0$$
$$6 - 2(I_2 - I_1) - I_2 - 2 = 0 \qquad (1/2)(V_2 - V_1) + V_2 - 4 = 0$$

In matrix form these become:

$$\begin{bmatrix} 3 & -2 \\ -2 & 3 \end{bmatrix}\begin{bmatrix} I_1 \\ I_2 \end{bmatrix} = \begin{bmatrix} -2 \\ 4 \end{bmatrix} \qquad \begin{bmatrix} 3/2 & -1/2 \\ -1/2 & 3/2 \end{bmatrix}\begin{bmatrix} V_1 \\ V_2 \end{bmatrix} = \begin{bmatrix} 8 \\ 4 \end{bmatrix}$$

Reducing the matrices we have:

$$\begin{bmatrix} 3 & -2 \\ 0 & 5/3 \end{bmatrix}\begin{bmatrix} I_1 \\ I_2 \end{bmatrix} = \begin{bmatrix} -2 \\ 8/3 \end{bmatrix} \qquad \begin{bmatrix} 3/2 & -1/2 \\ 0 & 4/3 \end{bmatrix}\begin{bmatrix} V_1 \\ V_2 \end{bmatrix} = \begin{bmatrix} 8 \\ 20/3 \end{bmatrix}$$

Solving these matrix equations we obtain:

$$I_1 = 2/5 \text{ mA} \qquad\qquad V_1 = 7 \text{ V}$$
$$I_2 = 8/5 \text{ mA} \qquad\qquad V_2 = 5 \text{ V}$$

Circuit currents and voltages are:

2/5 mA L to R through R_1 7 mA down through R_4
6/5 mA up through R_2 1 mA L to R through R_5
8/5 mA L to R through R_3 5 mA down through R_6

2/5 V across R_1 IHS more positive   7 V across R_4 top more positive
12/5 V across R_2 bottom more positive   2 V across R_5 LHS more positive
8/5 V across R_3 LHS more positive   5 V across R_6 top more positive

4. The only differences between this circuit and the one in question 2 are the 4.7 kΩ and 2.4 kΩ resistors. These will not affect current and voltage distributions among the other components, but will affect only the current drawn from the voltage generator and the voltage across the current generator. The current down through the 4.7 kΩ resistor is 0.85 mA. The voltage across the 2.4 kΩ resistor is 4.8 V, RHS more positive.

EQUIVALENT CIRCUITS

The methods of circuit analysis we have studied so far in this programme have allowed us to calculate all the voltages and currents in a circuit we are analysing. Such information is certainly sometimes required and the methods we have examined are used in the development of algorithms for the production of computer programs for the complete analysis of very large circuits.

In many cases, however, more limited information is required about a particular circuit. We may need to know only the current drawn from a generator for example. Alternatively we may be interested only in changes of voltage across a load resistor as different load values are used. In such cases as these, methods of circuit analysis other than those we have used so far may lead to a quicker answer. In carrying out these more limited calculations we often make use of the concept of an 'equivalent circuit'. In effect we try to replace part of the circuit by a simpler circuit which will produce exactly the same effect in the components we are interested in as the circuit it replaces. The concept is again best illustrated by some examples.

Suppose, in the circuit given here, we want to know the current drawn from the generator. What we want to know, in effect, is what value of resistor, if connected to the generator, would cause the same current to be drawn as the circuit given here.

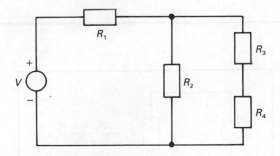

We can tackle the problem in stages. To begin with resistors R_3 and R_4 could be replaced by a single resistor of value $R_3 + R_4$.

This 'equivalent resistor' is in parallel with R_2, so R_2, R_3 and R_4 can, in fact, all be replaced by a single resistor of appropriate value.

Can you re-draw the diagram, replacing resistors R_2, R_3 and R_4 by a single resistor which would have the same effect on the generator and R_1 as these three components? Give the value of this new resistor.

59

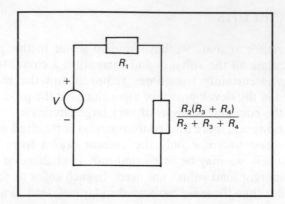

R_2 is in parallel with the series combination of R_3 and R_4 so the value of the resistor equivalent to these three resistors can be calculated by the rule used in programme 1. With this reduction of the circuit we have lost information about how currents and voltages are distributed among these three components, but this does not matter since we do not need to know this.

Now draw a diagram reducing the circuit
to the generator and a single resistor.

60

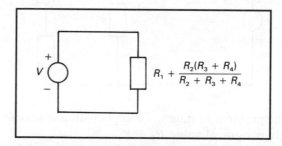

The single resistor is 'equivalent to' the network of resistors insofar as their effect on the generator is concerned. The value of this resistance is often referred to as the 'input resistance' of the resistor network. Using it in Ohm's Law allows us to determine the current that would be taken from any generator connected to the network. Any network of resistors to which a generator can be connected has an input resistance defined in this way.

61

Here is an example for you to try. What is the input resistance of the resistor network in this diagram? What current would be taken from a 6 V generator having the network as a load? What voltage would be developed across the network if it was fed by a 10 mA current generator?

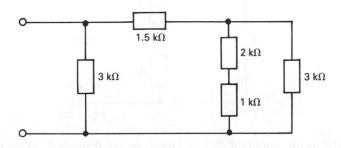

62

> The input resistance is 1.5 kΩ.
> The current drawn would be 4.0 mA.
> The voltage developed would be 15 V.

Working from the right we have 3 kΩ in parallel with (1 + 2) kΩ, giving 1.5 kΩ
  This 1.5 kΩ is in series with the 1.5 kΩ at the top of the diagram, giving 3 kΩ
    This 3 kΩ is in parallel with the 3 kΩ nearest the terminals, giving 1.5 kΩ

Once the input resistance has been determined it can be used in Ohm's Law, just like the value of any other resistor. The two latter results above hence follow from the first.

The concept of input resistance is particularly useful when several networks are linked to each other, as we shall see in later frames. The concept has even more meaning when associated with circuits used for processing changing rather than direct electrical quantities. When analysing these we shall learn to think of 'electrical information' being passed from one circuit to another, the input resistance having a considerable effect on the way it changes as it enters a circuit. It seems reasonable that a circuit which is 'delivering information' should have associated with it an 'output resistance' too, so we will investigate this idea next. We shall see that networks can also have 'equivalent circuits' as seen from their output terminals. The ideas can be examined with direct generators and resistors.

63

EQUIVALENT CIRCUITS FOR NETWORKS WITH OUTPUT TERMINALS

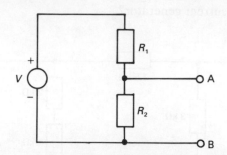

We first analysed the potential divider circuit in programme 2. Here it is again in the diagram above with a pair of 'output terminals' AB added. The implication of these is that we want to connect additional resistors or networks to these terminals as 'loads' on the potential divider.

We are, in effect, extending the idea of a load which was first introduced in programme 2, frame 41. We can now allow any network which contains an energy source to have a load on it at a place in the network where two terminals can be attached. Furthermore, from the work we did in frames 58 to 62 of this programme, we can regard any network into which energy can be fed as forming a load for another network.

Suppose we wanted to examine the effects of adding many different loads to the potential divider above. It would be advantageous, in carrying out the many different calculations which would be necessary, to be able to represent the circuit, as seen from its output terminals, in a simpler way. Because the circuit is already so simple, the only simplification we are likely to be able to make is to replace the potential divider by a (possibly different) generator and a single resistor.

Can you draw a diagram showing the way these two components *must* be connected if they are to be equivalent to the potential divider whatever is connected to the terminals?

Do not try to calculate values for the components but consider the effect of placing different resistors between the terminals A and B. Make sure you suggest a model which, given suitable component values, would allow the same voltage to be developed across a load resistor and the same current to flow through it whether it was connected to the potential divider or to its 'equivalent circuit'.

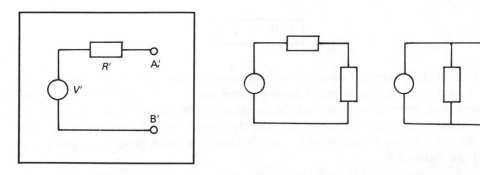

The voltage generator *must* be in series with the resistor as shown in the left-hand diagram above so that, when loads are added as shown in the centre diagram, the *voltage across* a load *and* the *current through* the load will depend on *the value of* the load. If the resistor was placed in parallel with the generator as shown in the right-hand diagram (the only possible alternative way of connecting two components) then, although different load currents could be obtained, the voltage across all loads would be that of the generator, so changing the load would change the current but not the voltage.

If the two circuits *are* to be equivalent then it follows that the same voltages must be developed across identical loads connected to terminals AB and to terminals A' B', and the same currents must flow through these loads. Both these conditions must be true whatever the value of the loads. In particular, they must be true if the loads are open-circuits (loads of infinite resistance) or short-circuits (loads of zero resistance). If the loads are both open-circuits then no current will flow through them, so we can simply equate open-circuit voltages. If the loads are short-circuits then there will be no voltage across them, so we can also equate short circuit currents.

Can you write down an equation for the two open-circuit voltages?

65

$$V' = VR_2/(R_1 + R_2)$$

If no load is connected (open-circuit), no current can flow through R'. There is therefore no potential drop across R', so all the generator voltage V' will appear across the terminals. We calculated the voltage across the resistors in a potential divider in frames 71 to 73 of programme 2.

Can you now write an equation for the two short-circuit currents?

66

$$V'/R' = V/R$$

The short-circuit current equation follows from the application of Ohm's Law to the two circuits. In the potential divider circuit the resistor R_1 is 'bypassed' by the short-circuit so no current flows in this resistor and no voltage is developed across it. The current in the wire which provides the short-circuit is thus dependent only on the value of the generator and on R_2. We can now solve these two equations to find the value of R'.

What is this value?

67

$$R' = R_1R_2/(R_1 + R_2)$$

This result can be obtained by dividing the voltage equation by the current equation. For either circuit it is thus the ratio of the open-circuit voltage to the short-circuit current. From the above expression we can see that R' can also be regarded as the resistance due to R_1 and R_2 in parallel. This is the resistance that would be measured between terminals A and B if the generator was replaced by a short-circuit. This example demonstrates, in fact, a simple version of one of the most useful and important theorems in circuit theory. The theorem is stated here in its most general form.

THEVENIN'S THEOREM

Any network of voltage and current generators and resistors with output terminals A and B is equivalent at these terminals to a single voltage generator in series with a single resistor. The value of this resistor is called the output resistance of the network. The voltage generator has a value equal to the open-circuit voltage between the terminals A and B. The output resistance has a value given by the ratio of the open-circuit voltage to the short-circuit current.

Provided all the generators are independent, the output resistance is the same as that which would be measured between the terminals A and B if all voltage generators were replaced by short-circuits and all current generators replaced by open-circuits.

In the next frame we will go through a proof of this theorem.

68

A PROOF OF THEVENIN'S THEOREM

Consider these two diagrams:

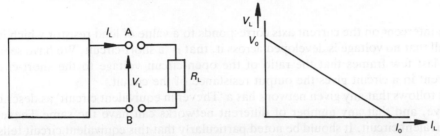

The diagram on the left represents an unknown network of direct voltage and current generators and resistors with a single pair of output terminals AB. The diagram on the right is the graph which would be obtained by connecting a range of values of load resistor R_L to the terminals and plotting corresponding values of V_L and I_L, the voltage across the load and the current through the load. V_0 and I_0 are the intercepts on the voltage and current axes respectively. Such a graph could be found experimentally for any given network. Its linear form may be predicted from the fact that all components of the network are linear. That is, they obey Ohm's Law.

From this graph it is impossible to say exactly what network is 'behind the terminals' inside the 'black box'. There can, in fact, be any number of different networks which would give identical graphs. One of these, however, must be a simple network consisting of a single voltage generator in series with a single resistor. In frames 48 to 56 of programme 2 we found that such a simple network produced such a graph. It follows therefore that the converse must be true. That is, given such a graph, it must be possible to find values for a single voltage generator in series with a single resistor that will produce the graph.

Can you say, by looking at the graph, what
the value of the voltage generator must be?

69

> The value of the voltage generator must be V_0,
> the intercept on the voltage axis of the graph.

The intercept corresponds to a load value which is so large that no current flows, that is, an open-circuit, so V_0 is the open-circuit voltage.

What is the value of the resistor?

70

> The value of the resistor will be the ratio of the intercept on the voltage axis to that on the current axis.

The intercept on the current axis corresponds to a value of load resistor which is so small that no voltage is developed across it, that is, a short-circuit. We have seen in the last few frames that the ratio of the open-circuit voltage to the short-circuit current in a circuit gives the output resistance of the circuit.

It follows that any given network has a 'Thevenin equivalent circuit' as described above, and that any number of different networks can have the same Thevenin equivalent circuit. It should be noted particularly that this equivalent circuit tells us nothing about the voltage, current and power distributions *inside* the network. It does say, however, that any load resistor connected to any one of the networks represented by a given Thevenin equivalent will have a voltage across it and a current flowing through it whose values can be calculated by consideration of the equivalent circuit alone.

What are the Thevenin equivalent circuits as seen looking back into the terminals AB and A′ B′ for the two networks in this diagram?

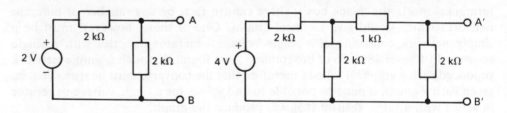

71

Both networks have the same Thevenin equivalent circuit. The generator and resistor values are the ones shown in the diagram on the right.

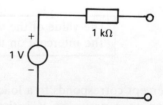

The network on the left of the diagram at the bottom of frame 70 is the same as the one used in the example in frames 63 to 67. The Thevenin equivalent circuit can be deduced simply by substituting values in the expressions derived in these frames.

The network on the right of the same diagram could be analysed by mesh or nodal analysis as illustrated in the frames at the beginning of this programme. If either of these methods was used, the circuit would have to be analysed twice: once to find the open-circuit voltage and a second time with a short-circuit connected between the terminals to find the short-circuit current. Here is another method of analysis which makes use of Thevenin's theorem itself.

First let us imagine the circuit to be divided into two parts as shown in the diagram below. The components to the right of this diagram can be regarded as a load for the circuit on the left.

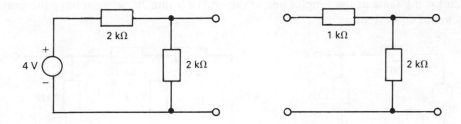

The circuit on the left can be seen to be a simple potential divider. It can therefore be replaced by a Thevenin equivalent circuit using the methods developed in the last few frames. If this Thevenin equivalent circuit is then reconnected to the components on the right-hand side of the diagram above, it will produce the same voltage and current distributions in these components so will make no difference to the open-circuit voltage at the output and the current which would flow in a short-circuit connected between the output terminals.

Can you re-draw the complete diagram making the appropriate replacement with suitably calculated values for the Thevenin equivalent generator and resistor? Calculate values for the Thevenin equivalent circuit of the components on the left above and then draw these Thevenin equivalent components reconnected to the components on the right.

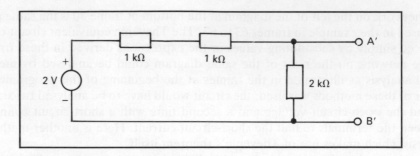

The operations suggested in the previous frame produce the above diagram. We can now proceed as follows. The two 1 kilohm resistors in this diagram are in series so can be replaced by a single 2 kilohm resistor giving the circuit below left. But this circuit is the same as the simpler one at the end of frame 70, so must have the same Thevenin equivalent as it.

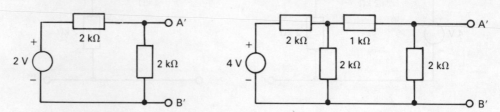

The more complicated circuit at the end of frame 70 is shown again above right. We will now check that the Thevenin equivalent resistance for this circuit could also be calculated by finding the resistance looking back into the output terminals with the generator short-circuited. The generator in this circuit is certainly independent. The output voltage it gives does not depend on any voltages developed or currents drawn in this or any other circuit. If we 'short out' the generator we get the diagram below.

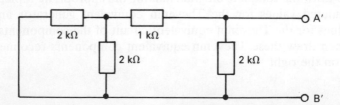

To *calculate* the resistance seen looking back into the terminals we must start from the *left-hand side* of the diagram. Looking from right to left, the two two-kilohm resistors on the left can be seen to be in parallel. Can you now re-draw the diagram with these two resistors replaced by the single resistor to which they are equivalent?

73

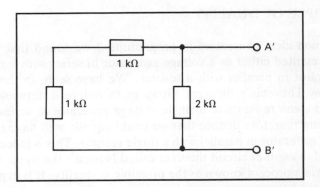

The 1 kilohm resistor on the left above is the replacement for the two 2 kilohm resistors in the original circuit. The rest of the circuit is unaltered. We can now look back from the terminals of this new circuit to arrive at the final value for the output resistance. Can you explain the last two steps in calculating the output resistance by this method?

74

> 1. The two 1 kilohm resistors on the left are in series, so can be combined into a 2 kilohm resistor.
> 2. The two 2 kilohm resistors thus formed are in parallel so can be combined into a 1 kilohm resistor.

In arriving at the above statements we are again considering the circuit 'looking from right to left', so we deal with the components on the left-hand side of the diagram first.

The output resistance calculated by this method is thus indeed the same as that obtained by ratioing the open-circuit voltage to the short-circuit current. When generators *are* independent, this is often the simplest process.

This example illustrates the fact that two quite different networks can have the same equivalent circuit. If we wanted to investigate the effect of connecting different loads to one of the networks, we could do all the calculations using the Thevenin equivalent rather than repeatedly analysing the original network with a new load connected for each new analysis. This could plainly save quite a lot of work, especially if the original network given had been the more complicated one.

75

THE PRINCIPLE OF DUALITY

In analysing non-ideal generators in programme 2 we found that any generator could be represented either as a voltage generator in series with a resistor or as a current generator in parallel with a resistor. We have seen, in the previous few examples, how Thevenin's theorem allows us to reduce a network containing a generator and some resistors to a single voltage generator in series with a single resistor. We can therefore deduce that we could equally well have reduced it to a single current generator in parallel with a single resistor. This is indeed true and the result is stated in another circuit theorem called Norton's theorem. We will derive this theorem via a process known as the principle of duality. It is explained below.

You may have been struck, as you have been working through the programmes in this text, that, whenever a mathematical result has been obtained involving the voltages in a circuit, a very similar mathematical result can be obtained involving the currents. Kirchhoff's two laws are mathematically very similar for example: the sum of voltages round a mesh is zero; the sum of currents at a node is zero. This similarity between results for voltages and results for currents is formalised in the principle of duality which can be stated as follows:

> Given a mathematical relationship amongst certain properties of a circuit, the substitution of the duals of those properties will lead to an equally valid mathematical relationship amongst the duals.

We must define duals. If the relationship is expressed in the usual words and symbols, the changes below will produce the dual relationship:

> Wherever there is a voltage V, replace it with a current I
> Wherever there is a current I, replace it with a voltage V
> Wherever there is a resistance R, replace it with a conductance G
> Wherever there is a conductance G, replace it with a resistance R
> Wherever the word *series* appears, write the word *parallel*
> Wherever the word *parallel* appears, write the word *series*
> Wherever the word *open-circuit* appears, write the word *short-circuit*
> Wherever the word *short-circuit* appears, write the word *open-circuit*

Corresponding pairs are called duals, and one property in a pair is said to be the dual of the other. After making the replacements suggested above it is sometimes necessary to adjust the wording of the rest of the relationship slightly so that it makes proper sense in English, but the two essential mathematical relationships will be identical except that the names and meanings of the variables used in them will have changed.

Now apply this process to Thevenin's theorem to obtain Norton's theorem.

NORTON'S THEOREM

Any network of current and voltage generators and resistors with output terminals A and B is equivalent at these terminals to a single current generator in parallel with a single resistor, the output conductance of the network. The current generator has a value equal to the short-circuit current between the terminals A and B. The output conductance has a value given by the ratio of the short-circuit current to the open-circuit voltage.

In this instance, simply exchanging the words voltage and current and open-circuit and short-circuit and replacing the word resistance with the word conductance produce the required effect. No other adjustments to the statements are necessary. Notice that, in the definition of the properties of the output resistor, the reciprocal relationship between resistance and conductance and the exchanging of the words open-circuit and short-circuit give the correct algebraic result. It would, of course, be perfectly valid to express the property of the resistor in this theorem in terms of its resistance rather than its conductance, but the theorem would not then be the exact dual of Thevenin's theorem as it was enunciated in frame 67. Changing words in the statement following Thevenin's theorem in frame 67 concerning the alternative way of evaluating the output resistance simply gives the statement the same meaning expressed in a slightly different way.

Having established this principle of duality you may find it instructive to look back over some of the results obtained in earlier frames to see how it applies to them. We have already mentioned Kirchhoff's Laws. The expressions for resistances in series and parallel also have meaningful duals. There are many others.

It is also worth remarking that the principle of duality is not restricted to electrical circuit theory alone. It occurs in many other situations when physical properties are expressed in mathematical terms. You should find it interesting to look out for other examples of its use.

Another very useful circuit theorem which often helps in simplifying the analysis of circuits describes the principle of superposition. It is given in the following frame.

77

THE SUPERPOSITION THEOREM

In a linear circuit containing any number of generators, the currents and voltages which are produced in the circuit may be calculated by considering each of the generators in turn and summing the results. During the calculation for any particular generator all other generators must be 'removed', voltage generators being replaced by short-circuits and current generators by open-circuits.

The proof of this theorem is most easily achieved using more complicated matrix theory than will be dealt with in this text. A few examples will show how it can be used, however. It can often be combined with Thevenin and Norton's theorems to reduce the amount of work required in analysing a particular circuit. We will look at an example in the next frame.

78

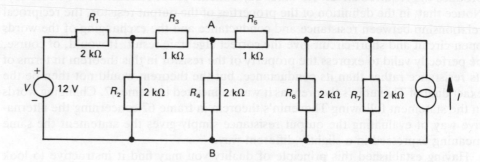

Calculate the current in R_4, the 2 kΩ resistor between points A and B in this circuit.

There are many ways of tackling this problem even allowing that we want to make use of the superposition theorem. We could first of all replace the current generator, I, by an open-circuit as required and then analyse the resulting circuit by mesh or nodal analysis, using the mesh current or node voltage values to calculate the contribution of V to the current in R_4. We would then replace the voltage generator, V, by a short-circuit and calculate the contribution of I to the current in R_4 by a similar process, finally adding the two results together. This method would, however, involve the solution of two sets of simultaneous equations and would be very lengthy.

We will tackle the problem a different way. Having first replaced I by an open-circuit, we will reduce the components to the left of AB to a Thevenin equivalent and those to the right of AB to a single equivalent resistor. Can you do this? Draw a new diagram and mark the component values on it.

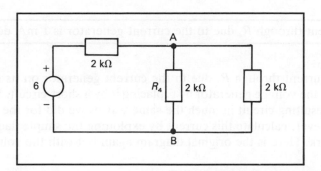

79

The Thevenin components to the left can be calculated in two stages. The voltage generator, R_1 and R_2 can first be separated off as we did in the example in frame 71, to be replaced by a generator of value 6 V in series with a 1 kΩ resistor. This 1 kΩ resistor can then be combined in series with the 1 kΩ resistor R_3 to give the 2 kΩ resistor shown in the diagram at the top of this frame. On the right of AB in the diagram with the current generator removed, the two 2 kΩ resistors R_6 and R_7 can be seen to be in parallel giving a 1 kΩ resistor. This is in series with the 1 kΩ resistor R_5 giving the 2 kΩ resistor shown above.

These reductions to the circuit have left R_4 unchanged so this simpler circuit can now be analysed to find the current through R_4 due to the voltage generator alone. If we first calculate the total load on the generator we can then deduce the current drawn from it. We can then calculate how this current divides between R_4 and the other 2 kΩ resistor to its right. Can you do these calculations and say what the current through R_4 is?

> The current through R_4 due to the voltage generator is 1 mA downwards.

To find the total load we can first observe that R_4 and the 2 kΩ resistor to the right of it are in parallel so can be combined to give a 1 kΩ resistor. This 1 kΩ resistor is then seen to be in series with the generator and the remaining 2 kΩ resistor. The total load on the generator is thus 3 kΩ so the current drawn from it is 6/3 = 2 mA. This current flows through the 2 kΩ resistor in series with the generator towards point A. Here it divides equally between the two 2 kΩ resistors so the current in R_4 due to this source is 1 mA downwards.

Can you now find the current through R_4 due to the current generator alone?

81

> The current through R_4 due to the current generator is 1 mA downwards.

To find the current through R_4 due to the current generator on its own, we must first 'remove' the voltage generator by replacing it by a short-circuit. We could then analyse the resulting circuit in much the same way as we did for the previous one. We will, however, calculate this current by exploiting the simple 'ladder' structure of this network. Here is the original diagram again but with the voltage generator removed:

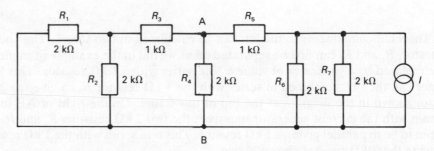

Starting at the left-hand end and looking from right to left we see that R_1 and R_2 are in parallel, giving a 1 kΩ resistor. This 1 kΩ is in series with R_3 giving a 2 kΩ resistor. This 2 kΩ resistor is, in turn, in parallel with R_4 giving another 1 kΩ resistor which, in its turn, is in series with R_5 giving another 2 kΩ resistor. This 2 kΩ is in parallel with R_6, R_7 and the 6 mA current generator. The current thus splits equally three ways, so the current from right to left through R_5 is 2 mA. However, bearing in mind the calculations we have just done above, the current in R_5 must divide equally between R_4 and the components to its left which have an equivalent resistance of 2 kΩ. Hence the current through R_4 is 1 mA downwards.

> The total current in R_4 is thus 1 mA + 1 mA = 2 mA.

It is worth noticing that the current through R_3 also divides into two, equal currents of $\frac{1}{2}$ mA flowing through R_1 and R_2. Circuits of this kind in which currents are successively divided into two as they pass successive nodes in a circuit are widely used in digital-to-analogue converters. These are circuits used to change quantities held, for example, in digital form in computer memories into currents or voltages which can then be further processed in analogue form, possibly within a control system. It should be emphasised that the kind of calculation performed above can usually only be done easily on circuits such as these. It could, in principle, be done on any circuit but the sums involved would, in general, become very unwieldy.

Another example exploiting Thevenin's theorem is given in the next frame.

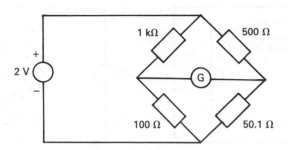

The circuit in this diagram is a 'bridge' circuit. Such circuits are used in instruments for measuring component values and in measurement techniques where small changes in component values are to be monitored. The 50.1 Ω resistor could, for example, be a strain gauge – a resistor whose value varies in a predictable manner as it is put under a mechanical strain. If the value of the resistor is known, the amount of mechanical strain can be estimated. G is a galvanometer – a sensitive ammeter, the reading on which can be calibrated to give an estimate of the change in value of the 50.1 Ω resistor and thus of the strain it is subjected to. It is desirable that the current drawn by the galvanometer should be small compared with other currents flowing in the bridge.

What value should the resistance of the galvanometer have if the current through it is to be less than 2 μA with the bridge components shown? If the galvanometer resistance has a value such that the current through it is exactly 2 μA with the bridge components shown, what will be the current if the value of the 50.1 Ω resistor changes to 50.2 Ω?

This is a problem which is relatively easy to solve by using Thevenin's theorem but quite difficult by other methods. The first step is to treat the galvanometer as a 'load' for the rest of the circuit and thus, in the initial analysis, to disconnect it from the circuit. The Thevenin equivalent of the rest of the circuit can then be calculated. Treating part of a circuit as a load in this way and obtaining an equivalent circuit for the remaining components is one of the standard ways of using Thevenin's theorem in problem solving.

Can you now do this? Calculate the Thevenin equivalent voltage generator and resistor for the circuit without the galvanometer and then re-draw the circuit in its equivalent form with the galvanometer 'load' replaced in the circuit. Remember that you are analysing the circuit 'looking back into the terminals from which the galvanometer has been disconnected'.

83

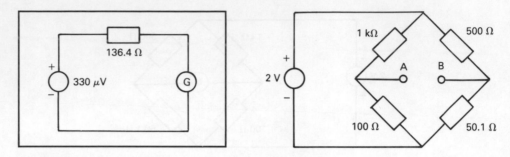

The left-hand diagram above shows the equivalent circuit with the galvanometer replaced ready for the next part of the calculation.

The problem of calculating the values shown in this circuit is best tackled by first re-drawing the original circuit with the galvanometer removed as shown in the right-hand diagram. A pair of terminals AB have been added for reference. We now want to calculate the voltage between A and B and the resistance which would be seen looking back into A and B with the voltage generator replaced by a short-circuit.

A little thought shows us that the bridge is 'balanced' (no current in the galvanometer because the potential at A equals that at B) when the 50.1 Ω resistor is reduced to 50 Ω. With 50.1 Ω in circuit, then, the potential at B will be slightly greater than that at A. Current in the galvanometer flows from B to A. We will therefore calculate $V_B - V_A$. V_B is obtained by the potentiometric action of the 500 Ω and 50.1 Ω resistors on the 2 V generator; V_A by the same action of the 1 kΩ and 100 Ω resistors. V_B and V_A can thus be calculated separately and their difference taken. Thus we have:

$$V_B - V_A = 2\left(\frac{50.1}{50.1 + 500} - \frac{100}{100 + 1000}\right) = \frac{200}{550.1 \times 1100} = 330 \ \mu V$$

Visualising the resistor configuration when the generator is short-circuited takes a little care. The 1 kΩ and 100 Ω resistors are effectively in parallel as are the 500 Ω and 50.1 Ω resistors. As seen between A and B, these two sets of parallel resistors are in series. If you have difficulty visualising this, re-draw the diagram with the generator replaced by a wire and then adjust the lines as necessary until it becomes obvious to you. Then:

$$R_{AB} = \frac{100 \times 1000}{100 + 1000} + \frac{50.1 \times 500}{50.1 + 500} = 90.9 + 45.5 = 136.4 \ \Omega$$

Now, using the equivalent circuit in the left-hand diagram above, can you calculate a minimum value for the internal resistance of the galvanometer?

$$\boxed{R > 28.6 \ \Omega}$$

If the current is to be less than 2 μA we have the inequality:

$$\frac{330 \times 10^{-6}}{136.4 + R_G} < 2 \times 10^{-6}$$

$$\text{so} \quad 136.4 + R_G > \frac{330 \times 10^{-6}}{2 \times 10^{-6}}$$

$$\text{thus} \quad R_G > 165 - 136.4$$

$$\text{so} \quad R_G > 28.6 \ \Omega$$

To complete the second part of the problem, we must recalculate the values of the components making up the Thevenin equivalent circuit and then calculate the new current using the above value for R_G. We can use the expressions from frame 83, simply replacing the 50.1 Ω resistor with one of 50.2 Ω. What is the new current?

$$\boxed{\text{The new current is } 4.00 \ \mu A}$$

The expressions from frame 83 with the new values substituted are:

$$V_B - V_A = 2\left(\frac{50.2}{50.2 + 500} - \frac{100}{100 + 1000}\right) = \frac{400}{550.2 \times 1100} = 661 \ \mu V$$

$$R_G = \frac{100 \times 1000}{100 + 1000} + \frac{50.2 \times 500}{50.2 + 500} = 90.9 + 45.6 = 136.5 \ \Omega$$

The Thevenin equivalent resistance has hardly altered but the Thevenin equivalent generator has slightly more than doubled. Thus

$$I_G = \frac{661 \times 10^{-6}}{136.5 + 28.6} = 4.00 \ \mu A$$

The problem is extended in the next frame.

86

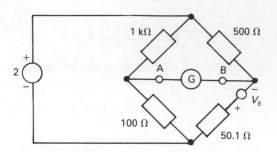

In this diagram the original circuit has been modified to include a voltage generator in the arm of the bridge containing the 50.1 Ω resistor. This generator could represent a thermo-electrically induced voltage. Assuming the 50.1 Ω resistor is nominally 50 Ω, use the superposition theorem to find the value of induced voltage that just cancels out the effect of the 0.1 Ω increase in the 50 Ω resistor to bring the bridge back into balance. Note: at balance the galvanometer takes no current so it can be removed.

87

The generator value is 363 μV

In frame 83 we found that the voltage between A and B with only the 2 V generator in circuit was 330 μV. By superposition, we therefore require the induced generator *alone* to produce an exactly equal and opposite voltage to this at balance. Re-drawing the circuit for this calculation we have:

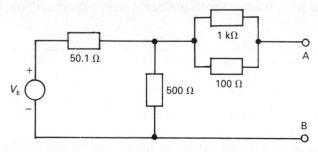

The generator value to produce a 330 μV voltage at the output is given by:

$$500 \, V_{E}/(500 + 50) = 330 \, \mu V \quad \text{so} \quad V_{E} = 330 \times 550/500 = 363 \, \mu V$$

Notice that the parallel combination of the 100 Ω and 1000 Ω resistors does not enter into the calculation for the open-circuit voltage. Because the output is open-circuit, no current flows through these resistors.

Here is another problem which shows another way of calculating a Thevenin equivalent circuit. This method has the advantage that it can also be used for networks containing dependent generators and will give the correct value for output resistance as well as equivalent generator voltage. Since such networks cannot be analysed using Thevenin's theorem, the equivalent circuit components in such cases cannot strictly be called Thevenin equivalents. The concept of an 'equivalent source voltage' and an equivalent output resistance is still, however, very useful and widely used in electronic circuit modelling.

Here is a circuit diagram together with a Thevenin equivalent version of it:

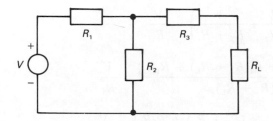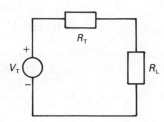

We will deduce the Thevenin equivalent by calculating the current through the resistor R_L for both circuits and comparing the two expressions. Can you first write an expression for the current through R_L in the simpler circuit?

$$I_{R_L} = \frac{V_T}{R_T + R_L}$$

The result is obtained by straightforward application of Ohm's Law to the circuit. Examining this expression shows us the form we must look for in the expression derived from the other circuit. We want an expression with R_L as a separate term in the denominator. The other term will then be R_T, the Thevenin resistance. The numerator will be V_T, the Thevenin equivalent voltage generator.

To begin the next part of the analysis, can you now write down a nodal equation for the left-hand circuit? Use the symbol V_1 for the voltage at the junction of resistors R_1, R_2 and R_3.

90

$$\frac{V_1 - V}{R_1} + \frac{V_1}{R_2} + \frac{V_1}{R_3 + R_L} = 0$$

Since the circuit has only two principal nodes, the single node equation above is sufficient to solve for all currents and voltages in the circuit. It is obtained by applying Kirchhoff's Current Law to the node at the top of the diagram with the notation that all currents flow out of the node.

Hence $\quad V_1 \left(\dfrac{1}{R_1} + \dfrac{1}{R_2} + \dfrac{1}{R_3 + R_L} \right) = \dfrac{V}{R_1}$

So $\quad \dfrac{V_1 \{R_2(R_3 + R_L) + R_1(R_3 + R_L) + R_1 R_2\}}{R_1 R_2 (R_3 + R_L)} = \dfrac{V}{R_1}$

And thus $\quad \dfrac{V_1 \{(R_1 + R_2) \times (R_3 + R_L) + R_1 R_2\}}{R_1 R_2 (R_3 + R_L)} = \dfrac{V}{R_1}$

Hence $V_1 = \dfrac{V R_2 (R_3 + R_L)}{(R_1 + R_2)(R_3 + R_L) + R_1 R_2}$

The current through the load resistor in this circuit in fact flows from V_1 through R_3 and R_L in series. Can you now write an expression for this current from the above value for V_1?

91

$$I_{R_L} = \frac{V R_2}{(R_1 + R_2)(R_3 + R_L) + R_1 R_2}$$

This expression for the current is obtained simply by dividing the expression for V_1 by $R_3 + R_L$. It is not, however, in the form we require for comparison with the expression obtained earlier for the simpler circuit. To bring it into the appropriate form we need to have R_L on its own in the denominator. Can you re-write the expression in this form and hence deduce values for the Thevenin equivalent voltage generator and Thevenin equivalent resistor?

The current through $I_{R_L} = \dfrac{\dfrac{VR_2}{R_1 + R_2}}{\dfrac{R_1 R_2}{R_1 + R_2} + R_3 + R_L}$
the load resistor is

The Thevenin equivalent generator is $\dfrac{VR_2}{R_1 + R_2}$

The Thevenin equivalent resistor is $R_3 + \dfrac{R_1 R_2}{R_1 + R_2}$

To obtain R_L on its own in the denominator of the expression in frame 91 we must divide throughout the denominator by $(R_1 + R_2)$. We must therefore also divide throughout the numerator by the same expression. The result is the expression at the top of this frame.

The Thevenin equivalent generator is the numerator of the new expression.

The Thevenin equivalent resistance is made up of the terms other than R_L in the denominator of the new expression.

Calculating the values by the more usual method, we see that the open-circuit voltage at the output (R_L disconnected, since it is regarded as a load) is $VR_2/(R_1 + R_2)$. As in the problem in frame 60, R_3 does not affect this calculation since no current flows through it when R_L is disconnected. The resistance looking back towards the rest of the circuit with R_L disconnected and V short-circuited is R_3 in series with the parallel combination of R_1 and R_2. Thus $R_T = R_3 + R_1 R_2/(R_1 + R_2)$. These two Thevenin components thus correspond with those calculated above.

This completes the essential material covered in this programme. The problem in the next frame illustrates the application of the method used in the last few frames to the analysis of an operational amplifier with feedback. Even if you have not previously studied operational amplifiers, you should be able to follow the circuit analysis if you are prepared to accept the statements made about these amplifiers at the beginning of the frame. Notice that, because of the 'feedback' from output to input, the output voltage is obtained as a 'function of itself as well as the input voltage'. This means that the generator used to model the circuit is dependent on both output and input voltages, so does not accord with the rules for the application of a Thevenin analysis. The 'open circuit voltage' and 'resistance looking back' give quite a different (and wrong!) answer for the equivalent output resistance of the circuit from that obtained by the recommended method of analysis. The recommended method however provides a valid way of assigning this property to the circuit.

93

An operational amplifier is an electronic circuit which is very widely used in many different kinds of application. It is generally used with some kind of *feedback* from output to input. In circuit configurations employing feedback the properties of the circuit with feedback are predictable to quite a high degree of accuracy, variations in the properties without feedback (the *open loop parameters*) being compensated for by the feedback. The circuit we shall analyse here is the *voltage follower*. This circuit produces an output voltage which is the same as the input voltage but also acts as a *resistance buffer*. It has a very high input resistance which therefore produces very little loading effect on circuits to which it is connected. Its output resistance, on the other hand, is very low so circuits connected to it do not load it very heavily.

The open loop properties characterising an operational amplifier are as follows. (1) A very high voltage gain A. The amplifier has two inputs v_+ and v_- (lower case letters are conventionally used with operational amplifier circuits for reasons which will become clear later in this text). The output v_o is given as $v_o = A(v_+ - v_-)$. $(v_+ - v_-)$ is called the *differential input voltage*. (2) A very high input resistance R_i. In this example we shall take the input resistance to be infinite. (3) A low output resistance R_o. In this example we shall calculate the ouput resistance with feedback.

The following circuit diagrams show an operational amplifier connected in the voltage follower configuration together with an equivalent circuit for the amplifier that can be used for analytical purposes.

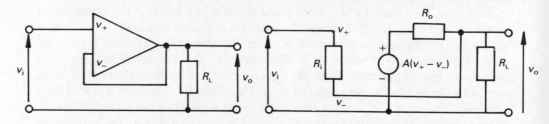

Looking at the circuit, the differential input voltage can be written as

$$v_+ - v_- = v_i - v_o$$

The amplifier equivalent voltage generator is therefore $A(v_i - v_o)$.

Because of the assumption of infinite input resistance we can assume that the output is not loaded by the feedback connection to the input. By potentiometric division between R_o and R_L, the output voltage is thus:

$$v_o = \frac{A(v_i - v_o)R_L}{R_o + R_L}$$

Hence $\quad v_o (R_o + R_L) = v_i A R_L - v_o A R_L$

So $\quad v_o(R_o + R_L + A R_L) = v_i A R_L$

$$v_o = \frac{A v_i R_L}{R_o + (1 + A)R_L}$$

Dividing top and bottom of this expression by $(1 + A)$ we have:

$$v_o = \frac{\dfrac{A v_i R_L}{(1 + A)}}{\dfrac{R_o}{(1 + A)} + R_L}$$

Comparing this expression with the expression for v_o obtained from a simple generator/resistor circuit, we have the following results:

Equivalent voltage generator $v_T = \dfrac{A v_i}{1 + A}$

$\qquad\qquad\qquad\qquad\qquad\quad = v_i$ if A is very large

Equivalent output resistance $R' = \dfrac{R_o}{1 + A}$

The open loop output resistance of the amplifier is thus seen to be reduced by a factor $(1 + A)$ due to the feedback connection.

An attempted Thevenin analysis for this circuit 'looking back into the output' with R_L disconnected and the generator replaced by a short-circuit would give the value of R_o as the output resistance of the circuit. From the above analysis this is clearly not correct.

By the same kind of analysis the 'Thevenin equivalent voltage generator' with the output open-circuit would be given by the equation:

$$v_o = A(v_i - v_o)$$

$$\text{so } v_o = \frac{A v_i}{1 + A}$$

By comparison with the result above, this value is, in fact, correct.

An attempted Thevenin analysis thus gives us the correct value for the equivalent voltage generator but the wrong value for the equivalent output resistance. Thevenin-type analysis is thus not reliable for circuits including active elements in feedback configurations. The method used above, however, will give the correct result under all circumstances.

94

SUMMARY OF PROGRAMME 2

1. The topology of an electric circuit (that is, the way in which the various components which comprise it are interconnected) can be described in terms of its branches, loops or meshes and nodes. A branch is a path between two 'terminals' within a circuit through which current can flow. A node is the junction of two or more branches. A loop or mesh is a closed path made up of two or more branches.

2. *Kirchhoff's First Law (the Current Law)*: In any electric circuit in which currents are flowing, the algebraic sum of currents entering and leaving a node is always zero.

3. *Kirchhoff's Second Law (the Voltage Law)*: In any electric circuit containing components with voltages across them, the algebraic sum of the voltages around any mesh in the circuit is zero.

4. *Maxwell's cyclic currents in mesh analysis*: A clockwise cyclic or circulating current is postulated in each adjacent mesh of the circuit being analysed. A matrix equation can then be set up to solve for the unknown currents. The full rules for setting up the matrix are given in frames 12 to 18. The matrix has as many rows and columns as there are meshes in the circuit. All diagonal elements of the matrix contain terms which are positive and formed by the sums of resistances in the meshes of the circuit. All off-diagonal elements contain terms which are either negative or zero and are formed by the values of resistances common to two meshes in the circuit. Each term in the column vector on the right-hand side contains terms related to the values of generators in a given mesh.

5. *Nodal analysis*: One of the principal nodes of the circuit is taken as a reference node. Unknown voltages referred to this node are postulated at all other principal nodes of the circuit. A matrix equation can then be set up to solve for the unknown voltages. The full rules for setting up the matrix are given in frames 31 to 39. The number of rows and columns in the matrix is one less than the number of principal nodes in the circuit. All diagonal elements of the matrix contain terms which are positive and formed by the sums of conductances in the branches connected to a given node of the circuit. All off-diagonal elements contain terms which are either negative or zero and are formed by the values of conductances between two nodes in the circuit. Each term of the column vector on the right-hand side contains terms related to the values of generators in the branches connected to a given node.

6. Any network of resistors to which connection can be made via a pair of terminals can be represented by a single equivalent resistor for purposes of calculating currents drawn from generators connected to the terminals or voltages developed between these terminals. The value of the equivalent resistor can be called the input resistance of the network.

7. *Thevenin's theorem*: Any network of voltage and current generators and resistors with output terminals A and B is equivalent at these terminals to a single voltage generator in series with a single resistor, the output resistance of the network. The voltage generator has a value equal to the open-circuit voltage between the terminals A and B. The output resistance has a value given by the ratio of the open-circuit voltage to the short-circuit current.

Provided all the generators are independent, the output resistance is the same as that which would be measured between the terminals A and B if all voltage generators were replaced by short-circuits and all current generators replaced by open-circuits.

8. *Norton's theorem*: Any network of current and voltage generators and resistors with output terminals A and B is equivalent at these terminals to a single current generator in parallel with a single resistor, the output conductance of the network. The current generator has a value equal to the short-circuit current between the terminals A and B. The output conductance has a value given by the ratio of the short-circuit current to the open-circuit voltage.

Provided all the generators are independent, the output conductance is the same as that which would be measured between the terminals A and B if all current generators were replaced by open-circuits and all voltage generators replaced by short-circuits.

9. *The principle of duality*: Given a mathematical relationship among certain properties of a circuit, the substitution of the duals of those properties will lead to an equally valid mathematical relationship among the duals. A list of duals is given in frame 51.

10. *The superposition theorem*: In a linear circuit containing any number of generators, the currents and voltages which are produced in the circuit may be calculated by considering each of the generators in turn and summing the results. During the calculation for any particular generator all other generators must be 'removed', voltage generators being replaced by short-circuits and current generators by open-circuits.

REVISION QUESTIONS ON PROGRAMME 3

1. What is the input resistance of the network of resistors shown here?

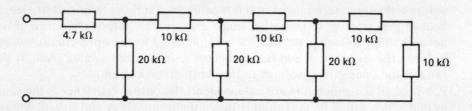

2. Draw the Thevenin equivalent and Norton equivalent circuits for the following circuit as seen at the terminals A and B. Hence calculate the current through and voltage across a 4.7 kΩ resistor connected between the terminals.

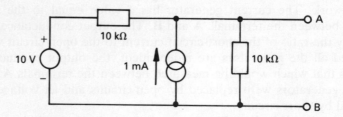

3. Using the superposition theorem and any appropriate circuit reduction techniques, calculate the current through and voltage across the 9.1 kΩ resistor in this circuit.

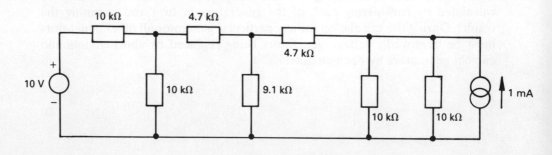

SOLUTIONS TO REVISION QUESTIONS ON PROGRAMME 3

1. Input resistances are calculated from right to left, that is, back *towards* the input.

$$\text{So } 10 + 10 = 20 \quad 20 \mathbin{/\!/} 20 = 10 \quad 10 + 10 = 20 \quad 20 \mathbin{/\!/} 20 = 10$$

$$10 + 10 = 20 \quad 20 \mathbin{/\!/} 20 = 10 \quad \text{and finally} \quad 10 + 4.7 = 14.7 \text{ k}\Omega$$

2. The Thevenin and Norton equivalent circuits can be fully determined when o/c voltage and s/c currents are known. Calculate these using superposition taking each generator in turn.

o/c voltage: with 1 mA o/c the 10 V generator gives $\dfrac{10 \times 10}{20}$ 5 V at AB

with 10 V s/c the 1 mA generator gives $\dfrac{1 \times 10}{20} \times 10 = 5$ V at AB

By superposition, total volts at AB = 10 V

s/c current: with 1 mA o/c the 10 V generator gives $\dfrac{10}{10} = 1$ mA in s/c at AB

the 10 kΩ between A and B is 'shorted out'

with 10 V s/c the 1 mA generator gives 1 mA in s/c at AB

All the generator current flows through the s/c at AB

By superposition, total current in s/c at AB = 2 mA

Thevenin or Norton resistance $= \dfrac{10 \text{ V}}{2 \text{ mA}} = 5 \text{ k}\Omega$

Check: with 10 V s/c and 1 mA o/c, 'resistance looking back' into AB is:

$$10 \mathbin{/\!/} 10 = \frac{10 \times 10}{10 + 10} = 5 \text{ k}\Omega$$

Thevenin equivalent circuit is 10 V in series with 5 kΩ
Norton equivalent generator is 2 mA in parallel with 5 kΩ

With a 4.7 kΩ load $V_{AB} = 10 \times \dfrac{4.7}{4.7 + 5} = 10 \times \dfrac{4.7}{9.7} = 4.85$ V

$$I_{AB} = 2 \times \frac{5}{4.7 + 5} = 2 \times \frac{5}{9.7} = 1.03 \text{ mA}$$

3. Using Thevenin's theorem on the 10 volt generator and the two 10 kilohm resistors close to it, we can reduce these components to a 5 volt generator in series with a 5 kilohm resistor.

Using Thevenin's theorem on the 1 milliamp generator and the two 10 kilohm resistors close to it, we can reduce these components to a 5 volt generator in series with a 5 kilohm resistor.

The circuit can thus be re-drawn as shown below:

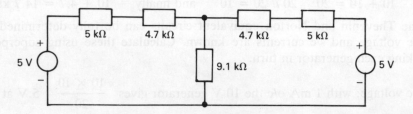

The circuit is thus seen to be symmetrical. The current through the 9.1 kilohm resistor due to one generator alone must therefore be the same as that due to the other generator alone. The total current in the 9.1 kilohm resistor must therefore, by superposition, be twice the current due to one generator alone.

For one generator alone the circuit may be redrawn as shown below (the other generator is replaced by a short-circuit):

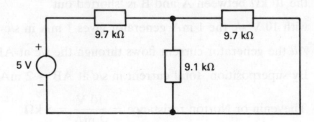

The current from the generator is

$$\frac{5}{9.7 + \dfrac{9.1 \times 9.7}{9.1 + 9.7}} = 0.347 \text{ mA}$$

The current in the 9.1 kilohm resistor is thus $\dfrac{9.7 \times 0.347}{9.7 + 9.1} = 0.179 \text{ mA}$

Total current is therefore 0.358 mA. Voltage across 9.1 kΩ is 3.262 V.

TEST ON PROGRAMME 3

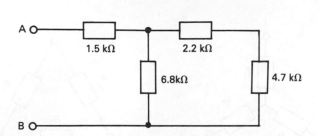

1. What is the input resistance of the circuit in the diagram above? What current would be drawn from a 10 volt generator connected between the terminals A and B? What voltage would be developed across a 2 milliamp current generator connected between the terminals A and B?
2. Calculate the current through and voltage across each resistor in the circuit in the diagram above when a 10 volt voltage generator is connected between the terminals A and B. Solve this problem (a) by using mesh analysis and (b) by using nodal analysis.
3. Repeat question 2 but with the 10 volt generator replaced by a 2 milliamp current generator.
4. The circuit in the diagram above has a 10 volt generator connected between the terminals A and B. Calculate the Thevenin equivalent circuit as seen looking back into the other end of the circuit when the 4.7 kilohm resistor is removed. Hence calculate the current through and voltage across this 4.7 kilohm resistor if it were replaced. What currents would flow through (a) a 2.4 kilohm resistor and (b) a 9.1 kilohm resistor connected instead of the 4.7 kilohm resistor?
5. Use the superposition theorem to calculate the current in the 6.8 kilohm resistor in the circuit below.

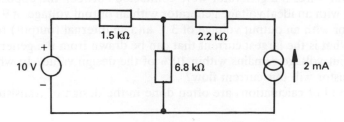

FURTHER QUESTIONS ON PROGRAMME 3

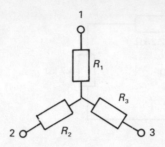

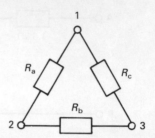

1. The two resistor configurations shown above are to be equivalent whatever is connected to terminals 1, 2 and 3.

(a) Express R_1, R_2 and R_3 in terms of R_a, R_b and R_c.

(b) Express R_a, R_b and R_c in terms of R_1, R_2 and R_3.

The combination of R_1, R_2 and R_3 is called a star, T or Y connection.
The combination of R_a, R_b and R_c is called a delta or π connection.
The relationship derived in (a) is called the delta–star transformation.
The one derived in (b) is called the star–delta transformation. These connections and transformations are widely used in the analysis of three-phase power circuits.

2. A wire cube is made by soldering together twelve pieces of wire of equal length, each of which has a resistance of 1 Ω. What is the resistance which can be measured between opposite corners of the cube? *Note*: Take two corners which are *not* opposite corners of a single face.

Hint: By looking at the symmetry of the cube, consider how currents would flow in the wires if a generator were connected between the opposite corners.

3. Starting with an ideal voltage generator with an output voltage of 9 V, design a generator with an output voltage of 3 V and an internal (output) resistance of 4 kΩ. What is the largest current that can be drawn from the generator so that the output voltage remains within 10% of the design value? In what value of load resistor will this current flow?

These kind of calculations are often done in the design of transistor circuits.

4. Starting with an ideal voltage generator with an output voltage of 12 V, design a potential divider which acts as a generator with an output of 3 V when supplying a current of 50 µA and an output of 2.9 V when supplying a current of 100 µA. What are the nearest preferred values in the 1% range to the values in your design?

5.

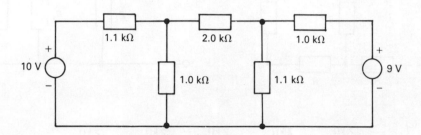

Find the currents drawn from the generators and the voltage across the 2.0 kΩ resistor in the circuit above.

6.

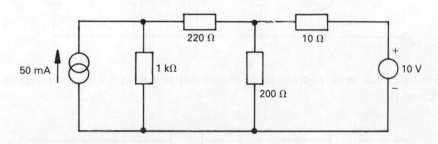

In the circuit above, the 200 Ω and 220 Ω resistors are to be selected from ranges having maximum power ratings of 250 mW, 500 mW or 1.0 W, the cost of a component being higher the more power it can dissipate. Which range should each of the two above resistors be selected from to minimise the cost of these components?

7. Calculate the input resistance of the circuits below:

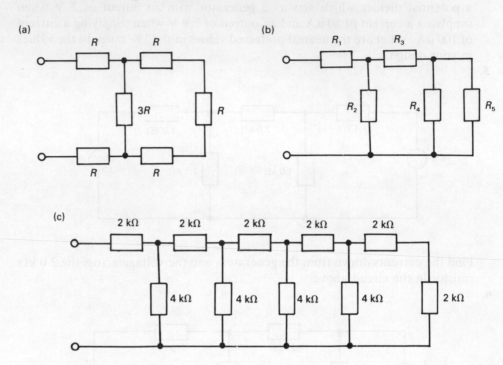

(a)

(b)

(c)

8. Find the Thevenin equivalent of the circuit below as seen at the terminals A and B:

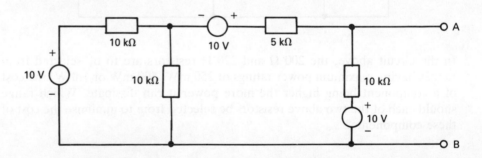

9. Find the Norton equivalent of the circuit below as seen at the terminals A and B:

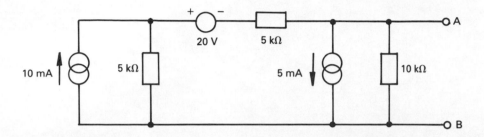

10. The galvanometer in the circuit below should ideally give full scale deflections in positive and negative directions for currents of ±100 µA. What must its internal resistance be? With the value of internal resistance that you calculate, what is the scale error when the variable resistance is 100.5 Ω?

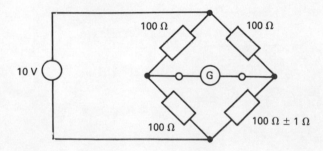

Programme 4

WAVEFORMS, PHASORS
AND
REACTIVE CIRCUIT
ELEMENTS

INTRODUCTION

In programmes 2 and 3 we studied several ways of analysing circuits which were made up of resistors and direct current and voltage generators. In most electronic circuits, however, the so-called 'd.c. conditions' are only the starting point. The usefulness of a circuit usually depends on how it affects changing voltages and currents which are applied to it as 'inputs'. We shall begin the study of this kind of circuit operation in this programme.

A voltage or current which changes with time is generally known as a 'waveform'. The name is derived from the graphs of such functions when their size or 'amplitude' is plotted against time. 'Regular' or 'periodic' waveforms often have a characteristic undulating or wave-like appearance. The name has become generally accepted, however, for any time-varying function of voltage or current. When such waveforms are applied to circuits as inputs they are often referred to as 'signals' and the way in which they are changed as they pass through the circuits is called 'signal processing'.

A standard terminology or 'jargon' of the subject has grown up to describe the properties of waveforms. In the first part of this programme you will learn how to use this terminology and will come to recognise what characterises a waveform in terms of those properties which may be affected by an electrical or electronic circuit. You will see how many of the important properties of one of the most widely used waveforms (the sine wave) can be represented by vector-like quantities known as phasors.

In the latter part of the programme you will be introduced to two additional circuit components, the capacitor and the inductor, and will learn how to apply 'phasor analysis' to circuits containing them. These components differ from resistors in the way in which they affect signals passing through circuits which contain them. They possess a property known as 'reactance'. This property will be seen to have some things in common with resistance (it has the same dimensions for a start) but also to have some very important differences. You will see how it is affected by the 'frequency' of signals passing through the circuit and how the time-varying voltages and currents in the circuit depend on it.

All the terms used above are fully explained in the programme so, if any of them are new or unfamiliar to you, you will learn what they mean as the programme progresses. When you have completed the programme you will know how to describe waveforms, how to represent sinusoidal waveforms by phasors and how to apply phasor analysis to circuits containing both resistive and reactive components to see how sinusoidal signals are affected by them.

PERIODIC FUNCTIONS

In programmes 2 and 3 we dealt only with direct currents and voltages, that is, quantities which are constant with time. In the analysis of electric circuits, however, many quantities will be encountered which vary with time and can be expressed as functions of time. A generalised function of time is often depicted mathematically as being 'of the form' $f(t)$. A voltage which varied as a known function of time could be depicted as $v(t)$, a current as $i(t)$ and so on. Small or lower-case letters are conventionally used to depict quantities which vary with time. Quantities which vary regularly with time are called periodic functions.

Periodic functions obey a relationship of the form $f(t) = f(t + T)$

The time T is called the repetition time or period of the function. Such a function is called a waveform and may be depicted graphically thus:

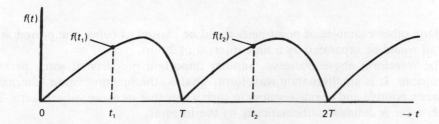

The time t is most conveniently measured between two well-defined points on the waveform such as points where the function crosses or meets the time axis. Points 0 and T above are ideal. Any two points on the waveform which are separated by a time interval T will, however, give the same value of $f(t)$ and the waveform will pass though both points in the same sense and with the same slope. Points t_1 and t_2 above illustrate these concepts.

What is the period of the waveform below? Give two different pairs of points separated by one period: one pair on the time axis and one pair not.

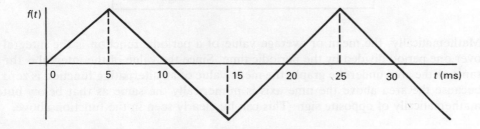

2

> The period of the waveform is 20 milliseconds (ms).
> Points separated by one period are at 0 and 20 ms and at 5 and 25 ms

Here is the waveform again:

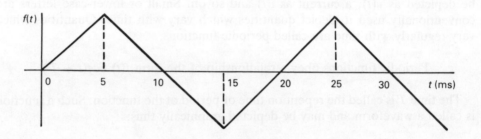

Many other examples of point-pairs could be chosen as being one period apart but all would be separated by a time interval of 20 ms.

The waveform above possesses another important property of some periodic waveforms. It is an alternating waveform. That is, the function value 'alternates' between positive and negative values in such a way that its *mean value* is zero. The mean value is defined mathematically by the integral:

$$\text{Mean value} = \frac{1}{T}\int_{t}^{t+T} f(t)\,\mathrm{d}t \quad \text{and is sometimes written } \overline{f}(t)$$

What is another name for mean value?

3

> Mean value is the same as average value.

Mathematically, the mean or average value of a periodic function is the integral over one period divided by the periodic time. Since the value of the integral is the same as the area under the graph, the mean value of an alternating function is zero because the area above the time axis is numerically the same as that below but mathematically of opposite sign. This can be clearly seen in the function above.

4

SINUSOIDAL WAVEFORMS

The most important alternating function is the sinusoidal function. Such functions are frequently encountered in the transmission and use of electrical power and in many electronic circuits.

A voltage which varies with time according to the expression $v = V_p \sin \omega t$ is called a sinusoidally varying voltage waveform or just a 'voltage sinewave'. The quantity V_p is called the 'peak voltage', 'voltage amplitude' or 'voltage magnitude' of the waveform.

The quantity ω is called the 'angular frequency' of the waveform. Since ωt appears as the argument of a sine function it must be dimensionless, as shown in programme 1. The quantity t has dimensions of time so the quantity ω must have dimensions of 1/time or 'per second'. It must therefore be a frequency. Why it is an angular frequency will be explained shortly.

A sinewave may be depicted graphically as shown below. The amplitude V_p and period T are clearly marked on the graph.

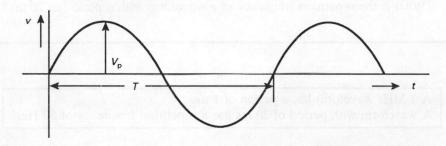

Another property of a periodic function which is often used in describing the function is its 'repetition frequency'. The repetition frequency is defined as the number of times per second that the waveform repeats itself. It has the symbol f and is the reciprocal of the period so $f = 1/T$.

Now, since a sine function is mathematically defined in terms of an angle – the argument of the function – we can obtain a relationship between the quantity ω and the angular values defining the sine function. It is the quantity ωt which corresponds to the angle, and comparing the graph with time on the horizontal axis to that for a sine function plotted for angular values, we see that $v = 0$ when $\omega t = 0$ and again when $\omega t = 2\pi$, the sense of the sinewave at both these points being the same. That is, the transition through zero is negative to positive in both cases. The value of t when $\omega t = 2\pi$ must therefore be the period T.

What are T and f in terms of ω?

151

5

$$T = \frac{2\pi}{\omega}, \quad f = \frac{\omega}{2\pi} \quad \text{so} \quad \omega = 2\pi f$$

Since $t = T$ when $\omega t = 2\pi$, then $\omega T = 2\pi$ and so $T = 2\pi/\omega$. $f = 1/T$ so $f = \omega/2\pi$. It is very important when making frequency calculations not to forget the factor of 2π when it should be included.

The units of repetition frequency, f, are cycles per second (c.p.s.), now known as Hertz (Hz) after the German scientist Heinrich Hertz (1857–1894). The quantity ω is measured in radians per second. The above relationship between ω and f shows why ω is called an *angular* frequency. We shall investigate a graphical representation of this relationship shortly. The period T is, of course, measured in seconds. For a given waveform it is useful to remember the period/frequency pair or to be able to calculate one from the other quickly.

What is the period of a 1 MHz waveform?
What is the repetition frequency of a waveform with a period of 20 ms?

6

A 1 MHz waveform has a period of 1 μs.
A waveform with period of 20 ms has a repetition frequency of 50 Hz.

Two further quantities used in describing waveforms are the 'peak-to-peak' voltage V_{pp} and the 'root mean square' or r.m.s. voltage V_{rms}. The peak-to-peak voltage is a measure of the 'total amplitude excursion' of the waveform and is simply the difference between the largest voltage it reaches and the smallest. The r.m.s. voltage is defined mathematically as:

$$V_{rms} = \sqrt{\left\{ \frac{1}{T} \int_{t}^{t+T} (v(t))^2 dt \right\}}$$

It is the square root of the average or mean over one period of the square of the function. It has a particular physical meaning which we shall investigate shortly and can be defined for any periodic function. Calculation of the integral is most easily achieved over the period from 0 to T.

Can you evaluate the r.m.s. voltage of the sine function $v = V_p \sin \omega t$?

> The r.m.s. value of a sinewave $v = V_p \sin \omega t$ is $\dfrac{V_p}{\sqrt{2}}$

Substituting the expression for v into the integral we have:

$$V_{rms} = \sqrt{\left\{ \frac{1}{T} \int_t^{t+T} (V_p \sin \omega t)^2 \, dt \right\}}$$

Before carrying out the integral it is worth checking the dimensions of the terms involved. The function being integrated is $(V_p \sin \omega t)^2$. This has dimensions of voltage squared since the sine term is dimensionless. Integration with respect to time is the same as multiplying by a quantity having the dimension of time since it is the limit of a summation of values of the function multiplied by small elements of time. The integral is divided by the period which has dimensions of time so the result of this operation is again a voltage squared. Finally the square root is taken so the end result is a voltage. In the expression above we can take the constant term V_p^2 outside the integral. We can then use a trigonometrical identity on the sine squared term to give:

$$V_{rms} = V_p \sqrt{\left(\frac{1}{T} \int_0^T (\sin \omega t)^2 \, dt \right)} = V_p \sqrt{\left(\frac{1}{T} \int_0^T \frac{1}{2} (1 - \cos 2\omega t) dt \right)}$$

$$= V_p \sqrt{\left(\frac{1}{T} \times \frac{1}{2} \left[t + \frac{\sin 2\omega t}{2} \right]_0^T \right)} = \frac{V_p}{\sqrt{2}}$$

The sine term is zero at both limits: $\sin 0 = 0$ and $\sin 2\omega T = \sin 2\omega(2\pi/\omega) = \sin 4\pi = 0$. The only non-zero term left in the integral is the t term set to the value T from the upper limit. This cancels with the T in the denominator to produce the result given at the beginning of this frame.

From the diagram of the sinewave in frame 4 it can be seen that $V_{pp} = 2V_p$. We can therefore also express the r.m.s. voltage in terms of the peak-to-peak voltage as:

$$V_{rms} = \frac{V_{pp}}{2\sqrt{2}}$$

Now turn to the next frame where we will examine another frequently encountered waveform.

8

THE SQUARE WAVE

The waveform below is a square wave. What are its amplitude, peak-to-peak voltage, mean value voltage and root-mean-square voltage?

9

The amplitude is V_p.	The peak-to-peak voltage is V_p.
The mean value voltage is $V_p/2$.	The root-mean-square voltage is $V_p/\sqrt{2}$.

The amplitude and peak-to-peak voltage can be seen directly from the waveform diagram. Both have the same value in this case. The other quantities can be evaluated using the area property of graphs. The mean value depends on the integral over one complete period of the function describing the voltage variation with time.

The function in this case is 'discontinuous'. It has a constant value V_p from $t = 0$ to $t = T/2$ and then changes suddenly at the 'discontinuity' to a value of zero. This value is held from $t = T/2$ to $t = T$ where there is another discontinuous change back to the value V_p. This pattern is then repeated indefinitely.

The integral from 0 to T must be evaluated in two parts over regions in which the function is continuous. That is from $t = 0$ to $t = T/2$ and from $t = T/2$ to $t = T$. This is standard practice for the integration of discontinuous functions. The integral from $t = 0$ to $t = T/2$ is the area under the graph between these limits. The area is thus $V_p T/2$. The 'area under the graph' between the limits $t = T/2$ and $t = T$ is zero because the value of the function is zero over this region. The total area over the whole period is thus $V_p T/2$. Dividing this by T (the whole period) to get the average gives $v_{mean} = V_p/2$.

The root-mean-square value can be obtained by similar reasoning. The values of the square of the function over the two regions of integration are respectively V_p^2 and zero. The integrals are thus again the two areas $V_p^2 T/2$ and zero, and the integral over the whole period is $V_p^2 T/2$. Dividing this value by the period T gives $V_p^2/2$ and taking the square root gives $V_p/\sqrt{2}$.

10

DIAGRAMMATIC DERIVATION OF SINEWAVES

A sinewave may be generated by considering the projection onto a diameter of a circle of a point moving around the circumference of the circle at uniform angular velocity. Consider the following diagram:

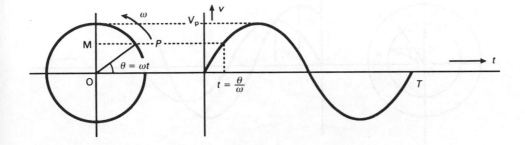

   The point P is moving round the circle centre O in an anticlockwise direction with uniform angular velocity. OM is the projection of OP onto a fixed diameter of the circle. Now imagine a strip of paper moving at constant speed from right to left across the page beneath the circle at right angles to the diameter chosen above. The projection of the point M onto the paper traces out a sinewave as the point P moves round the circle.

   If the radius of the circle represents a voltage V_p, can you write a mathematical expression for the sinewave as a voltage which varies with time?

11

$$\boxed{\text{The sinusoidal voltage is } v = V_p \sin \omega t}$$

The expression for the sinewave can be deduced as follows: if the point P moves through an angle θ in time t then $\theta = \omega t$. Thus, on the time axis, the corresponding value of OM occurs at a time $t = \theta/\omega$. A complete 'cycle' of 2π radians is completed in a time T, so $\omega T = 2\pi$ and $T = 2\pi/\omega$. If the point P continues to move round the circle and the paper continues to move across the page at the same constant speed, more cycles of the sinewave will be traced out as time progresses. The above analysis gives an alternative interpretation of the 'angular frequency' ω used in earlier frames.

12

'PHASE' RELATIONSHIPS WITH SINEWAVES

Now consider the following diagram containing two concentric circles:

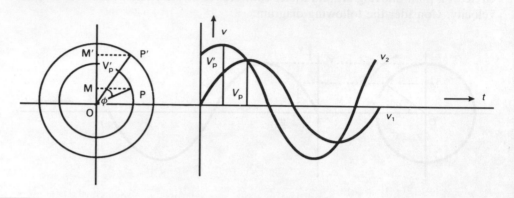

The second circle has radius V'_p. A point P' moves round the circumference of this circle also at constant angular velocity but so positioned that OP' makes an angle ϕ with OP. If the same strip of paper moved beneath these two circles, a second sinewave would be traced out by the projection of OM' onto the same diameter as OM. If the equation of the original sinewave represents a voltage $v_1 = V_p \sin \omega t$, can you write an equation for the voltage v_2 represented by the second sinewave?

13

> The equation of the second sinewave is $v_2 = V' \sin(\omega t + \phi)$

When OP lies along the time axis, OP' makes an angle ϕ with this axis. The projection of OM' onto the axis at right angles is then $V' \sin \phi$ at this instant. As t increases, this angular difference is added to all values of ωt to give values of v_2 describing the second sinewave. Two sinewaves have thus been produced both having the same repetition frequency $\omega/2\pi$ but displaced with respect to each other by the angle ϕ. The two waveforms are spoken of as being 'out of phase' by the angle ϕ, and ϕ is termed the 'phase angle' between the waves. The voltage v_2 is said to 'lead' the voltage v_1 by the phase angle ϕ or to be 'in advance of' v_1 by the angle ϕ. The voltage v_1 is said to 'lag' the voltage v_2 by the phase angle ϕ.

14

ADDITION OF SINUSOIDAL VOLTAGES

Suppose two voltages $v_1 = V_1 \sin \omega t$ and $v_2 = V_2 \sin(\omega t + \phi)$ are supplied by two 'alternating voltage generators' wired in series and connected to a resistor R as shown in the diagram below. Kirchhoff's Voltage Law holds for alternating generators at any given instant of time, so the total voltage across the resistor at any instant is the sum of the two sinusoidal voltages.

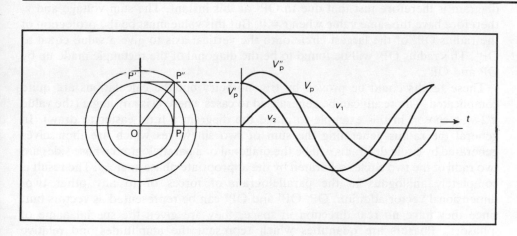

$v_1 = V_1 \sin \omega t$

$v_2 = V_2 \sin (\omega t + \phi)$

R

Can you draw a circle and sinewave diagram like the one in frame 11 to represent the two separate voltages and their sum if $V_1 = 3\,V$, $V_2 = 4\,V$ and $\phi = \pi/2$? You will find that the sum voltage is also a sinewave. Plot out the two voltages separately first and then sum them point by point. You must draw these diagrams carefully to scale. It will take you quite a long time but this is the best way to understand how these two voltages combine.

15

V_p''

V_p'

V_p

v_1

v_2

P'

P''

O

P

t

What line on the circle diagram corresponds to the rotating radius which generates the sum voltage sinewave? Try to determine this by projecting back from the sinewave representing the sum voltage onto the circle diagram.

16

> OP″, the radius generating the sum waveform, is the
> diagonal of the rectangle whose sides are OP and OP′

Here is the complete circle diagram together with the sinewaves generated from it. OP and OP′ are at right angles since $\phi = \pi/2$.

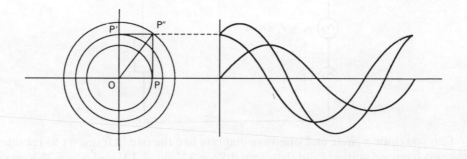

To check the above assertion first note that the amplitude of the sum waveform is 5 V. If you have drawn your diagram carefully you should be able to measure this. A circle of this radius can therefore be drawn concentric with the other two. Now consider the situation where OP lies along the horizontal axis. OP′ is therefore along the vertical axis. The contribution to the sum voltage on the sinewave diagram is therefore just that due to OP′ at this instant. The sum voltage and v_2 therefore have the same value when $t = 0$. But this value must be the projection of the radius OP″ of the largest circle onto the vertical axis to give a value equal to OP′. This radius OP″ will be found to be the diagonal of the rectangle made up by OP and OP′.

These results could be proved by trigonometry but the calculations are quite complicated. The result can be generalised to cases where ϕ is any angle (the value $\pi/2$ was chosen in this example to make the diagram a little easier to draw). In general the radius generating the sum of two sinewaves which are themselves generated by circle diagrams will be the diagonal of a parallelogram whose sides are two radii of the two circles separated by the appropriate phase angle ϕ. The result is completely analogous to the parallelogram of forces or to any other two-dimensional vector addition. OP, OP′ and OP″ can be represented as vectors but, since they have no real direction in space, they are given the special name of 'phasors'. Phasors are quantities which represent the amplitudes and relative phases of alternating sinewaves as generated from the appropriate circle diagrams. They add in exactly the same way as two-dimensional vectors.

17

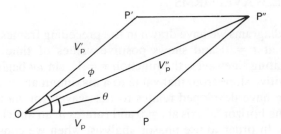

The diagram above shows a more general set of three phasors which could be used to generate three sinewaves. OP is regarded as the 'reference' phasor. OP' is at an angle ϕ to OP, and OP'' is the diagonal of the parallelogram whose sides are OP and OP'. OP'' is at an angle θ to OP. If all three phasors were made to rotate anticlockwise at the same angular frequency ω, the sinewave generated via OP'' would be found to be the sum of the sinewaves generated via OP and OP'. If the reference phasor is taken as generating the sinewave $v_1 = V_p \sin \omega t$, then this 'phasor diagram' carries all necessary information to deduce the relationship of v_2 and $v_1 + v_2$ with respect to v_1. With the above assumption what are the expressions for v_2 and $v_1 + v_2$ in terms of the quantities shown on the diagram?

18

$$v_2 = V'_p \sin (\omega t + \phi), \qquad v_1 + v_2 = V''_p \sin(\omega t + \theta)$$

The assumption made about the reference phasor OP is the same as assuming that, at the instant of time $t = 0$, the reference phasor lies along the horizontal axis. There is no loss of generality in this since the phasor diagram relates only to the *relative* positions of the three phasors. The assumption does, however, allow expressions for the other phasors to be written very simply. The phasor OP' is of length V'_p and makes an angle ϕ with OP, so a phase angle ϕ must be added to the angle ωt in the expression for the sinewave generated by the reference phasor. The equation of the sinewave generated by OP' is thus $v_2 = V'_p \sin(\omega t + \phi)$. Similarly the sum sinewave generated by OP'' is $v = V''_p \sin (\omega t + \theta)$.

Phasor diagrams provide us with a way of analysing circuits which are energised by alternating voltages and currents. We have seen how phasors can be added in the same way as two-dimensional vectors. It must be emphasised, however, that phasors do not obey other vector properties such as scalar or vector products. These concepts have no meaning in phasor algebra.

19

STEADY STATE WAVEFORMS

In the waveform diagrams we have drawn in the preceding frames, the (horizontal) time axis begins at $t = 0$ and shows positive values of time. When we have considered alternating sinewaves, the function $v = V_p \sin \omega t$ begins at $t = 0$, $v = 0$ and rises with positive slope from that value to a maximum at $t = \pi/2\omega$. The phasor representation we have developed relates to this waveform via a rotating phasor which lies along the horizontal axis at $t = 0$ and rotates in an anticlockwise direction as time increases. In order to use phasor analysis, when we consider these waveforms applied to electric circuits it is necessary to imagine that these waveforms have been in existence for some considerable time. The instant of time $t = 0$ simply determines *the moment at which we start to take an interest in the waveforms*. If, for a waveform which has been in existence for some time, we choose different moments to 'start looking at it', the effect on the mathematical function used to describe it will be evident in the phase angle associated with the argument of the sine term. Here is an example:

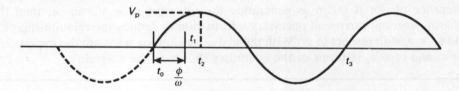

This diagram represents a portion of a sinewave which has been in existence for some time and will continue for some time into the future. Several different points are marked on the time axis. If we choose the point t_0 as our time reference $t = 0$, the mathematical function representing the sinewave will be $v = V_p \sin \omega t$. What will be the functions representing the sinewave if we choose first the point t_1, then the point t_2 and finally the point t_3 as the time reference $t = 0$?

20

> Choosing t_1 the function is $v = V_p \sin(\omega t + \phi)$
> Choosing t_2 the function is $v = V_p \cos \omega t$
> Choosing t_3 the function is $v = V_p \sin \omega t$

Note that the waveform is the same. It is the expression that represents it which changes and only the argument of the sine term is affected.

If t_0 is taken as the time reference $t = 0$, the value of v at t_1 can be ascertained as V_p sin ϕ by substituting $t = \phi/\omega$ into the expression V_p sin ωt. If this value of v is to be the value of the function at $t = 0$ when t is taken as the time reference $t = 0$, then the function must be $V_p \sin(\omega t + \phi)$. Substituting $t = 0$ in this expression again gives the value $v = V_p$ sin ϕ at t_1. If t_2 is chosen as the time reference $t = 0$, the waveform takes the familiar cosine shape. If t_3 is taken, the waveform is again correctly represented as $v = V_p$ sin ωt. Mathematically, times to the left of the chosen time reference represent 'negative time'. In practical terms this is 'time past'.

In phasor terms, as we saw in frames 16 and 17, the significance of the instant $t = 0$ is that a reference phasor lying along the horizontal axis at this instant will generate a waveform V_p sin ωt as it rotates. If we '*start looking at*' the phasor some time later, it will generate a waveform of the form $v = V_p \sin(\omega t + \phi)$.

Consideration of these matters is necessary because, in practical circuits, wave-forms take some time to 'settle down' after any power sources or generators in the circuit have been switched on. There is a period of time during which voltages and currents in the circuit take on '*transient*' values. (We shall analyse such phenomena in a later programme). After all 'transients' have 'died away', the waveforms in the circuit are said to have attained their *steady state*' values. It is only during this steady state that phasor analysis can be used, because phasor analysis depends on all waveforms being sinusoidal in character and all having the same frequency. Since this is such an important concept, you complete the following sentence:

> Phasors can be used only for the . . . . analysis
> of sinusoidal waveforms having the same . . . .

21

> Phasors can be used only for the *steady state* analysis of
> sinusoidal waveforms having the same *frequency*.

Provided the same time-zero reference is taken for all waveforms in a given circuit, they will all bear the correct *relative* relationships to each other. Similarly, the *relative* positions of all phasors representing the waveforms will be the same. All the important practical information is thus preserved. Generally, the most con-venient time-reference is chosen in the analysis of each particular circuit. Now turn to the next frame for a summary of the preceding work and then try the revision examples which follow.

22

SUMMARY

1. A periodic function of the form $v(t) = v(t + T)$ can be plotted as a graph of value against time and can be characterised by a number of parameters:

   (i) its peak value is the greatest value it reaches above the zero axis;

   (ii) its peak-to-peak value is the difference between its largest value and its smallest value;

   (iii) its period is the time taken for a complete 'cycle' of the function – it is the time T in the expression above;

   (iv) its frequency is the number of cycles of the function in one unit of time – frequency is the reciprocal of period;

   (v) its mean value is defined by the expression:

   $$v_{mean} = \frac{1}{T} \int_{t}^{t+T} v(t) dt$$

   (vi) its root mean square (r.m.s.) value is defined by the expression:

   $$v_{rms} = \sqrt{\left\{ \frac{1}{T} \int_{t}^{t+T} (v(t))^2 \, dt \right\}}$$

2. A periodic function whose mean value is zero is called an alternating function. The most important alternating function is the sine function. When representing an alternating voltage, this has the form $v(t) = V_p \sin \omega t$. Its peak value (also called its amplitude) is V_p; its peak-to-peak value is $2V_p$; its mean value is zero; its r.m.s. value is $V_p / \sqrt{2}$; its period is $2\pi/\omega$ and its frequency is $\omega/2\pi$. ω is called its angular frequency.

3. The relative amplitude and phase relationships of sinewaves having the same frequency can be represented on a phasor diagram. Phasors can be associated with the radii of circles from which the sinewaves can be generated by the method shown in detail in frames 9 and 10 of this programme.

4. If two voltage sinewaves are described by the expressions $v_1 = V_p \sin \omega t$ and $v_2 = V_p' \sin(\omega t + \phi)$, they are said to be 'out of phase' by the angle ϕ. v_2 is said to 'lead' v_1 by the phase angle ϕ. v_1 is said to 'lag' v_2 by the phase angle ϕ. If lines representing V_p and V_p' are drawn to scale from the same point with an angle ϕ between them as two adjacent sides of a parallelogram, the diagonal of the parallelogram drawn from the common point will generate a sinewave representing the sum of v_1 and v_2 as the three phasors rotate anticlockwise at an angular frequency ω.

┌─────────────────────┐
│ REVISION QUESTIONS │
└─────────────────────┘

1. The waveform in this diagram is called a half-wave-rectified sinewave. It can be derived from a sinewave using an electronic circuit incorporating one or more diodes. Between $t = 0$ and $t = \pi/\omega$ it has the same mathematical form as a sinewave. Between π/ω and $2\pi/\omega$ it is zero. What are its period, frequency, peak voltage, peak-to-peak voltage, mean voltage and root mean square voltage?

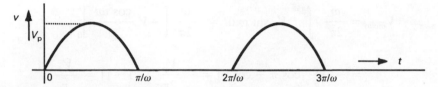

2. The waveform in this diagram is one variation of a group of waveforms called saw-tooth waveforms. What are its peak voltage, peak-to-peak voltage, mean voltage, root mean square voltage, period and frequency? Is it an alternating waveform? (*Hint:* To evaluate integrals, write equations for the graph over regions where it is a continuous function. See frame 9.)

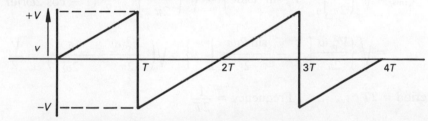

3. Two voltage waveforms are described by the equations $v_1 = 10 \sin 2000\pi t$ and $v_2 = 10 \cos 2000\pi t$. Draw a phasor diagram for the two waveforms and their sum. What is the amplitude of the sum waveform? What is its frequency? What is its period? Does the sum waveform lead or lag v_1 and v_2 and by how much? (*Hint:* A cosine function can be written as a sine function with a 'phase shift' of $\pi/2$ or 90°.)

4. Here is a phasor diagram representing the outputs of two alternating voltage generators giving outputs at a frequency of 50 Hz. Write equations for the waveforms generated and their sum. Call the phase shift of the sum waveform ϕ and give an expression for $\tan \phi$.

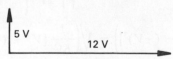

$$\boxed{\text{SOLUTIONS TO REVISION QUESTIONS}}$$

1. Period $= \dfrac{2\pi}{\omega}$ Frequency $= \dfrac{\omega}{2\pi}$

Peak voltage $= V_p$ Peak-to-peak voltage $= V_p$

Mean voltage:

$$V_{mean} = \frac{\omega}{2\pi} \int_0^{\pi/\omega} V_p \sin \omega t\, dt = \frac{\omega}{2\pi} \left[-V \frac{\cos \omega t}{\omega} \right]_0^{\pi/\omega}$$

$$= -\frac{V_p}{2\pi} [\cos \pi - \cos 0] = -\frac{V_p}{2\pi} [-1 - 1] = \frac{V_p}{\pi}$$

(The integral from π/ω to $2\pi/\omega$ is zero, but the period is from 0 to $2\pi/\omega$.)
r.m.s. voltage

$$V_{rms} = \sqrt{ \left\{ \frac{\omega}{2\pi} \int_0^{\pi/\omega} V_p^2 \sin^2 \omega t\, dt \right\} } = \sqrt{ \left\{ \frac{V_p^2 \omega}{2\pi} \int_0^{\pi/\omega} \frac{1}{2} (1 - \cos 2\omega t) dt \right\} }$$

$$= \sqrt{ \left\{ \frac{V_p^2 \omega}{2\pi} \left[\frac{t}{2} - \frac{\sin 2\omega t}{2} \right]_0^{\pi/\omega} \right\} } = \sqrt{ \left(\frac{V_p^2 \omega}{2\pi} \cdot \frac{\pi}{2\omega} \right) } = \frac{V_p}{2}$$

2. Period $= 2T$ Frequency $= \dfrac{1}{2T}$

Peak voltage $= V$ Peak-to-peak voltage $= 2V$

Mean voltage $= 0$ (area above axis $=$ area below axis)

It *is* an alternating waveform.

r.m.s. voltage
The equation of the line from T to $3T$ is $v = -V + V(t - T)/T$

$$V_{rms} = \sqrt{ \left\{ \frac{1}{2T} \int_T^{3T} \left(-V + \frac{V}{T} (t - T) \right)^2 dt \right\} } = \sqrt{ \left\{ \frac{1}{2T} \left[\frac{\left(-V + \frac{V}{T}(t - T) \right) \frac{T}{V}}{3} \right]_T^{3T} \right\} }$$

$$= \sqrt{ \left(\frac{1}{6V} [(-V + 2V)^3 - (-V)^3] \right) } = \sqrt{ \left(\frac{1}{6V} [V^3 - (-V)^3] \right) } = \sqrt{ \frac{V^2}{3} } = \frac{V}{\sqrt{3}}$$

3.

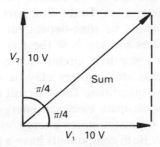

Sum waveform amplitude = $10\sqrt{2}$ = 14.142 V

Frequency of sum waveform = 1000 Hz

Period of sum waveform = 1.0 ms

Sum waveform leads v_1 by $\pi/4$ radians (45°)

Sum waveform lags v_2 by $\pi/4$ radians (45°)

Sum waveform is $v_3 = 14.142 \sin(2000\pi t + \pi/4)$

4.

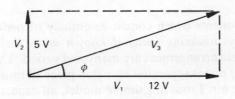

$v_1 = 12 \sin 100\pi t$

$v_2 = 5 \cos 100\pi t$

$v_3 = 13 \sin(100\pi t + \phi)$

$\tan \phi = 5/12 = 0.4167$

25

REACTIVE CIRCUIT ELEMENTS

In programmes 2 and 3, all the circuits we studied were made up of resistors and direct current and voltage generators. In the first part of this programme we saw how voltages and currents could be time-dependent quantities. We studied, in particular, sinusoidal quantities and saw how these could be represented by phasors. We will now look at some new circuit elements with which circuits for processing alternating currents and voltages may be constructed and which are sensitive to the phase of these quantities. These circuit elements are *capacitors* and *inductors*. Whereas resistors dissipate electrical energy, capacitors and inductors are capable of storing it. A capacitor stores energy '*electrostatically*', an inductor stores it '*electromagnetically*'. Both components have a property which is related to alternating currents and voltages in the same way that the resistance of a resistor is related to direct currents and voltages. This property is not a true resistance, however, and is given the name '*reactance*'. Circuits constructed with a mixture of components may exhibit properties both of resistance and reactance in the presence of alternating currents and voltages. They are spoken of as exhibiting an '*impedance*'.

We will look briefly at the energy storage properties of these components and then go on to see how they are used as circuit elements. We shall make use of the phasor analysis developed in the first part of the programme.

26

CAPACITORS

Capacitors are components which consist essentially of *two pieces of conducting material separated by insulating material known as a 'dielectric'*. The physical realisations of this basic arrangement are many and varied. The simplest consists of two flat parallel metal plates separated by a thin piece of insulating material which may, for example, be air. From this simple model, all capacitors are spoken of as having two '*plates*'. Capacitors store energy when electric charges are moved onto the plates. The existence of charge on the plates of a capacitor results in the development of a voltage across the capacitor and an *electrostatic field* in the region between its plates. Charge is placed on the plates of the capacitor by an electric current flowing for a given time. Energy is thus used in placing a charge on a capacitor. With an ideal capacitor this energy can be stored indefinitely until other components are connected to the capacitor, allowing the charge to be removed. Removal of the charge again results in a flow of current for a given time so the energy stored can be transferred to other components.

The basic capacitor circuit symbol (on the left below) also reflects its construction, looking like a side view of two parallel 'plates' separated by a small distance. Some types of capacitor need a 'polarising voltage' across them in order for them to work correctly. These are called 'electrolytic capacitors'. They are depicted by the right-hand symbol below where the plus and minus signs indicate the sense of the polarising voltage:

The diagram below shows a generator connected to a capacitor via a resistor to form a closed circuit. If the voltage across the capacitor is initially zero, current will flow in the circuit so that positive charge builds up on plate A and negative charge builds on plate B. Ultimately the voltage from A to B will equal the voltage of the ideal generator V.

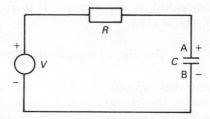

As the voltage is increasing the capacitor is said to be 'charging'. When the voltage reaches the value V the capacitor is said to be 'charged up' to this value. If components are connected to a charged up capacitor so that the voltage across it can reduce again it is said to be 'discharging'. While the voltage across the capacitor is building up from zero to the value V the current flowing in the circuit changes (we shall examine exactly how it does this in a later programme). One property of this changing current is very important to understand. It is in the nature of an electric field that, in a given time, exactly the same amount of positive charge will build up on plate A as the negative charge which builds up on plate B. The positive charge builds up as (negatively charged) electrons are attracted away *from* plate A *towards* the positive terminal of the generator. The negative charge builds up as electrons flow *from* the negative terminal of the generator *towards* plate B. But rate of change of charge is current so, at any instant, exactly the same current will flow *from* the positive terminal of the generator *to* plate A as flows *from* plate B *to* the negative terminal. *In terms of externally observable phenomena,* then, we can thus make exactly the same statement for changing currents and capacitors as we made in frame 1 of programme 2 for direct currents and resistors. You complete this sentence:

Changing currents flow . . . . a capacitor.

28

| Changing currents flow *through* a capacitor. |

Although no electrons actually pass through the capacitor from one plate to the other, the observable current flowing towards the positive plate is exactly the same as the observable current flowing away from the negative plate provided it is the instantaneous value of a changing current. It must be clearly understood, however, that, because there is no resistive path between the plates of a capacitor, it acts as an open-circuit to direct current. If a direct voltage generator is connected across the plates of a capacitor, no current will flow from one plate to the other through the capacitor. Practical components do, however, exhibit a '*leakage resistance*'.

When a charge Q is stored on a capacitor resulting in the development of a voltage V across it, the values of these two quantities are determined by a constant property of the capacitor called its capacitance. It is given the symbol C. The relationship between Q, V and C is:

$$Q/V = C \qquad \text{The unit of capacitance is the farad.}$$

As with most basic units when referenced to electronic circuits, capacitors whose values are measured in farads are seldom encountered in practice. The component sizes most widely used in circuit design are more likely to be measured in microfarads (farads $\times 10^{-6}$), nanofarads (farads $\times 10^{-9}$) or picofarads (farads $\times 10^{-12}$) – the latter known colloquially by designers as 'puffs'. The 'stray' capacitances associated with printed circuit board layouts and the interconnection capacitances found inside integrated circuits are typically of the order of a few puffs.

If a charge of 50 picocoulombs produces a voltage between the plates of a capacitor of 5 volts, what is the value of the capacitor?

29

| 10 pF |

Now suppose that a capacitor of value C is being charged by some kind of energy source and a small element of charge δq is added to the charge q on the plates when the changing voltage across the capacitor has an instantaneous value v. The work which must be done by the source in adding this charge is given by the expression $\delta w = v\delta q$. Now, using the defining relationship for capacitance given above, can you write an expression for δw which does not include the term in δq?

$$\delta w = Cv\delta v$$

Since $q = Cv$ then $\delta q = C\delta v$ which gives the above result on substitution. If the small quantities in this expression are now made infinitesimal by proceeding to the limit, they become 'differentials' and the expression becomes:

$$dw = Cvdv$$

This equation can now be integrated. If we assume that no work has been done when the voltage across the capacitor is zero and that W is the work needed to raise the voltage between the plates to a value V, we have an integral equation with definite integrals:

$$\int_0^W dw = C \int_0^V vdv$$

What is the result of carrying out this integration?

31

$$W = \tfrac{1}{2} CV^2$$

Since work and energy have the same dimensions, this value for W represents the energy stored on the capacitor when the voltage between its plates is V. Notice that, although an electric current must have been flowing whilst the charge was being stored, the final value of the stored energy does not depend on current but simply on the final value of the voltage between the plates of the capacitor.

We can, however, examine the relationship between the voltage across the capacitor and the current flowing 'through' it while these quantities are changing. To do this we return to the expression $q = Cv$ and differentiate it to obtain:

$$\frac{dq}{dt} = C\frac{dv}{dt}$$

But dq/dt can be interpreted in a different way. Can you re-write the above equation, replacing dq/dt by something to which it is equivalent?

32

$$i = C\frac{dv}{dt}$$

Rate of change of charge is current so we can replace dq/dt by i, the instantaneous value of the charging current. The above equation then tells us that, *when the current through and voltage across a capacitor are changing*, the current at any instant is equal to the value of the capacitance multiplied by the rate of change of voltage at that instant.

So now, as with Ohm's Law for a resistor, we have an equation linking the current through a capacitor to the voltage across it. The difference between the two cases is of course that, with Ohm's Law, the quantities involved are *direct* (that is unchanging) quantities. In the case of the capacitor, the quantities involved are *the instantaneous values of changing quantities*.

The diagram below shows an alternating voltage generator giving an output of value $v = V \sin \omega t$ connected to a capacitor of capacitance C. What is the value of the current i in the circuit?

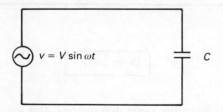

33

The current is $i = \omega CV \cos \omega t$

$$i = C\frac{dv}{dt} = C\frac{d}{dt}(V \sin \omega t) = C(\omega V \cos \omega t) = \omega CV \cos \omega t$$

Can you sketch graphs of the current through and voltage across the capacitor? Use the same scale on the time axis for both graphs and mark the amplitudes of the two quantities on the two graphs.

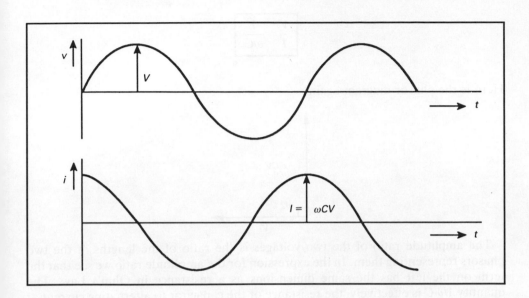

From the two graphs we see that the current and voltage waveforms have the same frequency but respective maxima are separated by a phase angle of $\pi/2$, the current waveform being in advance of the voltage waveform. *The current thus leads the voltage in a capacitor* energised by an alternating voltage generator. We can write the expression for the current as $i = I \cos \omega t$.

The two waveforms can be represented on a phasor diagram as shown below:

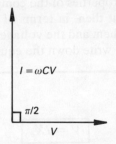

The voltage phasor (the sine function) is chosen as the reference phasor lying along the horizontal axis. From the graph, the amplitude of the current phasor is seen to be $I = \omega CV$ and its direction is at right angles to the voltage phasor. It points *upwards* because *the current leads the voltage.*

What is the ratio of the voltage amplitude to the current amplitude?

35

$$\frac{V}{I} = \frac{1}{\omega C}$$

Here is the phasor diagram again:

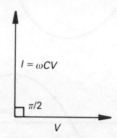

The amplitude ratio of the two voltages is the ratio of the lengths of the two phasors representing them. In the expression for the amplitude ratio we see that the term on the left has the same dimensions as a resistance in Ohm's Law. The quantity $1/\omega C$ is effectively 'the resistance of the capacitor to alternating current of angular frequency ω' and is called the *reactance* of the capacitor at the frequency ω. It is given the symbol X_c.

So $X_c = 1/\omega C$

The quantity X_c is measured in (reactive) ohms. A very important difference between resistance and reactance, however, is that, whereas resistance depends only on material properties, reactance *depends on the frequency of the applied signal* as well as the material properties of the component whose reactance is being considered. To a certain extent then, in terms of their reactances and the amplitudes of the currents through them and the voltages across them, capacitors obey a form of Ohm's Law. Now, you write down the equation for V in terms of I and X_c.

36

$$V = IX_c$$

This looks like Ohm's Law but with R replaced by X_c. Care must be exercised in using this relationship, however, because it relates only the amplitudes of the two quantities and takes no account of their relative phases. We shall investigate this problem shortly when we analyse some circuits involving both resistors and capacitors.

INDUCTORS

An inductor is a component which consists essentially of a coil of wire wound onto a former or bobbin in order to produce a *magnetic field* when a current flows in the wire. Energy is stored by virtue of this flow of current and the resulting magnetic field. Work must be done to change the current and the amount of work needed to produce a given change in current is a measure of the energy stored in effecting this change. In an ideal inductor the energy can be stored indefinitely by the flow of current. That is, *a given amount of energy will be stored in the inductor as long as a given current is maintained flowing through it*. Under these circumstances, because the inductor is ideal and therefore offers no resistance to the flow of direct current, the voltage across it will be zero. The energy can be transferred to other components if they can be connected into the inductor circuit in such a way that the current is made to change.

The electrical property of such an arrangement is called *inductance*. It acts so as to cause opposition to any change in the current flowing in a circuit into which it is incorporated. Frequently the centre or 'core' of the coil is made of *ferromagnetic* material since this gives a greater inductance than would be provided by the simple coil of wire on its own.

The circuit symbol for an inductor, like that for a capacitor, reflects its construction, appearing as a representation of a coil of wire. Here it is:

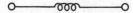

The diagram below shows a generator connected to an inductor to form a closed circuit. As soon as the circuit is completed, current will start to flow and will build up from zero to a final, fixed value. This final value will then be maintained indefinitely as a *direct* current flowing round the circuit and through the inductor. What is the final value of the current for the circuit given here?

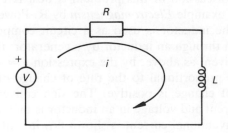

38

> The final value of the current is V/R

Once the current has ceased to change and become a direct current, the voltage across the inductor will be zero. The generator voltage V must therefore all appear across the resistor whose value thus determines the current. Here is the circuit diagram again:

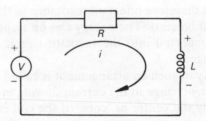

While the current in the circuit is changing there will be a voltage developed across the inductor in the sense shown in the diagram. Inductance is given the symbol L and the voltage across it is given by the expression:

$$v = L \frac{\mathrm{d}i}{\mathrm{d}t}$$ The unit of inductance is the Henry.

Confusion often surrounds this expression, particularly concerning whether or not the term on the right-hand side should have a minus sign in front of it or not. The problem arises because the very existence of a voltage depends on the fact that the current is *changing*. Faraday's Law states that, when the current in an inductive circuit changes, a voltage is induced in that circuit which opposes *changes* in the current and is proportional to the *rate* of change. When writing down Faraday's Law the opposition to current change is exemplified by writing the induced voltage as $-L\mathrm{d}i/\mathrm{d}t$. A fuller discussion of this problem is best left to a course in basic electromagnetism, for example *Electromagnetism* by R. Powell (in the same series as this text). When the inductor is used as a circuit component, however, and current is being driven through an inductor by a generator, the voltage across the inductor is correctly given, as above, by the expression $v = +L\mathrm{d}i/\mathrm{d}t$. The voltage across the inductor is proportional to the rate of change of current and is thus positive if this rate of change is positive. The sign convention used in circuit diagrams between current and voltage in an inductor is that shown in the diagram above. A positive conventional current is shown flowing into the terminal which becomes positive. Strictly, we should think of this as an increasing current.

39

ENERGY STORAGE IN AN INDUCTOR

The energy stored in an inductor can be evaluated by considering the work done in establishing a given current in the inductor. Suppose that a variable source of electrical energy is connected to the inductor so that, at a given instant in time, the current through the inductor is i and the voltage across it is v. The instantaneous power supplied to the inductor is then:

$$vi = L i \mathrm{d}i/\mathrm{d}t$$

Since power is rate of doing work and, therefore, work is power multiplied by time, in an element of time t, an element of work δw is done where:

$$\delta w = (L i \mathrm{d}i/\mathrm{d}t)\delta t$$

In the limit we can write:

$$\mathrm{d}w = (L i \mathrm{d}i/\mathrm{d}t)\mathrm{d}t = L i \mathrm{d}i$$

If we now let the energy source be so varied that the current in the inductor is raised from zero to a value I and, in doing this, the total work done is W, we can find an expression for W by integrating the above expression for $\mathrm{d}w$.

What is the value of W?

$$\boxed{W = \tfrac{1}{2}LI^2}$$

Carrying out the integral, we have:

$$\int_0^W \mathrm{d}w = L \int_0^I i\,\mathrm{d}i = \tfrac{1}{2}LI^2$$

When L is in Henries and I in amps, W is in Joules.

41

ALTERNATING CURRENTS AND VOLTAGES IN AN INDUCTOR

Returning now to the expression linking current and voltage in an inductor, $v = L\mathrm{d}i/\mathrm{d}t$, we can use it to find the relationship between alternating current and voltage in this component.

The diagram below shows an alternating current generator giving an output of value $i = I \sin \omega t$ connected to an inductor of inductance L. What is the value of the voltage v across the inductor?

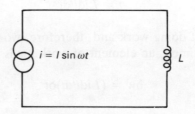

42

$$\boxed{\text{The voltage is } v = \omega L I \cos \omega t}$$

$$v = L \frac{\mathrm{d}i}{\mathrm{d}t} = L \frac{\mathrm{d}}{\mathrm{d}t} (I \sin \omega t) = L(\omega I \cos \omega t) = \omega L I \cos \omega t$$

Can you sketch graphs of the current through and voltage across the inductor? Use the same scale on the time axis for both graphs and mark the amplitudes of the two quantities on the two graphs.

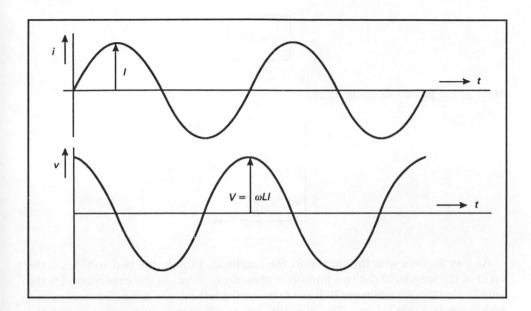

From the two graphs we see that the current and voltage waveforms have the same frequency but respective maxima are separated by a phase angle of $\pi/2$, the voltage waveform being in advance of the current waveform. The voltage thus leads the current in an inductor energised by an alternating current generator. We can write the expression for the voltage as $v = V \cos \omega t$.

The two waveforms can be represented on a phasor diagram as shown here:

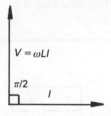

The current phasor (the sine function) is chosen as the reference phasor lying along the horizontal axis. From the graph, the amplitude of the voltage phasor is seen to be $V = \omega L I$ and its direction is at right angles to the voltage phasor.

What is the ratio of the voltage amplitude to the current amplitude?

44

$$\boxed{\frac{V}{I} = \omega L}$$

Here is the phasor diagram again:

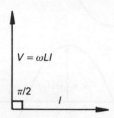

$V = \omega L I$

$\pi/2$

I

As was the case with the capacitor, the amplitude ratio of the two voltages is the ratio of the lengths of the two phasors representing them. In the expression for the amplitude ratio we again see that the term on the left has the same dimensions as a resistance in Ohm's Law. The quantity ωL is effectively 'the resistance of the inductor to alternating current of angular frequency'. It is called the reactance of the inductor at the frequency ω. It is given the symbol X_L.

$$\text{So } X_L = \omega L$$

The quantity X_L is measured in (reactive) ohms. So, just like capacitors, in terms of their reactances and the amplitudes of the currents through them and the voltages across them, inductors too obey a form of Ohm's Law. Now, you write down the equation for V in terms of I and X_L.

45

$$\boxed{V = IX_L}$$

Like the expression we had earlier for the capacitor, this looks like Ohm's Law but this time with R replaced by X_L. Once again the expression relates only the amplitudes of the two quantities so we must again be careful how we use it, especially when analysing circuits containing both resistors and inductors. Before doing this, however, we will study the power relationships in components energised by alternating energy sources.

POWER CONSIDERATIONS WITH ALTERNATING QUANTITIES

In frame 7 of this programme we defined the r.m.s. value of a sinewave. The power carried by a sinewave gives this definition a physical meaning.

The diagram below shows a resistor connected to a source of alternating voltage $v = V \sin \omega t$.

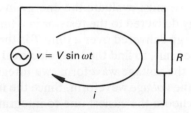

The current flowing in the resistor is $i = (V/R) \sin \omega t = I \sin \omega t$.
The instantaneous power dissipated in the resistor is:

$$vi = V \sin \omega t \times I \sin \omega t = VI \sin^2 \omega t = \frac{VI}{2}(1 - \cos 2\omega t)$$

In this form we see that the power has a constant term $VI/2$ and a fluctuating term $(VI/2)\cos 2\omega t$ whose frequency is twice that of the voltage and current waveforms. Here is a graph of the power expression:

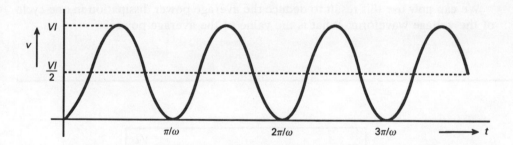

Notice that the graph is wholly above the time axis so the power is always positive. That is, even though the instantaneous power in the resistor is fluctuating, the generator always transfers power to the resistor. The power is '*dissipated*' in the resistor. That is, over a given time, the electrical energy used to produce it is converted into heat energy. What is the energy transferred to the resistor in one complete cycle of the voltage waveform?

47

> The energy transferred in one cycle is $\dfrac{VI\pi}{\omega}$

Energy is a product of power and time. Since, in the circuit in frame 45, the power is continuously changing we must evaluate the energy in a given time by a process of integration. The energy delivered to the resistor in a time δt when the power in it is vi is $vi\delta t$. The total energy delivered over a time T is the sum of all such products over the interval T. In the limit, to find the total electrical energy converted to heat energy over one cycle of the voltage waveform, we integrate the *power* waveform over a complete cycle of the *voltage* waveform. Since the integrals over all complete cycles are the same, we choose the easiest one to integrate over; that is, from 0 to $2\pi/\omega$. The right-hand side of the expression for the instantaneous power given in frame 45 can be integrated directly:

$$\frac{VI}{2}\int_0^{2\pi/\omega}(1 - \cos 2\omega t)\mathrm{d}t = \frac{VI}{2}[t - \sin 2\omega t]_0^{2\pi/\omega}$$

The only term contributing a non-zero value to the answer is the t term evaluated at the upper limit. Hence:

$$\text{Energy in one cycle} = \frac{VI}{2} \times \frac{2\pi}{\omega} = \frac{VI\pi}{\omega}$$

We can now use this result to deduce the average power dissipation in one cycle of the voltage waveform. What is the value of the average power?

48

> The average power in one cycle is $\dfrac{VI}{2}$

This result is obtained by dividing the energy in one cycle by the cycle length. Note the dimensions of the terms involved. Energy divided by time equals power.

Now, recalling the expression for the r.m.s. value of a sinusoidal quantity derived in frame 7 of this programme, can you express the average power per cycle in terms of the r.m.s. values of the voltage and current?

49

> The average power per cycle is the product of the
> r.m.s. values of the voltage and the current

Calling the average power P_{av}, we have

$$P_{av} = \frac{VI}{2} = \frac{V}{\sqrt{2}} \times \frac{I}{\sqrt{2}} = v_{rms} \times i_{rms}$$

So the r.m.s. values of voltage and current which, up to now we have defined purely as mathematical expressions, now have a physical meaning. Their product represents the average power carried by a current sinewave flowing through a resistor as a result of a voltage sinewave being applied across it. What value of direct voltage applied to the same resistor would produce the same power dissipation in it and what would be the resulting current?

50

> A direct voltage $V/\sqrt{2}$ applied across a resistor R would produce
> the same power in it as a sinewave $v = V \sin \omega t$. The current
> would be $V/R\sqrt{2} = I/\sqrt{2}$.

Power with direct current and voltage is the product of the current and the voltage. From the equation in frame 48 we see that a direct voltage of $V/\sqrt{2}$ and a direct current of $I/\sqrt{2}$ produce a power equal to P_{av}. But a direct voltage $V/\sqrt{2}$ across a resistor R produces a current $V/R\sqrt{2} = I/\sqrt{2}$ since $I = V/R$. Thus the r.m.s. values of a sinusoidal voltage or current are equivalent to the same values of direct voltage or current as would produce the same heating effect (power dissipation) in a resistor. For this reason r.m.s. values are sometimes also known as 'equivalent values'.

Here is the graph of the power function again:

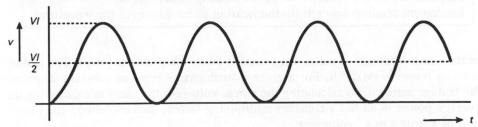

We can think of this power as having a direct component with an alternating component superimposed upon it. What is the value of the direct component?

51

> The direct component is $VI/2$

As we saw in frame 46, the power can be written as $P = (VI/2) - (VI/2)\cos 2\omega t$. The constant term $VI/2$ is, in effect a 'direct component' whilst the term $(VI/2)\cos 2\omega t$ shows the 'sinusoidal variation' about this direct component.

It is also worth noting that, since the average value of any alternating quantity is, by definition, zero, the average value of the combined function is just the equivalent direct value $VI/2$. Since the r.m.s. values of voltage and current lead to an average value of power, these r.m.s. values are sometimes referred to as the 'electrical mean values' of the two quantities.

Many instruments for measuring voltage and current are calibrated in r.m.s. values. Some of these respond simply to the peak value, assuming the waveform to be a perfect sinusoid. Their scales are calibrated by dividing this value by $\sqrt{2}$. These will give a true reading only if the waveform being measured *is* a perfect sinusoid. For all other waveforms, the reading will be in error. Care must therefore be exercised in using such instruments.

Some instruments, however, give a reading which is proportional to the heating effect of the waveform being measured when it is applied across a resistor inside the instrument. These instruments give a 'true r.m.s.' reading whatever the waveform. Now, by writing an expression for the power in a resistor with a voltage $v(t)$ across it and one for the definition of the r.m.s. value of a voltage $v(t)$, can you justify these two statements?

52

> By definition $v_{rms} = \sqrt{\left\{ \dfrac{1}{T} \displaystyle\int_{t}^{t+T} (v(t))^2 dt \right\}}$, but instantaneous power in a resistor is equal to $(v(t))^2/R$ thus the 'true r.m.s.' value is proportional to the square root of the heating effect. So the instrument reading depends on the heating effect whatever the waveform

In the integral for r.m.s. value, the function being integrated is $(v(t))$. The instantaneous power is $(v(t))^2/R$. For a given instrument, R remains constant whatever the voltage across it, so calculating the r.m.s. voltage is the same as calculating the average power in all but a constant multiplying factor, thus explaining the operation of a 'true r.m.s.' voltmeter.

53

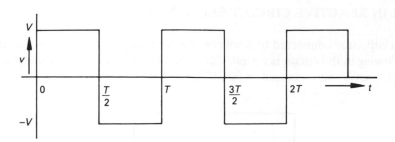

The diagram above is the graph of an alternating voltage square wave. What is its r.m.s. value? What power would be dissipated in a resistor R across which this voltage waveform could be measured?

54

> The r.m.s. value of the square wave is V
> The power dissipated in a resistor R is V^2/R

The square wave can be expressed mathematically as:

$$v(t) = V \quad \text{for } 0 < t < T/2 \quad \text{and} \quad v(t) = -V \quad \text{for } T/2 < t < T$$

over values of t defining its first cycle. We thus have:

$$v_{\text{rms}} = \sqrt{\left\{ \int_0^{T/2} V^2 \, \mathrm{d}t + \int_{T/2}^T (-V)^2 \, \mathrm{d}t \right\}}$$

$$= \sqrt{\left\{ \frac{1}{T} \left[\frac{V^2 T}{2} + \frac{V^2 T}{2} \right] \right\}} = \sqrt{\left(\frac{V^2 T}{T} \right)} = V$$

Note that the r.m.s. value is the same as the peak value. The power is obtained by dividing the integrals by a constant factor R without taking the square root. Thus $P = V^2 R$. The expression for the power is the same as would be obtained if a direct voltage of value V was measured across the resistor. It is intuitively reasonable that, if a resistor is at all times subject to the same peak voltage, then the power dissipated in it is constant. It does not matter which way the current in the resistor is flowing. It can therefore also be deduced that the r.m.s. value of the voltage is at all times V, even though its actual value alternates between $+V$ and $-V$.

An instrument which responded to the peak value of a waveform and then gave a scale reading of this value divided by $\sqrt{2}$ would not indicate a true r.m.s. reading if used to measure this waveform.

55

POWER IN REACTIVE CIRCUIT ELEMENTS

Here is a capacitor connected to a source of alternating voltage $v = V \sin \omega t$. The current flowing in the circuit is $i = \omega CV \cos \omega t$. The instantaneous power p is given by $p = vi = \omega CV \sin \omega t \cos \omega t = (\omega CV^2/2)\sin 2\omega t$.

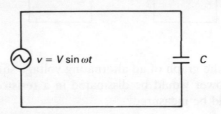

Here are graphs of the three waveforms:

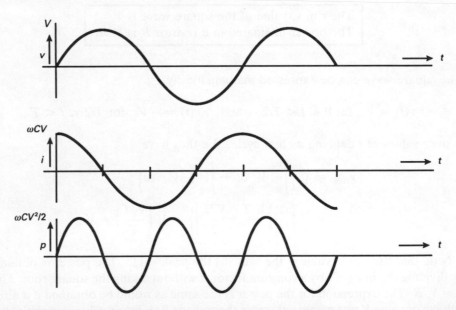

Just as was the case with the resistor, the power waveform has twice the frequency of the voltage and current waveforms. In this case, however, the power waveform is an alternating waveform and thus has a mean value of zero. In previous examples a positive value for power has denoted power being transferred from a generator to the component to which it is connected. The power waveform in this case is negative for half of each cycle. What is the meaning of 'negative power' in practical terms?

56

> When the power waveform is negative, power is being returned from the capacitor to the generator.

During the first half-cycle of the power waveform in the diagram in frame 54 power is positive and, as with previous examples we have seen, is transferred from the generator to the capacitor. During this half-cycle, energy is stored in the capacitor. The negative power in the second half-cycle implies that power is being absorbed by the generator. During this half-cycle, the power transfer is from the capacitor to the generator and, over the length of the cycle, energy is stored back in the generator. Since the waveform is repetitive, this 'ebb and flow' action of power from generator to capacitor and back continues as long as the circuit connections remain intact. Power ebbs and flows between the generator and the capacitor twice in every complete cycle of the voltage or current waveforms but the mean power transferred over a full cycle is zero. Now, can you complete the following sentence:

Unlike a resistor, a capacitor does not . . . . power.

57

> Unlike a resistor, a capacitor does not *dissipate* power.

This phenomenon is seldom a problem in 'electronic' circuits: radios, televisions, instruments, computers and so on. Here the power levels are likely to be measured in milliwatts or, at most, hundreds of watts, and generators can easily be designed to absorb these kinds of power level when necessary. When power generation at the Megawatt levels appropriate to a power station are considered, however, considerable problems are experienced in having to absorb such high levels of power in the generators and power transmission lines. Power generation companies prefer to deliver their power to resistive loads and impose cost penalties on customers whose loads do not appear to be so.

Another point is worth noticing about these waveforms before we move on. If we consider the first quarter-cycle of the voltage waveform we see that, during this time, the voltage increases from zero to V. In the same interval, the current falls from ωCV to zero. During this time the power curve is all above the time axis, so power is transferred from the generator to the capacitor. Integration of the power curve from $t = 0$ to $t = \pi/2\omega$ gives the energy stored in the capacitor during this time interval. What is this integral and is it consistent with earlier results?

58

> The value of the integral is $CV^2/2$
> It is consistent with the result in frame 30

The integral of the power curve gives the energy stored, because power is rate of doing work so work is power multiplied by time. The amount of work done in an interval is the same as the energy stored during that interval.

$$\text{Hence } \frac{\omega CV^2}{2}\int_0^{\pi/2\omega}\sin 2\omega t\,dt = \frac{\omega CV^2}{2}\left[\frac{-\cos 2\omega t}{2\omega}\right]_0^{\pi/2\omega} = \frac{CV^2}{4}\left[-\cos\pi - (-\cos 0)\right]$$

$$= \frac{CV^2}{4}[1+1] = \frac{CV^2}{2}$$

During the time interval from 0 to $\pi/2\omega$, the voltage on the capacitor increases from 0 to V. In frame 30 we found that the energy stored in producing such an increase was $CV^2/2$, so the two results are consistent.

Similar results can be obtained for an inductor connected to a current generator $i = I\sin\omega t$. Draw a diagram of such a circuit and write down the equations for the current through and voltage across the inductor and the instantaneous power in it. Does an inductor dissipate power?

59

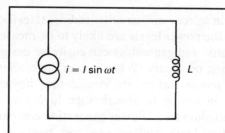

The current is $i = I\sin\omega t$
The voltage is $v = \omega LI\cos\omega t$
The power is $(\omega LI^2/2)\sin 2\omega t$
No power is dissipated

All the generator current flows through the inductor. Since the voltage across the inductor is given by the equation $v = L\,di/dt$, the voltage is $L(d/dt)I\sin\omega t = \omega LI\cos\omega t$. Power is $v \times i$ so $P = \omega LI^2\sin\omega t\cos\omega t = (\omega LI^2/2)\sin 2\omega t$. Since the power function is a sine wave, it has a mean value of zero so no power is dissipated. Just as for the capacitor, power ebbs and flows between the generator and the inductor. This again causes problems at very high power levels and, in fact, most industrial loads *are* partly inductive in character. Now, here is a summary of the programme so far.

SUMMARY

Capacitors

1. A capacitor consists basically of two pieces of conducting material – the plates – separated by insulating material – the dielectric. Energy is stored in capacitors electrostatically. In terms of externally observable phenomena, changing currents flow through capacitors. Capacitors appear as open-circuits to direct current.
2. The charge on and voltage across a capacitor are linked by the equation:

$$C = q/v \qquad \text{The unit of capacitance is the farad.}$$

3. When the current through and voltage across a capacitor are changing, the two quantities are linked by the equation:

$$i = C\,dv/dt$$

4. The energy W stored by a capacitor when the voltage between its plates is V is given by the equation:

$$W = (CV^2)/2$$

5. When an alternating voltage generator $v = V \sin \omega t$ is connected to a capacitor to form a closed circuit, the current flowing in the circuit is $i = \omega CV \cos \omega t$. The two quantities can be represented on a phasor diagram, the current phasor leading the voltage phasor as shown here:

6. The reactance of a capacitor energised by an alternating generator is the ratio of the voltage amplitude V to the current amplitude I where:

$$V/I = X_c = 1/\omega C$$

7. When a source of alternating voltage $v = V \sin \omega t$ is connected to a capacitor to form a closed circuit, power ebbs and flows between the generator and the capacitor. The instantaneous power is given by the equation:

$$p = (\omega CV^2/2)\sin 2\omega t. \qquad \text{A capacitor does not dissipate power.}$$

Inductors

1. An inductor consists basically of a coil of wire wound on to a former in order to produce a magnetic field when a current flows in the wire. Energy is stored in the field associated with the inductor electromagnetically. Inductors appear as short-circuits to direct current.

2. When the current through and voltage across an inductor are changing, the two quantities are linked by the equation:

$$v = L\mathrm{d}i/\mathrm{d}t \qquad \text{The unit of inductance is the Henry.}$$

3. The energy W stored by an inductor when the current through it is I is given by the equation:

$$W = (LI^2)/2$$

4. When an alternating current generator $i = I \sin \omega t$ is connected to an inductor to form a closed circuit, the voltage developed across the inductor is $v = \omega LI \cos \omega t$. The two quantities can be represented on a phasor diagram, the voltage phasor leading the current phasor as shown here:

5. The reactance of an inductor energised by an alternating generator is the ratio of the voltage amplitude V to the current amplitude I where:

$$V/I = X_L = \omega L$$

6. When a source of alternating current $i = I \sin \omega t$ is connected to an inductor to form a closed circuit, power ebbs and flows between the generator and the inductor. The instantaneous power is given by the equation:

$$p = (\omega LI^2/2)\sin 2\omega t \qquad \text{An inductor does not dissipate power.}$$

Power and r.m.s. values of voltage and current

1. The r.m.s. value of a voltage or current is that value which would produce the same heating effect (power dissipation) in a resistor as a direct voltage or current having the same numerical value.

2. A measuring instrument calibrated in r.m.s. values gives a true r.m.s. reading for all waveforms only if its movement is sensitive to the heating effect of the quantity being measured.

REVISION QUESTIONS

1. A voltage of $10 \sin(2000\pi t)$ is measured across the terminals of a 100 μF capacitor. What is the frequency of the waveform? What is the current through the capacitor?

2. A current of $20 \sin(500\pi t)$ flows through a 1 mH inductor. What is the frequency of the waveform? What is the voltage across the inductor?

3. Physically small 1 farad capacitors are now widely available as 'memory backup capacitors' for microprocessor equipment. How much energy is stored in a 1 farad capacitor charged up to 12 volts? Assuming the capacitor is connected to a circuit which draws a steady current of 10 mA without changing the voltage across its terminals, for how long can it support this circuit?

4. A steady current of 50 mA flows through a 100 mH inductor. What is the energy stored in the inductor?

5. A sinusoidal voltage of amplitude 10 volts and of frequency 1 kHz is applied (a) across a 5 μF capacitor and (b) across a 10 mH inductor. What r.m.s. current flows in each case? Draw graphs of the voltage, current and power waveforms for each component.

ANSWERS TO REVISION QUESTIONS

1. Waveform frequency = 1 kHz

$$i = C\mathrm{d}v/\mathrm{d}t = 100 \times 10^{-6} \times 10 \cos 2000\pi t \times 2000\pi \text{ A} = 2\pi \cos 2000\pi t \text{ A}$$

2. Waveform frequency = 250 Hz

$$v = L\mathrm{d}i/\mathrm{d}t = 1 \times 10^{-3} \times 20 \cos 500\pi t \times 500\pi \times 10^{-3} \text{ V} = 10\pi \cos 500\pi t \text{ mV}$$

3. $W = CV^2/2 = (1 \times 12^2)/2 = 72$ J (Joules)

$P = VI = 12 \times 10 \times 10^{-3}$ W   But $P = W/T$

So $T = W/P = 72/(12 \times 10 \times 10^{-3}) = 600$ s = 10 minutes

4. $W = LI^2/2 = \frac{1}{2}(100 \times 10^{-3} \times 50 \times 50 \times 10^{-6}) = 0.125$ mJ

5. (a) $i_{\text{rms}} \dfrac{\omega CV}{\sqrt{2}} = \dfrac{2\pi \times 1000 \times 5 \times 10^{-6} \times 10}{\sqrt{2}} = \dfrac{100\pi}{\sqrt{2}}\text{mA} = 0.222$ mA

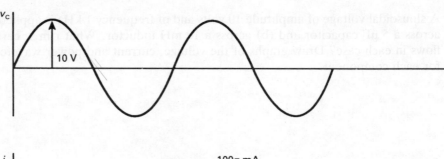

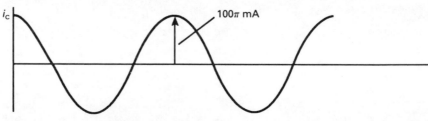

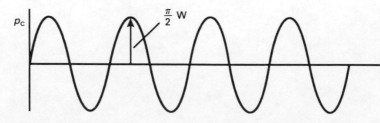

The power waveform has twice the frequency of the voltage and current waveforms, that is 2 kHz.

Its amplitude is the product of the r.m.s. values of the voltage and current waveforms, that is:

$$p = (10/\sqrt{2}) \times 50\sqrt{2} \times \pi \times 10^{-3} = 1.57 \text{ W}$$

5. (b) $i_{rms} = \dfrac{V}{\sqrt{2}\omega L} = \dfrac{10}{\sqrt{2} \times 2\pi \times 1000 \times 10 \times 10^{-3}} = \dfrac{1}{\sqrt{2} \times 2\pi} = 0.113 \text{ A}$

The power waveform has twice the frequency of the voltage and current waveforms, that is 2 kHz.

Its amplitude is the product of the r.m.s. values of the voltage and current waveforms, that is:

$$p = (10/\sqrt{2}) \times (1/2\sqrt{2\pi}) = 0.79 \text{ W}$$

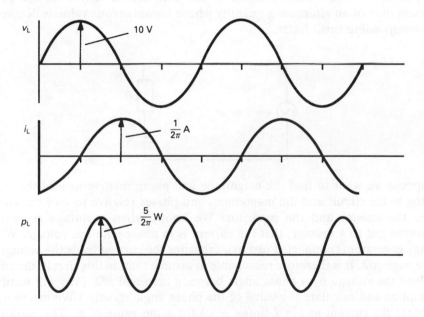

63

ALTERNATING CURRENTS AND VOLTAGES IN RESISTIVE/REACTIVE CIRCUITS

In the rest of this programme we will see how the phasor analysis we have developed in the earlier frames can be extended to circuits containing a mixture of resistors, capacitors and inductors. The phasor diagrams we shall analyse will no longer contain only phasors which are co-linear or orthogonal (that is, at right angles to each other). Phasors which represent the voltages across or currents through components in a complicated circuit are at various angles to each other. We will study some simple examples first.

THE SERIES RESISTOR/CAPACITOR CIRCUIT

Consider an alternating voltage generator connected to a resistor and a capacitor in series as shown in the diagram below. If we know the amplitude and frequency of the voltage waveform we can represent the output of the generator as $v = V \sin \omega t$. (Remember that we can choose the effective zero of time!) We can also represent it as a phasor V. It is normal practice to use bold capital letters for the phasor representation of an alternating quantity whose instantaneous value is denoted by the corresponding small letter.

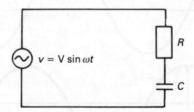

Suppose we want to find the magnitude and phase relative to v of the current flowing in the circuit and the magnitudes and phases relative to v of the voltages across the resistor and the capacitor. We know, when a voltage generator is connected just to a resistor, that the current is in phase with the voltage. When a voltage generator is connected just to a capacitor the current leads the voltage by a phase angle $\pi/2$. It is therefore reasonable to assume that, in this circuit, the current will lead the voltage by a phase angle between zero and $\pi/2$. (We will justify the assumption and calculate the value of the phase angle shortly.) We can therefore represent the current as $i = I \sin(\omega t + \phi)$ for some value of ϕ. The current can therefore be represented by a phasor I, where I leads V by the phase angle ϕ.

If we give the instantaneous voltage across the resistor the symbol v_R, can you write an expression for v_R? What symbol would you use to represent this quantity as a phasor?

> The resistor voltage is $v_R = IR \sin(\omega t + \phi)$
> It can be represented by the phasor V_R

Since the current through the resistor is $i = I \sin(\omega t + \phi)$ and the value of the resistor is R, the voltage across the resistor must be given by their product, so $v = IR \sin(\omega t + \phi)$. We use the bold letter V_R to denote the phasor representing v_R.

Now, the phasor V_R is a phasor of amplitude IR in the same direction as the phasor I since v_R is obtained from i by multiplying i by the scalar quantity R. We can therefore write:

$$V_R = IR$$

We saw in frames 32 to 35 that, if there is a current of amplitude I flowing through a capacitor C from a generator of angular frequency ω, then the voltage across the capacitor is of amplitude $IX_c = I/\omega C$ but lagging the current by a phase angle of $\pi/2$. The current i flows through the capacitor in this circuit, therefore the voltage across it lags this current by a phase angle $\pi/2$. But we saw above that the current and the voltage across the resistor are in phase. Therefore the voltage across the capacitor lags the voltage across the resistor by a phase angle $\pi/2$. But, as stated in frame 13, Kirchhoff's Laws hold for instantaneous values of current and voltage in a.c. circuits. So the voltage across the capacitor plus the voltage across the resistor must equal the voltage output of the generator. As shown in frames 14 to 17, this also means that the generator voltage phasor is the phasor sum of the resistor voltage phasor and the capacitor voltage phasor.

Referring to the diagram in frame 16 if necessary, can you draw a phasor diagram to show this? Draw the generator voltage phasor horizontally since we have taken this voltage as $v = V \sin \omega t$. Make sure orthogonal quantities are shown as such, and mark angles and amplitudes with the symbols used above. Do not bother about scales since we have not yet studied how to calculate the values involved. Your diagram will, in fact, be the basis for our calculations. This process is often used in phasor analysis: draw a rough diagram to get a general picture of the relative positions of quantities involved and then re-draw it to scale when some calculations have been done. So, bearing this in mind, can you now draw the initial sketch? When you have done that, use it to write an expression for the instantaneous value of the capacitor voltage v_c.

65

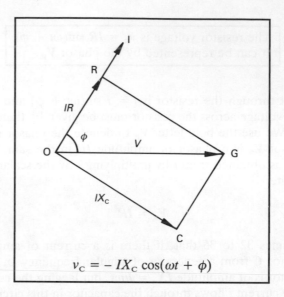

$$v_c = -IX_c \cos(\omega t + \phi)$$

If we first draw a horizontal line OG for the phasor representing the generator voltage we can then draw the line OI representing the current phasor at an angle ϕ to the first line since we have assumed that the current in the circuit leads the generator voltage. We do not know the value of ϕ at this stage so simply draw it as any angle between zero and $\pi/2$. The resistor voltage phasor OR must then be along the line OI since it is in the same direction as the current phasor. The capacitor voltage phasor OC must be at right angles to the resistor voltage phasor so this can be added to the diagram. But, in phasor diagram terms, the lines CG and RG must be the same length as OR and OC and must be equally good representations of the resistor and capacitor voltages respectively. That is, OCG must be a closed figure. In fact, it must be a triangle in which OG represents the generator voltage, OC represents the capacitor voltage and CG represents the resistor voltage. In practice triangles OCG and ORG carry the same information but, as we shall see shortly, triangle OCG is to be preferred when setting out the phasor diagram for the circuit being considered. Values of the terms involved are as shown on the diagram.

From frame 63, we know that the capacitor voltage phasor has amplitude IX_c. It lags the current phasor by $\pi/2$ so has phase relative to v, the generator voltage, of $((\pi/2) - \phi)$. The instantaneous value of v_c is thus:

$$v_c = IX_c \sin(\omega t - ((\pi/2) - \phi)) = IX_c \sin(\omega t + \phi - \pi/2) = -IX_c \cos(\omega t - \phi)$$

Now, because of the geometry of the diagram, we can establish some relationships between the quantities involved in drawing it. What is the relationship between V, I, R and X_c? Remember Pythagoras and make V the subject of the expression.

66

$$\boxed{V = I\sqrt{(R^2 + X_c^2)}}$$

By Pythagoras' Theorem: $V^2 = I^2R^2 + I^2X_c^2 = I^2(R^2 + X_c^2)$, hence
$V = I\sqrt{(R^2 + X_c^2)}$.
But $X_c = 1/\omega C$ so, if we know the values of V, R, C and ω, we can calculate the current amplitude I from the expression:

$$V = I\sqrt{(R^2 + 1/\omega^2 C^2)}$$

THE IMPEDANCE OF A CIRCUIT

The expression $\sqrt{(R^2 + 1/\omega^2 C^2)}$ is given the symbol Z and is called the '*impedance*' of the circuit or the impedance 'seen by the generator'. The term is applied to any circuit made up of a mixture of resistive and reactive components when connected to a source of alternating current or voltage. By definition, the *impedance* of a circuit with a pair of input terminals *is the ratio of the amplitudes of the voltage across the circuit and the current drawn by the circuit* when it is connected to an alternating energy source. This notation leads to another 'Ohm's Law' type of relationship like those in frames 35 and 44 between V and I. Can you write it down?

67

$$\boxed{V = IZ}$$

As with previous expressions of this kind, Z has the dimensions of resistance. Once again this relationship carries no information about the relative phases of the two quantities. Can you now write an expression for the phase angle ϕ between the generator voltage and current?

68

$$\boxed{\tan \phi = X_c/R = 1/\omega CR}$$

From the diagram, $\tan \phi = \text{RG/OR} = IX_c/IR$ hence the above result. In any circuit containing resistive and reactive components ϕ, the angle by which the voltage leads or lags the current, is called the *phase angle of the impedance*. The angle ϕ is positive if the voltage leads the current, negative if the current leads the voltage. Is ϕ positive or negative for the circuit we have just analysed?

69

$$\boxed{\phi \text{ is negative}}$$

We reasoned, in frame 62, that the current led the voltage hence ϕ is negative. To justify this assumption completely we need to relate the phasor diagram to the instantaneous values of the voltages across the resistor, the capacitor and the generator. What is the equation linking the instantaneous values of these three voltages?

70

$$\boxed{V \sin \omega t = IR \sin(\omega t + \phi) - IX_c \cos(\omega t + \phi)}$$

This result is obtained by collecting up the terms from frames 63 and 64. We also have the relationships $V = IZ$ where $Z = \sqrt{(R^2 + X_c^2)}$ and $\tan \phi = X_c/R$ which give $\sin \phi = X_c/Z$ and $\cos \phi = R/Z$. We can prove the above result by expanding the terms in $\sin(\omega t + \phi)$ and $\cos(\omega t + \phi)$ using trigonometrical identities and substituting the above expressions in the one at the beginning of this frame. Try to do this yourself before moving on to the next frame.

71

$$V \sin \omega t = IR \sin(\omega t + \phi) - IX_c \cos(\omega t + \phi)$$

$$= \frac{VR}{Z}(\sin \omega t \cos \phi + \cos \omega t \sin \phi) - \frac{VX_c}{Z}(\cos \omega t \cos \phi - \sin \omega t \sin \phi)$$

$$= \frac{VR}{Z}\left(\frac{R}{Z} \sin \omega t + \frac{X_c}{Z} \cos \omega t\right) - \frac{VX_c}{Z}\left(\frac{R}{Z} \cos \omega t - \frac{X_c}{Z} \sin \omega t\right)$$

$$= \frac{VR^2}{Z^2} \sin \omega t + \frac{VX_c}{Z^2} \sin \omega t$$

$$= V \sin \omega t \frac{(R^2 + X_c^2)}{Z}$$

$$= V \sin \omega t$$

This analysis shows that the left-hand side of the equation in frame 69 does indeed equal the right-hand side, which justifies our initial assumption that the current leads the voltage by a phase angle ϕ in this circuit.

72

A SYMBOLIC NOTATION FOR PHASORS

In frame 69 we obtained an equation by considering the instantaneous values of the voltages across the generator, the resistor and the capacitor. In terms of the symbols for these three quantities we can write:

$$v = v_c + v_R$$

We have also seen that the phasor representations of these three quantities add according to the rules of phasor addition, that is, taking their relative phases into account. We can therefore also write:

$$V = V_c + V_R$$

Suppose we want to relate the phasor V to the phasor I. We have the relationship $V = IZ$ relating the amplitudes but this gives no information about the relative phases. We know, however, from the analysis we have just completed, that V lags I by a phase angle ϕ. We use the following notation to denote this relationship in symbolic terms:

$$V = IZ\underline{/-\phi}$$

We have described ϕ in frame 67 as the phase angle of the impedance. The quantity $Z\underline{/-\phi}$ is thus a kind of 'phasor operator' which can multiply a current phasor I of amplitude I to produce a voltage phasor V of amplitude V (where $V = IZ$) and of phase angle $(-\phi)$ in relation to I. How would you relate the capacitor voltage phasor to the current phasor using this notation?

$$\boxed{V = IX_c \ \underline{/-\pi/2}}$$

The amplitude of the voltage across the capacitor is IX_c and it lags the current phasor by an angle $\pi/2$, hence the above notation.

When dealing with impedances using this notation it is more convenient to regard the current phasor as the reference phasor lying along the horizontal axis and thus representing the function $i = I \sin \omega t$. All information carried by the phasor diagram remains unchanged because phasors give only *relative* relationships. The orientation of the diagram may, however, be affected. Referring back to frame 64 if necessary, can you redraw the phasor diagram for the circuit we have been analysing but with the current taken as reference phasor. What are the corresponding expressions for the instantaneous values of the voltages in the circuit and how are they represented in the symbolic phasor notation?

74

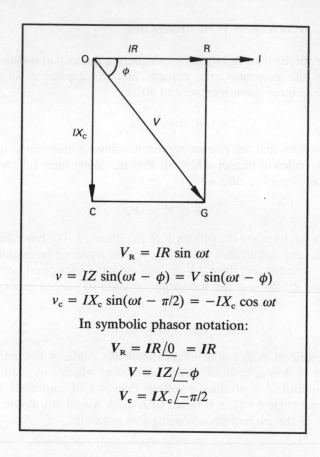

$$V_R = IR \sin \omega t$$

$$v = IZ \sin(\omega t - \phi) = V \sin(\omega t - \phi)$$

$$v_c = IX_c \sin(\omega t - \pi/2) = -IX_c \cos \omega t$$

In symbolic phasor notation:

$$V_R = IR\underline{/0} = IR$$

$$V = IZ\underline{/-\phi}$$

$$V_c = IX_c\underline{/-\pi/2}$$

With the current taken as reference phasor, the diagram is rotated clockwise through an angle ϕ but, otherwise, all lengths and angles are preserved. The instantaneous values all show a phase lag of ϕ compared with the original values but, as we saw in frames 18 to 20, this is, in effect, just shifting the zero-time reference which, in the steady state, makes little difference in practice. The current/voltage relationships in the symbolic phasor notation are unaltered, emphasising the fact that these are relative.

We need one further piece of notation to complete the body of knowledge required to perform steady state analysis of reactive circuits energised by alternating energy sources. It concerns the direction of current flow.

THE CURRENT FLOW CONVENTION IN REACTIVE CIRCUITS

In programme 2, frame 26 we defined a conventional direction for the flow of current in direct current circuits. Direct voltage generators have a positive and a negative terminal and we defined a conventional current as one which flows out of the positive terminal and back into the negative one. When it flows through a resistor it causes a potential difference to be developed across the resistor in such a sense that the more positive potential is at the end of the resistor that the current enters. With alternating voltage generators the potential between the terminals is changing continuously and 'alternates' between positive and negative values. The current thus flows for part of the cycle out of a given terminal and for another part of the cycle into the same terminal. As we have seen, there may also be a phase difference between the current and the voltage depending on the impedance of the circuit to which the generator is connected.

In spite of the differences between d.c. and a.c. circuits, a convention is adopted in a.c. circuits which is very similar to that used in d.c. circuits and which gives correct results when circuit equations are set up using it. Consider again the generator/resistor/capacitor circuit we have just been analysing. A polarity is assigned to the generator as shown on the diagram below. The direction of current flow is taken to be the same as would be consistent with conventional current flowing out of the positive terminal and potentials are considered set up across the components of the circuit with the polarities shown. That is, a positive polarity is assigned to the end of the component into which the current flows.

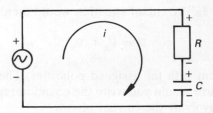

We can then write, for the circuit: $v = v_c + v_R$

This equation is consistent with the assigned polarities of the two voltages. If the current has an instantaneous value i, then $v_R = iR$. If i is taken as the reference waveform we have $v_R = IR \sin \omega t$. We know, however, that the current i is linked to the voltage across the capacitor v_c by the expression $i = C dv_c/dt$. Can you make v_c the subject of this expression?

76

$$v_c = \frac{1}{C} \int i\,dt$$

In steady state analysis, the constant of integration can be ignored. (We shall see how it is taken account of in general in a later programme.) Now, i is the reference current so $i = I \sin \omega t$. What is the expression for v_c?

77

$$v_c = -\frac{I}{\omega C} \cos \omega t$$

As, of course, it must be, this result is consistent with earlier results. The generator voltage can again be equated to the voltages across the resistor and the capacitor. (This appears as an exercise later.)

78

CURRENT FLOW IN PHASOR NOTATION

Now suppose, instead of taking it as an instantaneous value, we choose to think of the current as a phasor I. The circuit equation would then be:

$$V = V_c + V_R$$

This is again consistent with the assigned polarities. The addition, however, is now phasor addition. How would you write the equation replacing each voltage by the appropriate term involving the current phasor?

79

$$IZ \underline{/-\phi} = IX_c \underline{/-\pi/2} + IR$$

All the terms can be found in previous frames. This equation, in fact, leads to a method for constructing the phasor diagram accurately knowing only the voltage amplitude and frequency and the values of the circuit components. This is, in fact, the information usually known in a practical situation. The method of drawing the phasor diagram is given in the next frame.

DRAWING PHASOR DIAGRAMS

1. Draw a horizontal line at a convenient scale to represent the phasor V_R. The length of the line represents a voltage amplitude IR.
2. Draw a vertical line above the first and ending where the first began to represent the phasor V_c. The second line must be to the same scale as the first. Remember that the length of the first line represents a value IR while the length of the second represents a value $I/\omega C$. Since R, ω and C are known, the relative lengths of the two lines are determined.
3. Draw the line joining the ends of these two lines which must represent the generator voltage phasor V to the same scale. Since the length of the generator voltage phasor represents a known voltage amplitude, the scale of the whole diagram is determined. The values of the resistor and capacitor voltages may now be deduced and hence the current amplitude and phase angle.

The triangle constructed corresponds to triangle OCG in frame 64 but rotated so that it has the orientation of frame 73. The sense of addition of phasors on the phasor diagram corresponds with the sense of addition of voltages on the circuit diagram which is why OCG is preferred to ORG in frame 64. Here are the circuit and phasor diagrams again to illustrate this point.

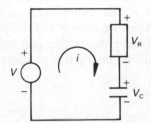 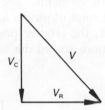

The minus sign on the capacitor is effectively at the same point on the circuit as the minus sign on the generator. The capacitor voltage phasor and the generator voltage phasor start at the same point on the phasor diagram. The highest potential on the resistor is at the same point on the circuit as the highest potential on the generator. The resistor voltage phasor and the generator voltage phasor end at the same point on the phasor diagram. Assigning a definite start and end to each phasor like this provides a consistent notation for drawing phasor diagrams. You can imagine the voltages on the phasor diagram 'following after each other end-to-end' just as the components follow after each other in the circuit diagram. You must, of course, always remember and take account of the relative phases of the different voltages. Now, can you re-draw the circuit diagram with the positions of the resistor and capacitor reversed and then draw the corresponding phasor diagram?

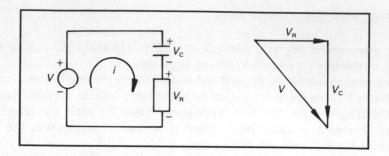

With the same components and generator, the *magnitudes* of the voltages will be as before but their relative positions in the phasor diagram are reversed just as the positions of the components in the circuit diagram are reversed.

A METHODOLOGY FOR DRAWING VOLTAGE PHASOR DIAGRAMS FOR CIRCUITS

In analysing the series R/C circuit we constructed the voltage phasor diagram for it. We were able to do this because it *was* a series circuit and so the current was common to both elements. The voltages across individual components added according to the rules of phasor algebra. When we transposed the positions of the two components, the relative positions of the phasors changed but their magnitudes and directions stayed the same. It will be instructive to study the following diagrams:

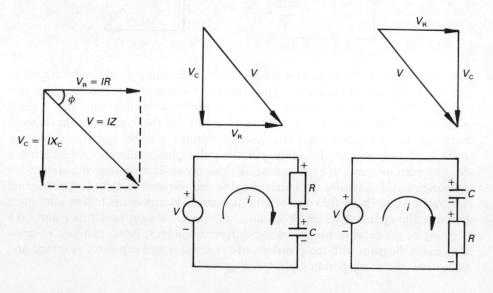

The left-hand phasor diagram serves to define the relative *directions* of all the phasors representing voltages across components in the circuit. We shall henceforth refer to it as the phasor direction-defining diagram. It shows clearly, in particular, that the capacitor voltage phasor lags the resistor voltage phasor by an angle $\pi/2$ and that the generator voltage phasor lags the resistor voltage phasor by an angle ϕ. The basis of the diagram is the current phasor which is taken as the reference phasor and drawn horizontally from left to right. The arrows on the phasors indicate the positive ends of the voltage phasors with respect to the assigned direction of the current phasor. Amplitudes of the phasors are shown in terms of the amplitude of the current phasor and the impedances in the circuit.

The centre phasor diagram corresponds to the circuit diagram below it. With the usual convention for polarities and current flow direction, the capacitor is at a lower potential than the resistor so the sense of the arrows is such that the resistor voltage phasor adds on to the end of the capacitor voltage phasor, the two phasors summing to the generator voltage phasor. Notice, however, that all phasors are in the directions determined by the diagram on the left.

The right-hand phasor diagram also corresponds to the circuit diagram below it. Again with the usual convention, the capacitor is at a higher potential than the resistor so the sense of the arrows is such that the capacitor voltage phasor adds on to the end of the resistor voltage phasor, the two phasors again summing to the generator voltage phasor. Again, all phasors are in the directions determined by the diagram on the left.

Do not worry that the arrows on the phasor diagram point down or across the page whereas the assigned potentials on the diagram are from top to bottom. You can imagine the phasor diagram rotated so that the generator phasor points up the page if you wish. The important thing is to make sure that corresponding 'tops' and 'bottoms' of phasors are in the right relative positions. For reasons which will become clear in a later programme, it is best to memorise the relative positions of the phasors from the phasor direction-defining diagram.

Now, here is a numerical problem for you to try. Draw the phasor diagram to scale and calculate the current amplitude and its phase relative to the generator voltage for a generator with an output of amplitude 3 volts at a frequency of $1000/2\pi$ Hz connected in series with a resistor of value $3 \text{ k}\Omega$ and a capacitor of value $0.25 \text{ }\mu\text{F}$, one end of the resistor being connected to the 'negative' side of the generator. What are the amplitudes of the voltages across the resistor and the capacitor, and what are their phases relative to the generator voltage?

82

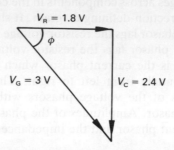

$V_R = 1.8$ V

ϕ

$V_G = 3$ V $V_c = 2.4$ V

$I = 0.6$ mA, $\phi = \arctan 4/3 = 53.13°$, current leading voltage
$V_R = 1.8$ V leading V_G by ϕ, $V_c = 2.4$ V lagging V_G by $((\pi/2) - \phi)$

$$f = \frac{1000}{2\pi} \text{ Hz} \quad \text{so} \quad \omega = 1000$$

Thus $X_c = \dfrac{1}{\omega C} = \dfrac{1}{1000 \times 0.25 \times 10^{-6}} = 4 \times 10^{-3}$ and $R = 3 \times 10^{-3}$

so the right-angled triangle has one side of 4 units and one of 3 units.

The hypotenuse must therefore be 5 units and this represents the generator voltage amplitude of 3 volts.

Thus $V_R = \dfrac{3 \times 3}{5} = 1.8 \ V$ and $V_c = \dfrac{3 \times 4}{5} = 2.4 \ V$

$I_R = \dfrac{1.8}{3000} = 0.6$ mA, $\arctan \phi = \dfrac{4}{3}$ so $\phi = 53.13°$

The diagram in frame 81 gives the lead/lag relationships.

It is also instructive to study the way in which the phasor diagram changes as the frequency of the applied voltage changes, the amplitude and the values of the components remaining the same. We will do this in the next frame.

83

CHANGES IN IMPEDANCE WITH FREQUENCY

Some interesting points can be noted from the following diagram:

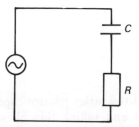
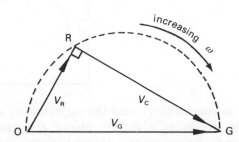

The generator voltage phasor has been drawn horizontal in this diagram because we are using it as the reference phasor in this piece of analysis. Suppose that, in a practical situation, we connect an alternating voltage generator into this circuit and vary its frequency from very low to very high values while keeping the voltage amplitude constant. Whatever the frequency, the generator voltage phasor can be represented by the same line (OG in the diagram). The capacitor voltage phasor (RG in the diagram) and the resistor voltage phasor (OR in the diagram) are at right angles to each other and meet at R. They must always sum to the generator voltage phasor. In the diagram the point R is at the apex of a right-angled triangle with its hypotenuse as base, so all points such as R for all values of frequency must lie on a semicircle with OG as diameter. (Remember the geometrical theorem which states that the 'angle in a semicircle is a right angle'.)

The CR combination may be thought of as a 'potential divider of alternating voltages' where OR and RG represent the 'components' of the generator voltage across the resistor and capacitor respectively. The position of R 'moves' round the semicircle in the direction shown as ω increases. When ω is zero (that is, for direct current), R is coincident with O and so all the generator voltage appears across the capacitor and there is no voltage across the resistor. As ω increases the capacitor voltage phasor decreases in size, the resistor voltage phasor increases in size and, for very large ω (that is, at very high frequencies), R becomes nearly coincident with G and therefore most of the generator voltage appears across the resistor and very little across the capacitor.

We may also say that, at very high frequencies, the impedance of the capacitor is negligible compared with that of the resistor. A capacitor 'looks like a short-circuit' at very high frequencies. At very low frequencies, the impedance of the resistor is negligible compared with that of the capacitor. A capacitor 'looks like an open-circuit' at very low frequencies.

84

THE SERIES RESISTOR/INDUCTOR CIRCUIT

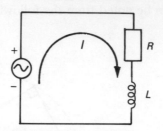

We can analyse this circuit the same way we analysed the series resistor/capacitor circuit. Assigning a current phasor I to the circuit and taking this phasor as reference, we can write a phasor voltage equation:

$$V = V_L + V_R$$

where the sense of the voltages relative to the direction of the current follows the notation introduced in frames 74 to 78.

Can you draw the diagram defining the relative directions of the current and voltage phasors and, from it, the phasor diagram for this circuit? By comparison with frame 78 if necessary, write an expression for each voltage in terms of the current phasor. Use Z and ϕ for the impedance of the circuit and its phase angle but do not evaluate Z and ϕ yet. What are the corresponding expressions for the instantaneous values of the voltages?

85

$$V_R = IR\underline{/0} \ = IR \qquad V_G = IZ\underline{/\phi} \qquad V = IX_L\underline{/\pi/2}$$

$$V_R = IR \sin \omega t$$

$$V_G = IZ \sin(\omega t + \phi) = V \sin(\omega t + \phi)$$

$$V_L = IX_L \sin(\omega t + \pi/2) = IX_L \cos \omega t$$

The inductor voltage and the generator voltage both lead the current and therefore also lead the resistor voltage. The phase angle ϕ is thus positive. Can you now write expressions for Z and ϕ in terms of R, L and ω?

$$\boxed{Z = \sqrt{(R^2 + \omega^2 L^2)}, \quad \tan \phi = \omega L / R}$$

An inductor has an impedance $X_L = \omega L$

The sides of the right-angled triangle can be written as IR, IX_L and IZ.

Hence $(IZ)^2 = (IR)^2 + (IX_L)^2$ so $Z^2 = R^2 + \omega^2 L^2$ and

$$Z = \sqrt{(R^2 + \omega^2 L^2)}$$

$$\text{Tan } \phi = IX_L / IR = X_L / R = \omega L / R$$

Can you draw a diagram similar to the one in frame 82 to show how the relative voltages across the two components vary with frequency? Regarding this circuit as a potential divider of alternating voltages, how does the generator voltage divide between the two components at high and low frequencies?

87

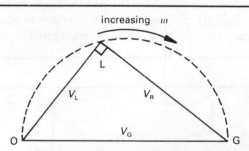

High frequency: most of the generator voltage appears across the inductor
Low frequency: most of the generator voltage appears across the resistor

---

Again the generator voltage phasor has been drawn horizontal in this diagram because we are using it as the reference phasor. The resistor voltage phasor and the inductor voltage phasor are at right angles and again sum to the generator voltage phasor. As ω increases the inductor voltage phasor gets longer as the resistor voltage phasor gets shorter, so for high frequencies most of the generator voltage appears across the inductor whereas at low frequencies most of the generator voltage appears across the resistor. At very high frequencies, the impedance of the resistor is negligible compared with that of the inductor. At very low frequencies, the impedance of the inductor is negligible compared with that of the resistor. A direct voltage 'sees' an inductor as a short-circuit, so these last statements are consistent with previous results.

88

THE SERIES INDUCTOR/CAPACITOR CIRCUIT

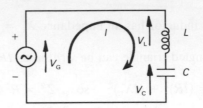

Analysis of this circuit yields some quite surprising results. Assigning a current phasor I to the circuit and taking this phasor as reference, we can, as before, write a phasor voltage equation:

$$V_G = V_C + V_L$$

Without, at this stage trying to calculate the relative sizes of the capacitor and inductor voltage phasors, can you draw the phasor diagram for this circuit? Draw the phasor direction-defining diagram first with the current phasor horizontal from left to right and deduce the voltage phasor diagram from it.

89

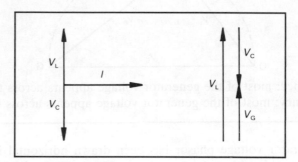

On the phasor direction-defining diagram we can show that the capacitor and inductor voltage phasors are both at right angles to the current phasor and in the same straight line but out of phase with each other by a phase angle π. To form the voltage phasor diagram we see that the generator voltage phasor must be equal in amplitude to the inductor voltage amplitude minus the capacitor voltage amplitude. Now write the algebraic equation relating these amplitudes, expressing the voltages in terms of the current amplitude I, the component values C and L and the frequency ω.

90

$$V_G = \omega LI - I/\omega C = I(\omega L - 1/\omega C)$$

You could justifiably have the signs in this equation reversed but, since the inductor voltage leads the current and is therefore plotted upwards from the origin, it is in the direction commonly taken as positive in most coordinate systems. The most important fact is that the inductor and capacitor voltages have opposite signs.

What is the impedance Z of this circuit?

91

$$Z = \omega L - 1/\omega C$$

By definition, impedance is the ratio of V and I, so the expression follows directly from the one in frame 89.

In answering the next question, bear in mind that this circuit is made up of ideal components. Problems using ideal components can sometimes result in mathematical results which are impossible in practice. As we have seen before, however, ideal components are very useful in helping us to model practical components. Now, what is the value of Z when $w = \sqrt{(1/LC)}$ and what is the current at this value of Z?

92

$$\text{When } \omega = \sqrt{(1/LC)}, Z = 0$$
$$\text{When } Z = 0, I = \infty$$

Substituting $w = \sqrt{(1/LC)}$ in the expression for Z in frame 90 gives $Z = \sqrt{(LC)} -\sqrt{(LC)} = 0$. Since V_G, the generator voltage amplitude, is non-zero and $I = V_G/Z$, then I must be infinite. Infinite currents and voltages cannot occur in practice because they imply infinite energy sources but, because these are ideal components, this infinity is mathematically correct.

Can you think of a reason why, in a practical circuit, this infinite current would not be possible? Does the circuit, as it is drawn in frame 87, represent something which could be wired up using real components?

93

> All practical circuits will contain some resistance which must limit the maximum current that can flow. If the circuit in frame 87 was wired up using real components, the wires joining them together would present a small but non-zero resistance.

It is worth bearing in mind, when working with real components, that they generally exhibit all three circuit properties of resistance, capacitance and inductance when used in real circuits. The leads of all components will be both resistive and inductive. There will inevitably be 'stray' capacitance between adjacent components on a circuit board or between a component and connections on the board. The skill you must try to develop is to recognise when one or other of these properties is negligible for the purposes of the analysis you wish to carry out.

If, however, we continue at present with the analysis of the ideal circuit in frame 87, what will be the values of the voltages across the capacitor and the inductor when $\omega = \sqrt{(1/LC)}$?

94

> Both voltages will be infinite

Once again we have a physically impossible situation brought about by the ideal components. Even with practical components we can deduce that the voltages across the capacitor and the inductor can be very much greater than the generator voltage in this circuit when $\omega = \sqrt{(1/LC)}$. Since this circuit can act as a voltage magnifier for a particular value of frequency, it is sometimes spoken of as a frequency-selective circuit. Such circuits are widely used in amplifier and filter design.

The property being exhibited by the circuit is called *resonance* and the value of ω at which resonance occurs is called the resonant frequency. It is of great importance in many branches of electrical and electronic circuit design and also occurs in mechanical systems. We shall come across several more examples of it in this text but, since whole books have been written about it, we shall not give it a full treatment.

The phase properties of the circuit are also of interest, particularly in the neighbourhood of the resonant frequency. Can you say what happens to the phase angle between the generator voltage and current when $\omega > \sqrt{(1/LC)}$ and when $\omega < \sqrt{(1/LC)}$?

When $\omega > \sqrt{(1/LC)}$, $\phi = +\pi/2$ When $\omega < \sqrt{(1/LC)}$, $\phi = -\pi/2$

Here is the phasor direction diagram again, together with graphs of impedance against frequency and the phase angle of the impedance against frequency for the circuit:

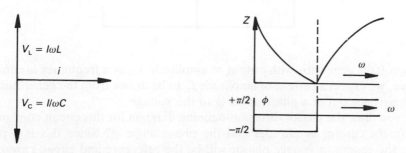

When $\omega > \sqrt{(1/LC)}$ then ωL, the reactance of the inductor, is greater than $1/\omega C$, the reactance of the capacitor. Hence V_L, the inductor voltage phasor, is longer than V_c, the capacitor voltage phasor, and the phasor representing the generator voltage is drawn upwards from the origin. It is thus at a phase angle $\pi/2$ in advance of (or leading) the current phasor. When $\omega < \sqrt{(1/LC)}$ then ωL, the reactance of the inductor, is less than $1/\omega C$, the reactance of the capacitor. Hence V_L, the inductor voltage phasor, is shorter than V_c, the capacitor voltage phasor, and the phasor representing the generator voltage is drawn downwards from the origin. It is thus at a phase angle $\pi/2$ behind (or lagging) the current phasor.

When $\omega > \sqrt{(1/LC)}$ and the inductor predominates, the circuit is said to 'look inductive'. It behaves approximately as an inductor. The greater the frequency becomes, the closer is this approximation met. When $\omega < \sqrt{(1/LC)}$ and the capacitor predominates, the circuit is said to 'look capacitive'. It behaves approximately as a capacitor. The lower the frequency becomes, the closer is this approximation met.

It is instructive to look at the above graphs for this circuit. Both graphs are discontinuous at the resonant frequency. The impedance graph shows a decreasing impedance as frequency increases from low values to the resonant frequency at which point the theoretical value zero is reached. Over this region the phase is everywhere $-\pi/2$. From the resonant frequency onwards, the impedance increases with frequency. The phase graph shows a step function at the resonant frequency, jumping to a value of $+\pi/2$ above it. It is emphasised again that this unusual behaviour is a result of using ideal components in the circuit. In a real circuit, the discontinuities would be replaced by smooth (but steep!) transitions.

96

THE PARALLEL RESISTOR/CAPACITOR CIRCUIT

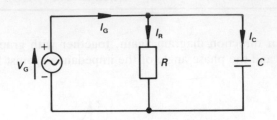

With a voltage generator with output of amplitude V_G at a frequency ω connected as above, we expect a current of amplitude I_G to be drawn from the generator at the same frequency but at a phase angle ϕ to the voltage.

Can you draw the phasor direction-defining diagram for this circuit configuration showing the current amplitudes and the phase angle ϕ? Since this is a parallel circuit, the generator *voltage* phasor will be the reference and circuit <u>currents</u> will be shown relative to it.

97

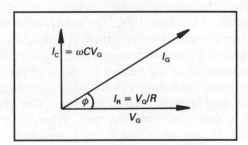

The generator voltage phasor V_G, drawn horizontally, is common to the generator, the resistor and the capacitor. The resistor current is in the same direction as this phasor and is of length V_G/R. The capacitor current leads the voltage phasor by an angle $\pi/2$ and is of length $V_G/(1/\omega C) = V_G\omega C$. The generator current must be the sum of the resistor and capacitor currents, so is at an angle ϕ leading the generator voltage.

Can you now draw the current phasor diagram and write an expression for the generator current amplitude in terms of the known component values, voltage amplitude and frequency? Remembering that $V_G = I_G Z$, can you then deduce the impedance of the circuit and its phase angle?

98

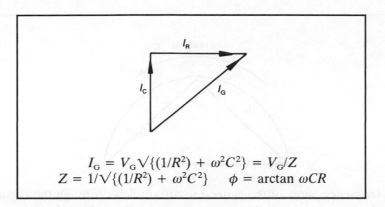

$$I_G = V_G\sqrt{\{(1/R^2) + \omega^2 C^2\}} = V_G/Z$$
$$Z = 1/\sqrt{\{(1/R^2) + \omega^2 C^2\}} \qquad \phi = \arctan \omega CR$$

All the quantities above are calculated from the properties of the right-angled triangle. It is sometimes convenient, in parallel circuits, to work with the reciprocals of impedance, resistance and reactance. These are respectively admittance $Y = 1/Z$, conductance $G = 1/R$ and susceptance $B = 1/X$.

Can you write an expression for Y in terms of R, ω and C, and then rewrite it in terms of G and B_c for the above circuit? Can you also then write expressions for the phasor V_G in terms of the impedance operator Z and its phase angle, and for the phasor I_G in terms of the 'admittance operator' Y and its phase angle.

99

$$Y = \sqrt{\{(1/R^2) + \omega^2 C^2\}} = \sqrt{\{G^2 + B_c^2\}}$$
$$V_G = ZI_G\underline{/-\phi} \qquad I_G = YV_G\underline{/+\phi}$$

Since $Y = 1/Z$, the first expression above comes directly from the first two expressions in frame 98. But $G = 1/R$ and $B_c = \omega C$ which gives the second expression for Y. The phasor expression $V_G = ZI_G\underline{/-\phi}$ embodies both the first and the third of the expressions in frame 98. Since $Y = 1/Z$ and $Z = V/I$, then $Y = I/V$. Thus $I = YV$. But I_G leads V_G as seen from the phasor diagram so, in phasor terms, $I_G = YV_G\underline{/+\phi}$. Since the phase angle of the impedance operator Z is negative, then the phase angle of the admittance operator Y is positive.

Can you now draw a diagram similar to the ones in frames 83 and 87 to show how changes in frequency affect the values of some of the quantities in the equations above? Think carefully which properties of the circuit can be illustrated in this kind of diagram.

100

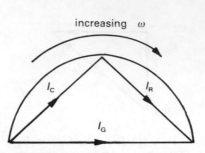

High frequency: most of the generator current flows through the capacitor
Low frequency: most of the generator current flows through the resistor

The appropriate diagram here is the current phasor diagram because it is the division of generator current between the capacitor and the resistor which varies with frequency. The generator current phasor has been drawn horizontally in this diagram because we are using it as the reference phasor. The resistor current phasor and the capacitor current phasor are at right angles and sum to the generator current phasor. As ω increases, the capacitor current phasor gets longer as the resistor current phasor gets shorter, so for high frequencies most of the generator current flows through the capacitor while at low frequencies most of the generator current flows through the resistor.

Since we have now carried out this kind of analysis several times, see if you can do the whole thing yourself for the parallel resistor/inductor circuit shown below before checking the results in the next frame.

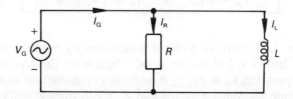

Draw the phasor direction-determining diagram and then the current phasor diagram. Use this diagram to write down the relationship between the currents in the circuit in phasor form, then deduce the amplitudes and relative phases of the voltage and currents. Write expressions for the impedance and admittance of the circuit and, finally, draw a diagram to show how the size of the currents through the two components varies with frequency.

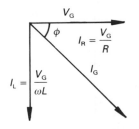 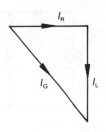

$$I_G = I_R + I_L$$

where $I_G = I_G\underline{/\phi}$ $I_R = I_R\underline{/0}$ $I_L = I_L\underline{/-\pi/2}$ when $V_G = V_G\underline{/0}$

and $I_R = V_G/R$ and $I_L = V_G/\omega L$

From the diagram $I_G = V_G\sqrt{\{(1/R^2) + (1/\omega^2 L^2)\}} = V_G/Z$

Thus $Y = \sqrt{\{(1/R^2) + (1/\omega^2 L^2)\}} = \sqrt{\{G^2 + B_L^2\}}$

$$\phi = \arctan R/\omega L$$

$$V_G = I_G Z\underline{/+\phi}$$

$$I_G = V_G Y\underline{/-\phi}$$

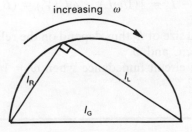

increasing ω

Low frequency: most of the generator current flows through the inductor
High frequency: most of the generator current flows through the resistor

All these results follow from recognising that the generator voltage is common to both components, so it and the resistor current (which it thus defines) can be taken as the reference phasors. The other phasors can thus be drawn and the calculations performed with reference to the diagrams.

We will complete the set of two-component parallel circuits by analysing a parallel inductor/capacitor circuit energised by a voltage generator. Can you draw the circuit and the phasor direction defining diagram?

102

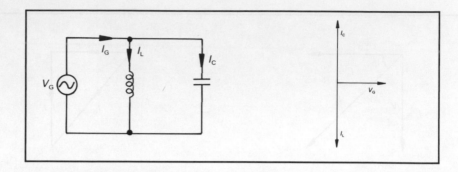

We have a similar situation here to the case of the same two components in series, but this time it is the currents which are in antiphase with each other (that is, out of phase by an angle π) and both are out of phase with the generator voltage by an angle $\pi/2$. Since the generator voltage phasor is common to both components, we choose it to define the reference direction. The capacitor current phasor is then drawn upwards and the inductor current phasor downwards to give them the correct orientation with respect to the reference phasor. The generator current is the difference between the two component currents and is itself out of phase with the generator voltage by an angle $\pi/2$. In terms of the three current amplitudes we thus have:

$$I_G = I_L - I_C = \{(1/\omega L) - \omega C\}V_G = (B_L - B_C)V_G$$

The resultant sign and size of I_G thus depend on the relative sizes of I_L and I_C and thus on the values of L, C and ω.

What happens to the circuit impedance when $\omega = 1/\sqrt{(LC)}$? How would you describe this frequency?

103

> Z is infinite when $\omega = 1/\sqrt{(LC)}$
>
> This is the resonant frequency of the circuit

By definition, Z is the ratio of the generator voltage amplitude to the generator current amplitude. That is, $Z = V_G/I_G$.

But $I_G = 0$ when $\omega = 1/\sqrt{(LC)}$, so Z is infinite if the size of V_G is fixed.

By comparison with frame 95 if necessary, can you plot graphs of the variation with frequency of the impedance and the phase of V_G relative to I_G?

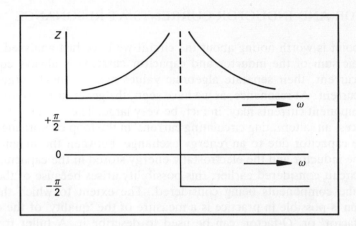

Z varies with frequency according to the expression:

$$Z = \frac{V}{I} = \frac{1}{(1/\omega L) - \omega C}$$

For very small values of ω, the term ωC is very small but the term $1/\omega L$ is very large, so Z tends to zero.

For very large values of ω the term $1/\omega L$ is very small but the term ωC is very large, so again Z tends to zero.

The infinity at $\omega = 1/\sqrt{(LC)}$ is therefore approached from both sides.

The phase diagram is best obtained by looking again at the phasor direction defining diagram. Here it is:

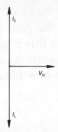

When $\omega = 1/\sqrt{(LC)}$, the lengths of the two current phasors are equal. When $\omega < 1/\sqrt{(LC)}$, the length of the inductor current phasor is greater and that of the capacitor current phasor less. The phase angle of the resultant current is thus $\pi/2$ so the circuit 'looks inductive'.

When $\omega > 1/\sqrt{(LC)}$, the length of the capacitor current phasor is greater and that of the inductor current phasor less. The phase angle of the resultant current is thus $-\pi/2$ so the circuit 'looks capacitive'.

105

CAPACITOR AND INDUCTOR CURRENTS AT RESONANCE

One final point is worth noting about the circuit we have just analysed. Although the algebraic sum of the inductor and capacitor currents is always equal to the generator current, their separate algebraic values may be much larger than the generator current. At resonance, as we have seen, the generator current is zero but the two component currents may, in fact, be very large. There could exist, in these circumstances, an 'alternating circulating current' in the loop comprising the inductor and the capacitor due to an 'energy exchange' between the magnetic energy stored in the inductor and the electrostatic energy stored in the capacitor. As with the series circuit considered earlier, this possibility arises because of the idealised nature of the components being considered. The extent to which this kind of phenomenon is possible in practice is a measure of the 'quality' of the circuit and a 'quality factor' or 'Q-factor' can be used to describe it. A fuller treatment of this topic belongs in a discourse on resonance which is not being treated in detail in this text.

106

SERIES–PARALLEL CIRCUITS

We have seen, in the last few examples, that, when constructing phasor diagrams, the current is used as the reference phasor in series circuits but the voltage in parallel circuits. This information may be used in constructing phasor diagrams for series–parallel circuits and may, in fact, be extended to quite complicated circuits. Keeping track of the relative positions of all the phasors becomes a considerable problem, however, as the size of the circuit increases.

A technique which overcomes many of these problems by the use of complex number notation is introduced in the next programme. Meanwhile there follows a summary of the important ideas in this programme. Make sure you have mastered these by completing the revision questions and the test exercise, and you will be in a strong position to understand the new ideas in the following programmes.

SUMMARY

1. A periodic function of the form $v(t) = v(t + T)$ is characterised by a number of parameters: its peak value, its peak-to-peak value, its period, its frequency, its mean value and its root mean square (r.m.s.) value. Its mean and r.m.s. values are expressed as:

$$v_{mean} = \frac{1}{T} \int_t^{t+T} v(t)dt \qquad v_{rms} = \sqrt{\left\{ \frac{1}{T} \int_t^{t+T} (v(t))^2 dt \right\}}$$

2. An alternating function is a periodic function whose mean value is zero. An alternating sine voltage can be written as $v(t) = V_p \sin \omega t$. It has a peak value (or amplitude) V_p; a peak-to-peak value $2V_p$; a period $2\pi/\omega$; a frequency $\omega/2\pi$; a mean value of zero; and an r.m.s. value of $V_p/\sqrt{2}$.

3. Phasor diagrams are used to show the relative amplitude and phase relationships of sinewaves having the same frequency. Phasors can be associated with the radii of circles from which the sinewaves can be generated. If two sinewaves are described by the expressions $v_1 = V \sin \omega t$ and $v_2 = V' \sin (\omega t + \phi)$, they are said to be 'out of phase' by the angle ϕ. v_2 is said to 'lead' v_1 by the phase angle ϕ. v_1 is said to 'lag' v_2 by the phase angle ϕ. If lines representing V and V' are drawn to scale from the same point O with an angle ϕ between them as two adjacent sides of a parallelogram, the diagonal of a parallelogram drawn from the common point will generate a sinewave representing the sum of v_1 and v_2 as the three phasors rotate anticlockwise at an angular frequency ω to form circles with centre O.

4. Circuits used to 'process' sinusoidal voltage and current waveforms are made from alternating voltage and current generators together with 'reactive' components called capacitors and inductors. These components have the following main properties:

4.1(a) A capacitor consists basically of two pieces of conducting material – the plates – separated by insulating materials – the dielectric. Energy is stored in capacitors electrostatically. In terms of externally observable phenomena, changing currents flow through capacitors. Capacitors appear as open circuits to direct current.

4.1(b) An inductor consists basically of a coil of wire wound onto a former in order to produce a magnetic field when a current flows in the wire. Energy is stored in the field associated with the inductor electromagnetically. Inductors appear as short-circuits to direct current.

4.2(a) The charge q on and voltage v across a capacitor are linked by the equation:

$$C = q/v \qquad \text{The unit of capacitance is the farad.}$$

When the current through and the voltage across a capacitor are changing, the two quantities are linked by the equation:

$$i = C dv/dt$$

4.2(b) When the current through and the voltage across an inductor are changing, the two quantities are linked by the equation:

$$v = L di/dt \qquad \text{The unit of inductance is the Henry.}$$

4.3(a) The energy W stored by a capacitor when the voltage between its plates is V is given by the equation:

$$W = (CV^2)/2$$

4.3(b) The energy W stored by an inductor when the current through it is I is given by the equation:

$$W = (LI^2)/2$$

4.4(a) When an alternating voltage generator $v = V \sin \omega t$ is connected to a capacitor to form a closed circuit, the current flowing in the circuit is $i = \omega CV \cos \omega t$. The two quantities can be represented on a phasor diagram, the current phasor leading the voltage phasor as shown below left.

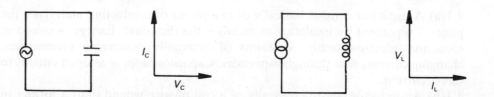

4.4(b) When an alternating current generator $i = I \sin \omega t$ is connected to an inductor to form a closed circuit, the voltage developed across the inductor is $v = \omega LI \cos \omega t$. The two quantities can be represented on a phasor diagram, the voltage phasor leading the current phasor as shown above right.

4.5(a) The reactance of a capacitor energised by an alternating generator is the ratio of the voltage amplitude V to the current amplitude I where:

$$V/I = X_c = 1/\omega C$$

4.5(b) The reactance of an inductor energised by an alternating generator is the ratio of the voltage amplitude V to the current amplitude I where:

$$V/I = X_L = \omega L$$

4.6(a) When a source of alternating voltage $v = V \sin \omega t$ is connected to a capacitor to form a closed circuit, power ebbs and flows between the generator and the capacitor. The instantaneous power is given by the equation:

$$p = (\omega C V^2/2) \sin 2\omega t \quad \text{An ideal capacitor does not dissipate power.}$$

4.6(b) When a source of alternating current $i = I \sin \omega t$ is connected to an inductor to form a closed circuit, power ebbs and flows between the generator and the inductor. The instantaneous power is given by the equation:

$$p = (\omega L I^2/2) \sin 2\omega t \quad \text{An ideal inductor does not dissipate power.}$$

5. Power and r.m.s. values of voltage and current.
    5.1 The r.m.s. value of a voltage or current is that value which would produce the same heating effect (power dissipation) in a resistor as a direct voltage or current having the same numerical value.
    5.2 A measuring instrument calibrated in r.m.s. values gives a true r.m.s. reading for all waveforms only if its movement is sensitive to the heating effect of the quantity being measured.
6. The impedance of circuits containing resistive and reactive components. If a circuit having a pair of terminals A and B is made up of resistive and reactive components and a sinusoidal voltage $V \sin \omega t$ connected to the terminals causes a current $I \sin (\omega t + \phi)$ to flow through the circuit via the terminals, then the circuit has an 'impedance' Z where $Z = V/I$. The angle ϕ is a measure of the 'phase difference' between the applied voltage and the current drawn, and is called the 'phase angle' of the impedance.

7. Phasor diagrams of circuits with resistive and reactive components.
   The relative amplitudes and phase relationships of currents and voltages in resistive/reactive circuits is readily shown on a phasor diagram of the circuit. The impedance of the circuit can also be deduced from the diagram. The relationships for the following two-component circuits are important:

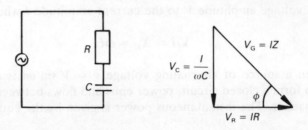

For the series RC circuit, $Z = \sqrt{(R^2 + 1/\omega^2 C^2)}$, $\tan \phi = 1/\omega CR$.

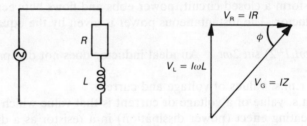

For the series RL circuit, $Z = \sqrt{(R^2 + \omega^2 L^2)}$, $\tan \phi = \omega L/R$.

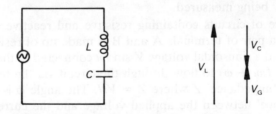

For the series LC circuit, $Z = \omega L - 1/\omega C$, $\phi = \pm\pi/2$.
When $\omega = 1/\sqrt{(LC)}$, $Z = 0$ and the circuit is said to be 'resonant'.

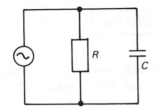 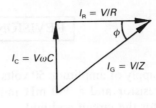

For the parallel RC circuit, $Z = 1/\{(1/R^2) + \omega^2 C^2\}$, $\tan \phi = \omega CR$.

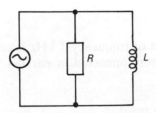 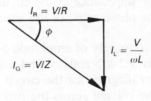

For the parallel RL circuit, $Z = 1/(1/R^2) + (1/\omega^2 L^2)$, $\tan \phi = R/\omega L$.

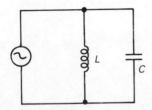 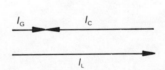

For the parallel LC circuit, $Z = 1/\{1/\omega L - \omega C\}$, $\phi = \pm\pi/2$.
When $\omega = 1/\sqrt{(LC)}$, $Z = \infty$ and the circuit is said to be 'resonant'.

REVISION QUESTIONS

1. An a.c. supply of amplitude 50 volts and of frequency 1 kHz is connected across a 2 kΩ resistor and a 300 mH inductor connected in series. Draw a phasor diagram for the circuit and find:
   (a) the current in the circuit
   (b) the amplitude of the voltage across the resistor
   (c) the amplitude of the voltage across the inductor
   (d) the impedance of the circuit
   (e) the phase angle of the impedance.

2. An a.c. supply of amplitude 5 milliamps and of frequency 1 kHz is connected across a 2 kΩ resistor and a 100 nF capacitor connected in parallel. Draw a phasor diagram for the circuit and find:
   (a) the voltage across the two components
   (b) the amplitude of the current through the resistor
   (c) the amplitude of the current through the capacitor
   (d) the impedance of the circuit
   (e) the phase angle of the impedance.

3. Superimpose phasor diagrams on each other for the meshes in the circuit below containing (i) the generator, R_1 and C_1 and (ii) the generator, R_2 and C_2 using the same line to represent the generator voltage for each mesh. Take care to show a general case and draw a line on the diagram which represents the voltage from A to B. Deduce conditions for the voltage from A to B to be (a) zero and (b) in phase with the generator voltage.

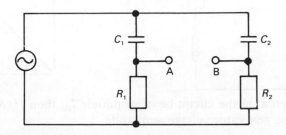

4. Draw the phasor diagram for the circuit below. Under what conditions will the generator voltage be in phase with the resistor voltage? How would you describe this condition? What is the impedance of the circuit and what is its value when the above condition holds?

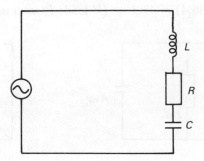

ANSWERS TO REVISION QUESTIONS

1.

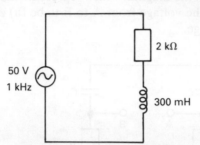 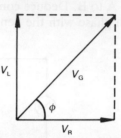

(a) Let the current in the circuit be of amplitude I_G, then $I_G^2(R^2 + \omega^2 L^2) = V_G^2$ where V_G is the generator voltage amplitude.

$$\text{So } I_G = \sqrt{\left\{ \frac{50^2}{4 \times 10^6 + 4\pi^2 \times 10^6 \times 9 \times 10^{-2}} \right\}} = 18.2 \times 10^{-3} = 18.2 \text{ mA}$$

(b) $V_R = 2 \times 10^3 \times 18.2 \times 10^{-3} = 36.4$ V
(c) $V_L = 2\pi \times 10^3 \times 300 \times 10^{-3} \times 18.2 \times 10^{-3} = 34.3$ V
(d) $Z = \sqrt{(R^2 + \omega^2 L^2)} = \sqrt{(4 \times 10^6 + 4\pi^2 \times 10^6 \times 9 \times 10^{-2})} = 2.75$ kΩ
(e) $\phi = \arctan(34.3/36.4) = 43.3°$ (*V* leads *I*, so ϕ is positive)

2.

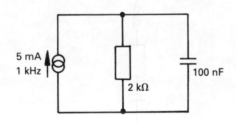 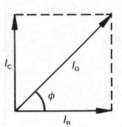

(a) Let the voltage across the circuit be of amplitude V_G, then $V_G^2\{(1/R^2) + \omega^2 C^2\} = I_G^2$ where I_G is the generator current.

$$\text{So } V_G = \sqrt{\left\{ \frac{5^2 \times 10^{-6}}{(1/4) \times 10^{-6} + 4\pi^2 \times 10^6 \times 10^4 \times 10^{-18}} \right\}} = 6.23 \text{ V}$$

(b) $I_R = 6.23/(2 \times 10^3) = 3.12$ mA
(c) $I_C = 6.23 \times 2\pi \times 10^3 \times 100 \times 10^{-9} = 3.91$ mA
(d) $Z = 1/\sqrt{\{(1/R^2) + \omega^2 C^2\}} = 1/\sqrt{\{(1/4) \times 10^{-6} + 4\pi^2 \times 10^6 \times 10^4 \times 10^{-18}\}}$
   $= 1.25$ kΩ
(e) $\phi = \arctan(3.91/3.12) = 51.4°$

3.

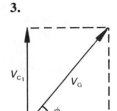 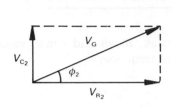 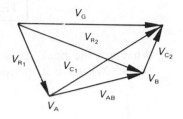

(a) By inspection of the phasor diagram, $V_{AB} = 0$ if $V_{R_1} = V_{R_2}$ and $V_{C_1} = V_{C_2}$. If the currents in the two branches are I_1 and I_2, this implies:

$$I_1 R_1 = I_2 R_2 \quad \text{and} \quad I_1/\omega C_1 = I_2/\omega C_2$$

Dividing these two equations gives $C_1 R_1 = C_2 R_2$.

(b) V_{AB} is in phase with V_G if the phasor V_{AB} is parallel to the phasor V_G.

Then $\arctan \phi_1 = \arctan(90 - \phi_2)$ so $V_{C_1}/V_{R_1} = V_{R_2}/V_{C_2}$

Thus $I_1/(\omega C_1 \times I_1 R_1) = I_2 R_2 \times \omega C_2/I_2$ so $\omega^2 = 1/C_1 C_2 R_1 R_2$ and $\omega = 1/\sqrt{(C_1 C_2 R_1 R_2)}$

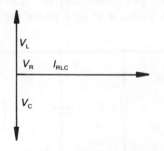 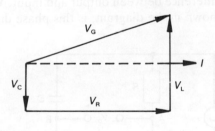

The phasor directions shown in the diagram on the left will be the same whatever the values of L, R and C. The lengths of the phasors will depend on the relative values of these components and the values of V_G and of ω.

In the phasor diagram on the right, note that V_L follows V_R which follows V_C with right angles as shown and the three phasors summing to V_G.

V_R is in phase with V_G when these two phasors are parallel, so $V_C = V_L$. Then $I_G \omega L = I_G/\omega C$ so $\omega L = 1/\omega C$ and $\omega = 1/\sqrt{(LC)}$. This is resonance.

$$Z = V_G/I_G = [\sqrt{\{(V_L - V_C)^2 + V_R^2\}}]/I_G = [\sqrt{\{(I_G \omega L - I_G/\omega C)^2 + I_G^2 R^2\}}]/I_G$$

$$= \sqrt{\{R^2 + (\omega L - 1/\omega C)^2\}} = R \text{ at resonance}$$

$$\boxed{\text{TEST ON PROGRAMME 4}}$$

1. What are the peak, peak-to-peak, mean and r.m.s. values of the waveform below? What are its period and frequency?

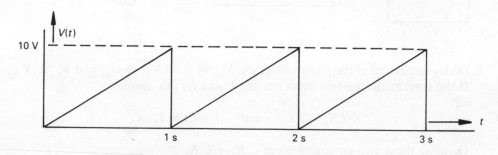

2. A sinusoidal current of amplitude 10 mA and frequency $(1/2\pi)$ kHz flows through (a) a 1 μF capacitor and (b) a 10 mH inductor. What r.m.s. voltage is developed across each component? Draw graphs of the current, voltage and power waveforms for each component.

3. Show that, in the circuit illustrated below left, the output and input voltages are equal in magnitude but differ in phase. Obtain an expression for the phase difference between output and input. With the output measured *from* A *to* B as shown in the diagram, is this phase difference a phase lead or a phase lag?

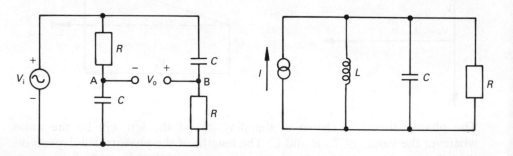

4. Draw a phasor diagram for the circuit illustrated above right and obtain an expression for the impedance of the circuit. Under what condition is the impedance purely resistive and what is its value? How would you describe this condition?

FURTHER QUESTIONS ON PROGRAMME 4

1. This waveform is called a fullwave rectified sinewave. What are its peak, peak-to-peak, mean and r.m.s. values? What are its period and frequency?

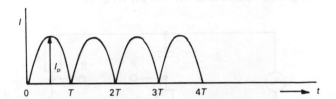

2. This is another form of saw-tooth waveform. What are its peak, peak-to-peak, mean and r.m.s. values? What are its period and frequency?

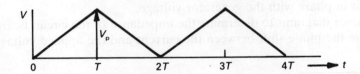

3. Two voltage sinewave generators with outputs $v_1 = V \sin \omega t$ and $v_2 = V \sin(\omega t + \pi/3)$ are connected in series with a resistor R to make a closed circuit. Write an expression for the current in the resistor.

4. A sinusoidal current of amplitude 5 mA and frequency 200 Hz flows through (a) a 10 kΩ resistor, (b) a 10 µF capacitor and (c) a 10 µH inductor. What r.m.s. voltage is developed across each component. Draw graphs of the voltage, current and power waveforms for each component and write time functions for each quantity using the same function for current in each case.

5. Phasor diagrams can be drawn using r.m.s. values of voltages and currents just as well as with their amplitudes. By considering how a phasor representing a sinusoidal quantity is related to the amplitude of that quantity, explain why the statement above is valid. A sinusoidal voltage generator is connected in series with a capacitor and a resistor. The voltage across the resistor is measured as 12 V r.m.s., the voltage across the capacitor as 5 V r.m.s. What is the voltage output of the generator (a) as an r.m.s. value and (b) in amplitude? If the resistor is of value 10 kΩ and the capacitor of value 10 µF, what is the frequency of the generator output?

6. A capacitance of 0.2 μF is connected in parallel with a resistance of 20 kΩ. A sinusoidal voltage of amplitude 20 V and of frequency 50 Hz is connected across this parallel combination. Find the current in each component and hence deduce the amplitude of the total current drawn from the generator and its phase relative to the applied voltage.

7. Show that when $CR_1 = L/R_2$ in the circuit below, then the potential difference between the points A and B is zero at all frequencies.

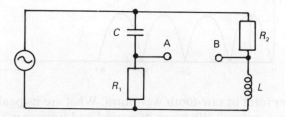

8. Find a value of ω at which the voltage measured from A to B in the circuit above is in phase with the generator voltage.

9. Use phasor diagrams to determine the impedance of the circuit below left and calculate the phase shift between the current and the applied voltage.

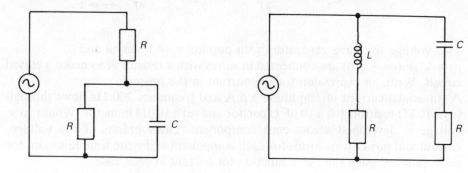

10. Show that when $R = \sqrt{(L/C)}$, the impedance of the parallel combination shown in the circuit above right is purely resistive and independent of frequency.

(*Note*: The last two problems above are interesting exercises in testing your understanding of phasor diagrams but are, in practice, more easily solved by the methods introduced in the next programme.)

Programme 5

THE USE OF j-NOTATION
IN CIRCUIT ANALYSIS

INTRODUCTION

In programmes 2 and 3 we established the main body of theory needed to analyse circuits containing direct voltage and current generators and resistors. We saw how a very wide range of circuit problems could be reduced, by the use of Thevenin and Norton's theorems, to the analysis of two simple forms: the potential divider and the current splitter. In programme 4 we investigated the nature of time-varying waveforms (voltages and currents which are not direct but whose values change with time) and learnt that sinusoidally varying signals in particular are very widely used in circuit design. In programme 4 we saw how the mathematical properties of such waveforms could be represented by a vector-like 'phasor notation' and went on to see how this notation could be used in circuit analysis.

In this programme we are going to investigate a new method of circuit analysis using j-notation – an analytical process based on the use of complex numbers. We will see how this method can be deduced from a knowledge of phasor notation and then go on to discover how it can be used to analyse circuits containing resistors, capacitors and inductors which are stimulated by sinusoidally varying generators. We will find out that, with this notation, such circuits can be analysed using the same kind of mathematical processes established in programmes 2 and 3 and how, once again, a very large range of circuit problems can be reduced to an analysis of the two basic forms.

The programme begins with a review of those properties of complex numbers necessary to understand their application to circuit analysis. Using complex number techniques, the simple circuits analysed using phasors in programme 4 are then re-analysed to see how the two methods compare. Further examples which would be very difficult using phasor techniques are then given to show the power of complex number methods. The j-notation versions of Thevenin's and Norton's theorems are stated and the way in which they differ from the d.c. versions emphasised.

The symbol j

It is standard practice, in electrical and electronic circuit theory, to use j rather than i to represent the square root of -1. The letter i is conventionally used in circuit analysis to represent a current and, as we shall see, there will be circumstances in the mathematical treatment of circuits where currents having imaginary parts will arise. Using the same letter for both current and the square root of -1 would therefore lead to confusion. It should be understood at this stage, however, that 'an imaginary current' is no more than a mathematical convenience. The currents flowing in a.c. circuits are no less real than those flowing in d.c. circuits. It is simply that a.c. properties can conveniently be described using complex numbers. This fact will become clear as this programme proceeds.

COMPLEX NUMBERS

Complex numbers arise in the solution of equations of the form:

$$ax^2 + bx + c = 0 \quad \text{when } b^2 < 4ac$$

Since

$$x = \frac{-b \pm \sqrt{(b^2 - 4ac)}}{2a}$$

the quantity under the square root sign will be negative when $b^2 < 4ac$. There is no real number which, when squared, is negative, so an *'imaginary number'* j' is postulated which has the property that $j^2 = -1$. Any real number, when multiplied by j becomes imaginary and such numbers are written in the form: j2; j7.5, j100 etc. A *complex number is a number which has both a real and an imaginary part*. 3+j4, for example, is a complex number.

Using this notation, we can write down the solutions to quadratic equations having roots which are not real.

The equation $x^2 - 2x + 5 = 0$ has roots . . . . and . . . .

2

$$\boxed{x = 1 + j2 \quad \text{and} \quad x = 1 - j2}$$

Substituting values in the formula given in frame 1 we have:

$$x = \frac{2 \pm \sqrt{(4 - 20)}}{2}, \text{ i.e. } x = \frac{2 \pm \sqrt{(-16)}}{2}$$

So $x = \dfrac{2 + j4}{2}$ and $\dfrac{2 - j4}{2}$ or $x = 1 + j2$ and $x = 1 - j2$

Complex numbers cannot be manipulated in quite the same way as real numbers – they have to be treated as 'ordered pairs', the *real part* preceding the *imaginary part*. Operations are performed on the real part and on the imaginary part separately. Due account must be taken of whether the result of the operation is real or imaginary, i.e. where it should be positioned in the new ordered pair produced. (In general, operations on complex numbers produce new complex numbers.) The rules of manipulation are best shown by example.

Addition: $a + jb + c + jd = a + c + j(b + d)$

Subtraction: $a + jb - (c + jd) = a - c + j(b - d)$

So $3 + j4 + 2 + j5 = \ldots$ and $5 + j7 - (1 + j2) = \ldots$

3

$$\boxed{5 + j9 \quad \text{and} \quad 4 + j5}$$

$$3 + j4 + 2 + j5 = 3 + 2 + j(4 + 5) = 5 + j9$$

$$5 + j7 - (1 + j2) = 5 - 1 + j(7 - 2) = 4 + j5$$

The real parts are added or subtracted to give the new real part; the imaginary parts are added or subtracted to give the new imaginary part.

Multiplication: $(a + jb)(c + jd) = (ac + jbc + jad + j^2bd)$

$$= ac + jbc + jad - bd = (ac - bd) + j(bc + ad)$$

So $(2 + j)(3 + j4) = \ldots .$

4

$$\boxed{2 + j11}$$

$$(2 + j)(3 + j4) = 2 \times 3 - 1 \times 4 + j(1 \times 3 + 2 \times 4)$$

$$= 6 - 4 + j(3 + 8) = 2 + j11$$

Multiplication is carried out as it would be if all terms in the brackets were real. Due account is then taken of whether the resulting terms are real or imaginary bearing in mind that $j^2 = -1$. Terms in the product are then placed in their correct position in the ordered pair.

Conjugation: This is an operation peculiar to complex numbers but which, among other things, is useful for the operation of division. A general complex number is usually given the symbol z, so:

If $z = a + jb$ then $\bar{z} = a - jb$ where $\bar{z}$ is the *complex conjugate* of z.

The numbers z and $\bar{z}$ have the property that their product $z\bar{z}$ is always real, positive and equal to the sum of the squares of the real part of z and its imaginary part; $z\bar{z} = a^2 + b^2$ for $z = a + jb$. Working this through we have:

$$z\bar{z} = (a + jb)(a - jb) = a + jab - jab - j^2b = a^2 + b^2$$

Remember $j^2 = -1$ so $-j^2 = 1$. Since $z\bar{z}$ is always positive, its square root is therefore always a real number. The positive value of this square root is called the *modulus* or *amplitude* of the complex number and is written $|z|$. We shall find that this is a very important property of complex numbers when we start using them in circuit analysis.

If $z = 2 + j3$, what is its conjugate and what is its modulus?

5

> If $z = 2 + j3$, its conjugate is $z = 2 - j3$, and its modulus is $\sqrt{13}$.

The conjugate is by definition just the original number with the sign of the imaginary part changed.

The modulus is given by
$$|z| = \sqrt{(z\bar{z})} = \sqrt{\{(2 + j3)(2 - j3)\}}$$
$$= \sqrt{(4 + 9)} = \sqrt{13}$$

Division:
$$\frac{a + jb}{c + jd} = \frac{(a + jb) \times (c - jd)}{(c + jd) \times (c - jd)} = \frac{ac + jbc - jad - j^2 bd}{c^2 + d^2}$$
$$= \frac{ac + bd}{c^2 + d^2} + \frac{j(bc + ad)}{c^2 + d^2}$$

So, to divide one complex number by another, we first multiply both numerator and denominator of the division sum by the complex conjugate of the denominator. This makes the denominator of the new expression real and positive. We can then separate the numerator into real and imaginary parts and divide both parts by the real denominator.

$$\text{So } \frac{4 + j3}{1 + j2} = \dots$$

6

> $2 - j$

$$\frac{4 + j3}{1 + j2} = \frac{(4 + j3)(1 - j2)}{(1 + j2)(1 - j2)} = \frac{4 \times 1 + 3 \times 2 + j(3 \times 1 - 4 \times 2)}{1 + 4}$$
$$= \frac{4 + 6}{5} + \frac{j(3 - 8)}{5} = \frac{10}{5} + \frac{j5}{5} = 2 + j$$

Equivalence: Two complex numbers are equivalent only if the real part of the first is equal to the real part of the second, and the imaginary part of the first is equal to the imaginary part of the second. So:

$$a + jb = c + jd \quad \text{only if} \quad a = c \text{ and } b = d$$
$$\text{Thus if } x + jy = 4 + j3 \quad \text{then} \quad x = \dots \text{ and } y = \dots$$

7

$$x = 4 \quad \text{and} \quad y = 3$$

Note that we have $y = 3$ and not $y = j3$.

THE POLYNOMIAL THEOREM

Before leaving numerical operations on complex numbers it is worth noting in passing that, if a quadratic equation such as that in frame 1 has *one root which is complex*, then *the second root is always the complex conjugate of the first*. In fact, this idea extends to polynomials of any order. If a polynomial is found to have one root which is a complex number, then the complex conjugate of this number will be a root also. So, in general, *the roots of a polynomial are either real or occur in complex conjugate pairs*. This very important property of polynomials is called the polynomial theorem.

Now, here are some more examples for you to try. You fill in the blanks:

The roots of $x^2 - 6x + 34 = 0$ are $x = \ldots$ and $x = \ldots$

$$6 + j2 + 3 - j4 = \ldots \qquad 6 + j2 - (3 - j4) = \ldots$$

If $a + jb = 2 - j3$ then $a = \ldots$ and $b = \ldots$

$$(3 - j7)(2 + j) = \ldots \qquad \frac{5 + j2}{3 - j} = \ldots$$

8

Here are the results in detail:

The roots of $x^2 - 6x + 34 = 0$ are $x = \dfrac{6 \pm \sqrt{(36 - 136)}}{2}$ or

$$x = 3 + j5 \text{ and } 3 - j5$$

$6 + j2 + 3 - j4 = 6 + 3 + j(2 - 4) = 9 - j2$

$6 + j2 - (3 - j4) = 6 - 3 + j(2 + 4) = 3 + j6$

If $a + jb = 2 - j3$ then $a = 2$ and $b = -3$. Don't forget the minus sign!

$(3 - j7)(2 + j) = 3 \times 2 - j^2 7 + j(-7 \times 2 + 3 \times 1)$

$\qquad = 3 \times 2 + 7 \times 1 + j(-14 + 3)$

$\qquad = 6 + 7 + j(-11) = 13 - j11$

$$\frac{5 + j2}{3 - j} = \frac{(5 + j2)(3 + j)}{(3 - j)(3 + j)} = \frac{5 \times 3 - 2 \times 1 + j(2 \times 3 + 5 \times 1)}{9 + 1}$$

$$= \frac{15 - 2}{10} + \frac{j(6 + 5)}{10} = 1.3 + j1.1$$

When you have got all these correct, move on to the next frame.

THE ARGAND DIAGRAM

The Argand diagram is a method of representing complex numbers graphically and is due to the French mathematician Argand from whom it takes its name. On an Argand diagram, real numbers and imaginary numbers are represented on two orthogonal axes (i.e. axes at right angles to each other). Complex numbers then lie anywhere on the plane defined by these two axes.

A general complex number is usually denoted by the letter z where $z = x + jy$. x is the real part (or real co-ordinate since the Argand diagram is really only a co-ordinate system for describing complex numbers), y is the imaginary part or imaginary co-ordinate. The complex number z then completely specifies a point P in the 'complex plane' or z-plane.

Here is an Argand diagram with some points plotted on it.

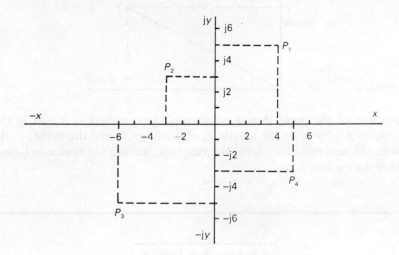

What complex numbers can be written to specify the points P_1, P_2, P_3 and P_4 in this Argand diagram? You fill in the blanks.

$$z_1 = \ldots \ldots \quad z_2 = \ldots \ldots$$

$$z_3 = \ldots \ldots \quad z_4 = \ldots \ldots$$

10

$$z_1 = 4 + j5, \; z_2 = -3 + j3, \; z_3 = -6 - j5, \; z_4 = 5 - j3$$

We can write a complex number as the *sum of its co-ordinates* in the complex plane because the j automatically tells us that the number following it is the imaginary co-ordinate.

COMPLEX NUMBERS IN POLAR AND EXPONENTIAL FORM

Comparison with the real plane gives us another way of representing a complex number. Real numbers in a wholly real plane described by axes x and y can be represented by Cartesian co-ordinates (x, y) or by polar co-ordinates (r, θ). The same is true of complex numbers as may be seen from the following diagram where only the positive quadrant is used in this case:

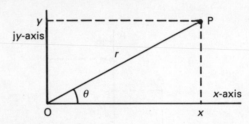

The position of the point P may be completely specified as it was in the previous frame by $x + jy$ or by the length, r, of the line OP and the angle, θ, that OP makes with the real axis. But, from the diagram, we can see that $x = r \cos \theta$ and $y = r \sin \theta$, so we can write . . . .

$$z = x + jy = \ldots \ldots \ldots$$

11

$$z = r \cos \theta + jr \sin \theta$$

This is called the polar form of z and we sometimes also write this as:

$$z = r\underline{/\theta} \text{ where } r = \surd(x^2 + y^2) \text{ and } \theta = \arctan y/x$$

θ is called the argument of z and is the angle whose tangent is the imaginary part of z divided by the real part of z. We can therefore also write:

$$\theta = \arg z = \arctan (\text{Im } z)/(\text{Rl } z)$$

We have seen an expression like that for r in terms of x and y in an earlier frame. We can therefore say that r is the . . . . of z.

12

> modulus

As we saw in frames 4 and 5, the modulus of a complex number is given by the square root of the sum of the squares of the real and imaginary parts.

We can therefore write $r = \sqrt{(z\bar{z})}$ which is sometimes written $r = \text{mod } z$.

We can obtain yet a further form for z by expanding $\cos \theta$ and $\sin \theta$ as power series and forming the sum of the $\cos \theta$ series and j times the $\sin \theta$ series. We find that this sum is a power series for $e^{j\theta}$. This is *Euler's theorem* and gives us the following expression for z in exponential form:

$$z = r(\cos \theta + j\sin \theta) = re^{j\theta} \text{ where } \theta \text{ must be expressed in radians}$$

This form gives some useful alternative expressions for multiplying and dividing complex numbers. Suppose we have two complex numbers z_1 and z_2 which we express in exponential form as $z_1 = r_1e^{j\theta_1}$ and $z_2 = r_2e^{j\theta_2}$. Remembering the rules for dealing with indices when two exponentials are multiplied or divided, can you complete the following equations?

$$z_1 \times z_2 = r_1e^{j\theta_1} \times r_2e^{j\theta_2} = \ldots\ldots\ldots \quad \text{and} \quad \frac{z_1}{z_2} = \frac{r_1e^{j\theta_1}}{r_2e^{j\theta_2}} = \ldots\ldots\ldots$$

13

> $$z_1 \times z_2 = r_1r_2e^{j(\theta_1+\theta_2)} \quad \text{and} \quad \frac{z_1}{z_2} = \frac{r_1}{r_2} e^{j(\theta_1-\theta_2)}$$

When *multiplying* together two complex numbers expressed in exponential form, we find the *product* of their *moduli* and the *sum* of their *arguments*. When *dividing* two complex numbers expressed in exponential form, we find the *quotient* of their *moduli* and the *difference* of their *arguments*.

These results give us some important corollaries for a few special cases of the numbers z_1 and z_2 which we shall use often in circuit analysis.

If $r_2 = 1$, $\theta_2 = \pi/2$ and $r_1 = a$, $\theta_1 = 0$ then $z_2 = e^{j\pi/2} = j$ and $z_1 = a$

If you are unsure how these results are formed, simply substitute the values in the expression given in Euler's theorem.

With these values for z_1 and z_2, what is the value of z_1z_2?

14

$$z_1 z_2 = ae^{j\pi/2} = ja$$

It is instructive to refer this answer to the Argand diagram shown below:

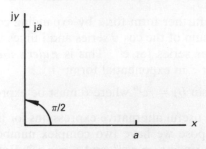

From this we see that, if z_1 is a real number and z_2 is simply j, then $z_1 z_2$ is the same size as z_1 but lies along the imaginary axis. In other words, multiplying a real number by j 'rotates it' in the complex plane by an anticlockwise angle $\pi/2$, where $\pi/2$ is the argument of j expressed in polar or exponential form.

If we extend this idea to the case where z_1 is a complex number, we find the same kind of relationship, i.e. multiplying a complex number by j preserves its amplitude but increases its argument by an angle $\pi/2$. This result follows directly from multiplying the two numbers together in exponential form.

If $z_1 = ae^{j\theta_1}$ and $z_2 = j = e^{j\pi/2}$ then $z_1 z_2 = ae^{j(\theta_1 + \pi/2)}$

Again we can think of this as rotating the r part of the polar form of z_1 by an anticlockwise angle $\pi/2$ in the complex plane as shown below:

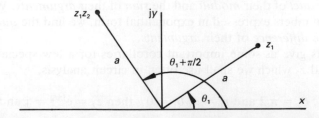

How would you express $-j$ in exponential form and what would be the effect of multiplying a complex number by $-j$? Express the complex number in exponential form and draw a sketch to help explain your result.

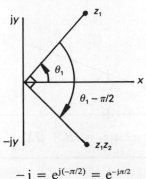

$$-j = e^{j(-\pi/2)} = e^{-j\pi/2}$$

If $z_1 = ae^{j\theta_1}$ and $z_2 = -j = e^{-j(\pi/2)}$ then $z_1 z_2 = ae^{j(\theta_1 - \pi/2)}$

Multiplying a complex number by $-j$ has the effect of reducing its argument by an angle $\pi/2$ without changing its amplitude. It is the same as rotating the r part of the polar form by a clockwise angle $\pi/2$ in the complex plane.

The above results follow directly by applying the rules for multiplication of complex numbers written in exponential form.

When we come on to circuit analysis we shall find that we often want to multiply a wholly real number by a complex number. As the example given below shows, this produces a complex number with the following properties: its amplitude is the product of the real number and the modulus (or amplitude) of the complex number; its argument is the same as the argument of the original complex number.

So, if $z_1 = a$ and $z_2 = be^{j\theta}$ then $z_1 z_2 = abe^{j\theta}$

Again, these results show up clearly on the Argand diagram:

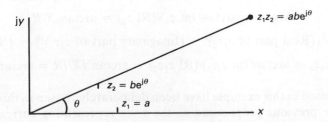

The results are, of course, equally valid if all the numbers are written in Cartesian form. Can you draw an Argand diagram to show the numbers $z_1 = I$, $z_2 = R + jX$, then evaluate their product and show this on the diagram too?

16

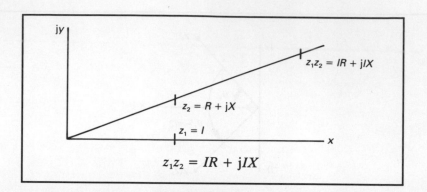

We established, in the previous frame, that multiplying a real number by a complex number results in another complex number having the same argument as the original one. Drawing the product of the two original numbers on the Argand diagram thus results in a line which is simply a scaling of the line representing the original complex number.

Can you now express both original numbers and their product in exponential form and hence show analytically that the original complex number and its product with the real number have the same argument?

17

$$z_1 = I, \ z_2 = [\sqrt{(R^2 + X^2)}]e^{j\theta} \text{ where } \theta = \arctan X/R$$
$$z_1z_2 = [\sqrt{\{I^2(R^2 + X^2)\}}]e^{j\theta} \text{ where } \theta = \arctan X/R$$

$z_1 = I$ in Cartesian or polar form

$$|z_2| = \sqrt{\{(\text{Real part of } z_2)^2 + (\text{Imaginary part of } z_2)^2\}} = \sqrt{(R^2 + X^2)}$$

$$\text{Arg } z_2 = \arctan(\text{Im } z_2)/(\text{Rl } z_2) = \arctan X/R$$

$$|z_1z_2| = \sqrt{\{(\text{Real part of } z_1z_2)^2 + (\text{Imaginary part of } z_1z_2)^2\}} = I^2R^2 + I^2X^2$$

$$\text{Arg } z_1z_2 = \arctan(\text{Im } z_1z_2)/(\text{Rl } z_1z_2) = \arctan IX/IR = \arctan X/R$$

The symbols used in this example have been deliberately chosen as those familiar to you from the previous programme as the ones representing current amplitude, resistance and reactance. You will see shortly how the above results can be used in circuit analysis using the complex number notation.

Now turn on to the next frame where we will look at the use of exponential notation in the division of two complex numbers which have the same argument.

18

The result of dividing two complex numbers expressed in exponential form is given here to remind you of it.

If $z_1 = r_1 e^{j\theta_1}$ and $z_2 = r_2 e^{j\theta_2}$ then $\dfrac{z_1}{z_2} = \dfrac{r_1}{r_2} e^{j(\theta_1 - \theta_2)}$

With the condition that $\theta_1 = \theta_2$, can you complete the following statement?

When two complex numbers having the same argument
are divided the result is a . . . .

19

| real number |

The argument of the quotient is $\theta_1 - \theta_2$, but $\theta_1 = \theta_2$ so the argument is 0 and $e^{j\theta} = 1$. The quotient is therefore just the quotient of the moduli and is thus real.

THE REPRESENTATION OF PHASORS ON THE ARGAND DIAGRAM

Having established all these results, we can now go on to examine the link between phasors and complex numbers which we obtain via the Argand diagram. The diagram below shows three points P_1, P_2 and P_3. The lines from O to the three points could represent phasors where OP_3 is the phasor sum or resultant of OP_1 and OP_2. However, if the lines OP_1, OP_2 and OP_3 are regarded as lines on an Argand diagram, the co-ordinates of P_1, P_2 and P_3, the endpoints of the phasors, can be represented by the complex numbers $z_1 = x_1 + jy_1$, $z_2 = x_2 + jy_2$ and $z_3 = x_3 + jy_3$.

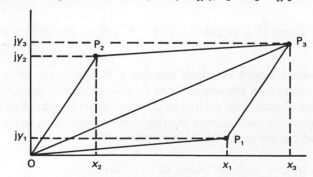

Can you write expressions for x_3 and y_3 in terms of x_1, x_2, y_1 and y_2?

20

$$x_3 = x_1 + x_2 \quad \text{and} \quad y_3 = y_1 + y_2$$

We obtain these results by studying the geometry of the figure and observing that $OP_1P_3P_2$ is a parallelogram. Now, using these results, we have:

$$z_3 = x_3 + jy_3 = (x_1 + x_2) + j(y_1 + y_2) = x_1 + jy_1 + x_2 + jy_2 = z_1 + z_2$$

This shows that, if we can express two phasors in terms of the (complex) co-ordinates of their endpoints, then we can use algebraic manipulation alone to derive the co-ordinates of the endpoint of their resultant. From these co-ordinates we can then calculate the amplitude of the resultant and its phase angle referred to the same axis as the phase angles of the two original phasors.

In terms of x_1, x_2, y_1 and y_2, we can write
$$|z_3| = \ldots \ldots \ldots \quad \arg z_3 = \arctan (\ldots \ldots .)/(\ldots \ldots .)$$

21

$$|z_3| = \sqrt{(x_1 + x_2)^2 + (y_1 + y_2)^2} \quad \arg z_3 = \arctan(y_1 + y_2)/(x_1 + x_2)$$

These results follow from the definitions for modulus and argument and the equations at the beginning of frame 20. Notice that, now we are dealing with phasors, it is more convenient to use the terms amplitude and phase angle for the quantities we have been calling modulus and argument up to now.

Looking at the diagram in frame 19 again we can see that the phase angle between the phasors representing z_2 and z_1 is $\theta_2 - \theta_1$, the phase angle between the phasors representing z_3 and z_1 is $\theta_3 - \theta_1$. We can write these as:

$$\theta_2 - \theta_1 = \arctan\frac{y_2}{x_2} - \arctan\frac{y_1}{x_1} \quad \text{and} \quad \theta_3 - \theta_1 = \arctan\frac{y_3}{x_3} - \arctan\frac{y_1}{x_1}$$

These expressions would be much simpler if θ_1 was zero. In most situations where we are dealing with phasors we shall be able to choose one of the phasors as a 'reference phasor' and, with no loss of generality, set its phase angle to zero. A property of phasors we encountered in progamme 4 enables us to do this. Can you remember it and complete the following statement?

A phasor diagram allows us to compare the . . . .
phase angles of two sinusoidally varying quantities.

relative

Remember that, when quantities are depicted as phasors, this notation preserves the relative phase angles of all phasors rotating at the same frequency. Remember, too, that these phasors represent sinusoidally varying quantities having the same frequency but different relative phases. Choosing one of these phasors as a reference phasor and setting its phase angle to zero is, as we saw in programme 4, in effect selecting the instant of time at which we wish to start observing the waveforms and ensuring that our reference waveform can be written as $A \sin \omega t$. All other waveforms can then be written in the form $kA \sin(\omega t + \phi)$ where k is a scaling factor and ϕ is the phase difference between the waveform in question and the reference waveform. All the calculations we need to do to find k and ϕ can now, however, be done using complex numbers.

Here is a problem for you to try. We did one just like this in programme 4 but then we did not have the benefit of being able to use complex numbers. The diagram below shows two voltage generators connected in series feeding a resistive load of 1 kΩ. If the amplitudes of the generator voltages given in the diagram are in volts, calculate the voltage v_R across the load resistor and the current i_R flowing through it. Give your answers in the same form as the voltages shown on the diagram are given.

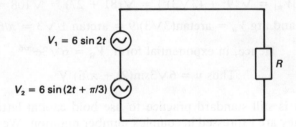

Hints: Draw a phasor diagram and then express the two voltages in complex exponential form. Turn these expressions into polar and then Cartesian forms so that you can combine them, then reverse the process to obtain the answers.

$$v_R = 6\sqrt{3}\sin(2t + \pi/6) \text{ volts}, \quad i_R = 6\sqrt{3}\sin(2t + \pi/6) \text{ milliamps}$$

Here is the phasor diagram and the working in full:

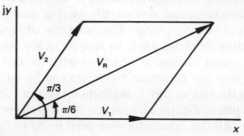

From the phasor diagram: $V_1 = 6$

$$V_2 = 6e^{j\pi/3} = 6(\cos\pi/3 + j\sin\pi/3)$$

$$= 6\cos\pi/3 + j6\sin\pi/3$$

$$= 6 \times (1/2) + j6 \times (\sqrt{3}/2)$$

$$= 3 + j3\sqrt{3}$$

So $V_R = V_1 + V_2 = 6 + 3 + j3\sqrt{3} = 9 + j3\sqrt{3}$

Thus $|V_R| = \sqrt{\{9^2 + (3\sqrt{3})^2\}} = \sqrt{(81 + 27)} = \sqrt{108} = 6\sqrt{3}$

and $\arg V_R = \arctan(3\sqrt{3})/9 = \arctan 1/\sqrt{3} = \pi/6$

Hence, in exponential form, $V_R = 6\sqrt{3}e^{j\pi/6}$

Thus $v = 6\sqrt{3}\sin(2t + \pi/6)$ V

Notice that it is still standard practice to use bold capital letters to represent phasors when they are expressed in complex number notation. We refer to them as *complex phasors*.

Since current and voltage in a resistor are in phase, we simply divide by R to get the current, so:

$$i = 6\sqrt{3}\sin(2t + \pi/6) \text{ mA}$$

In this particular problem you should be able to confirm the answer by studying the trigonometry of the phasor diagram. If the amplitudes and phases of the original voltages were different, however, the trigonometrical problem could be more difficult. The solution of the problem by complex numbers would, nevertheless, be much the same.

REVISION SUMMARY

1. Complex numbers can be represented in three forms:

   (a) in Cartesian form, we can write $z = x + jy$;
   (b) in polar form, we can write $z = r \cos \theta + jr \sin \theta$ or $z = r\underline{/\theta}$
   (c) in exponential form, we can write $z = re^{j\theta}$.

2. Complex numbers can be added, subtracted, multiplied and divided in Cartesian form, and multiplied and divided in exponential form. (All operations can, of course, be performed in all three forms, but those given here are the ones we shall find most useful in circuit analysis.)

3. Complex numbers can be depicted graphically on an Argand diagram which is also known as the complex plane.

4. Phasors can be represented on an Argand diagram. We sometimes talk of them as being 'mapped' onto the complex plane.

5. All the rules of combination of complex numbers can therefore be used to calculate the relative amplitudes and phases of phasors and thus of the sinusoidally varying waveforms they represent.

6. The amplitude of a phasor corresponds to the modulus of the complex number used to represent it. The phase angle of the phasor (referred to the horizontal axis) corresponds to the argument of the complex number used to represent it.

7. By choosing one phasor in a set as a reference and setting its phase angle to zero, it can be taken to represent a waveform $A \sin \omega t$. All other phasors having the same angular frequency can then be taken to represent waveforms of the form $kA \sin(\omega t + \phi)$ where k and ϕ can be calculated as above.

8. It is standard notation, when expressing phasors in complex number notation (usually called j-notation), to refer to them as complex phasors and to represent them with bold capital letters.

25

| REVISION QUESTIONS |

1. What are the roots of the equation $x^2 - 4x + 13 = 0$?
2. Express the complex number $z = 4\underline{/\pi/6}$ (a) in exponential form, (b) in polar form using Euler's theorem and (c) in Cartesian form.
3. Express the complex number $z = 2 + j2$ (a) in exponential form, (b) in polar form using Euler's theorem and (c) in polar form showing modulus and argument.
4. Plot on an Argand diagram the numbers in questions 2 and 3 and their complex conjugates.
5. Plot the sum of the numbers in 2 and 3 on an Argand diagram and write this sum in Cartesian and in exponential form.
6. Two current generators with outputs $i_1 = 3 \sin 5t$ and $i_2 = 4 \sin(5t + \pi/4)$ are connected in parallel and this parallel combination connected to a 2 kΩ resistor. Write an expression for the current through and voltage across the resistor in the same form as the two currents given above.

26

| ANSWERS TO REVISION QUESTIONS |

1. The roots are $\dfrac{4 \pm \sqrt{(16 - 4 \times 13)}}{2} = \dfrac{4 \pm \sqrt{-36}}{2} = \dfrac{4 \pm j6}{2} = 2 \pm j3$

2. $z = 4\underline{/\pi/6} = 4e^{j\pi/6} = 4 \cos \pi/6 + j4 \sin \pi/6 = 4\sqrt{3}/2 + j4/2 = 2\sqrt{3} + j2$

3. $z = 2 + j2$ so $|z| = \sqrt{(4 + 4)} = \sqrt{8} = 2\sqrt{2}$ and arg $z = \arctan 2/2 = \pi/4$

    Hence $z = 2\sqrt{2}e^{j\pi/4} = 2\sqrt{2} \cos \pi/4 + j2\sqrt{2} \sin \pi/4 = 2\sqrt{2}\underline{/\pi/4}$

4.

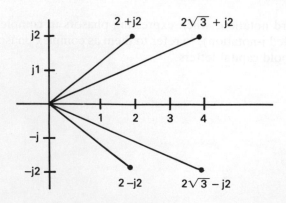

5.

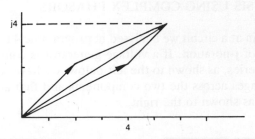

When $z_1 = 2\sqrt{3} + j2$ and $z_2 = 2 + j2$ then $z_1 + z_2$

$$= 2\sqrt{3} + 2 + j4 = 5.46 + j4$$

$$|z_1 + z_2| = \sqrt{\{(2\sqrt{3} + 2)^2 + 4^2\}} = \sqrt{\{12 + 8\sqrt{3} + 4 + 16\}}$$

$$= \sqrt{\{32 + 8\sqrt{3}\}} = 6.77$$

$$\text{Arg}(z_1 + z_2) = \arctan 4/5.46 = \arctan 0.73 = 0.63 \text{ rads}$$

$$\text{Thus } (z_1 + z_2) = 6.77e^{j0.63}$$

6. Current generators in parallel add, so we can draw a current phasor diagram, taking the current $i = 3 \sin 5t$ as the reference current:

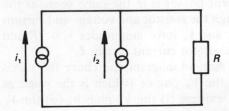
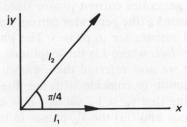

In complex phasor notation, $I_1 = 3$ and $I_2 = 4(\cos \pi/4 + j \sin \pi/4)$

$$\text{So } I_2 = 4(1/\sqrt{2} + j/\sqrt{2}) = 2\sqrt{2} + j2\sqrt{2}$$

The current sum in complex phasor notation is then:

$$I_R = I_1 + I_2 = 3 + 2\sqrt{2} + j2\sqrt{2} = 5.83 + j2.83$$

Now, $|I_R| = \sqrt{\{(5.83)^2 + (2.83)^2\}} = \sqrt{\{33.99 + 8\}} = 6.48$

and $\arg I_R = \arctan 2.83/5.83 = 0.45$ rads

Thus $i_R = 6.48 \sin(5t + 0.45)$ mA

and $v_R = 12.96 \sin(5t + 0.45)$ mA

27

CIRCUIT ANALYSIS USING COMPLEX PHASORS

Now let us look again at a circuit we analysed in programme 4 using phasors before we had the benefit of j-notation. If a voltage generator is connected to a resistor and an inductor in series, as shown to the left below, we have seen that the phasor diagram of the voltages across the two components and that across the generator can be represented as shown to the right.

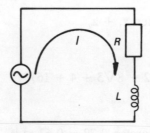 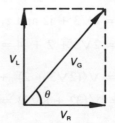

As we saw in programme 4, if the instantaneous voltages across the resistor and the inductor are v_R and v_L, then the phasors V_R and V_L represent these voltages in magnitude and phase and the phasor V_G represents their resultant, the generator voltage. The angle ϕ is the phase angle between the generator voltage phasor and the generator current phasor since the current phasor is in the same sense as the phasor V_R (the generator current flows through the resistor and voltage and current in a resistor are in phase). The phasors V_R and V_L have amplitudes $V = IR$ and $V = I\omega L$ where I is the amplitude of the generator current phasor I.

If we now referred these phasors to the Argand diagram and chose the x-axis direction to coincide with the direction of the V_R phasor (which is the same as saying that $v_R = V_R \sin \omega t$), how could we express (i) the V_R phasor, (ii) the V_L phasor and (iii) the V_G phasor in terms of the current phasor I, the values of the circuit components and the angular frequency ω?

28

$$\boxed{V_R = IR, \ V_L = jI\omega L, \ V_G = IR + jI\omega L}$$

The V_R phasor lies on the x-axis so is represented by a real number. The V_L phasor lies on the y-axis so is represented by an imaginary number. The V_G phasor is their resultant so is the sum of these two complex phasors.

From the last equation above, what are the amplitude and phase angle of V_G?

$$|V_G| = V_G = I\sqrt{(R^2 + \omega^2 L^2)} \quad \text{and} \quad \arg V = \phi = \arctan \omega L/R$$

These results follow directly from the rules of complex numbers. As we found using phasor notation in programme 4, we can again write $V_G = IZ$ where Z is the impedance of the R–L combination and V_G and I are the generator voltage and current amplitudes respectively.

The first two equations in frame 28 are similar to Ohm's Law with a '*phasor current*' I flowing through two impedances R and $j\omega L$. The third equation can be regarded as a very simple application of Kirchhoff's Voltage Law.

Now, treating the circuit below just as you did the d.c. circuits analysed in programmes 2 and 3, can you express V in terms of I, R and $j\omega L$? Use the same convention for potential differences as you did in the earlier programme.

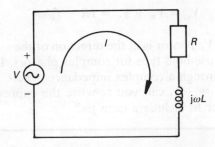

30

$$V = IR + Ij\omega L = I(R + j\omega L)$$

This equation is really the same as the third equation in frame 28, except that the j is now next to the ω. The power of complex number notation applied to circuits including reactive components is that we *can* write down these kind of equations directly. We assign a '*complex impedance*' $j\omega L$ to an inductor and then treat the circuit just as if it was a resistive circuit of the kind we have analysed before. The generator is 'assigned a polarity' as shown in the diagram and drives a current in the direction shown by the arrow. 'Potential differences' developed across the components are 'in opposition to the direction of current flow' just as they are in d.c. circuits.

Now, by analysing a voltage generator, a resistor and a capacitor in series and again choosing the resistor voltage phasor as a reference, can you obtain an expression for the complex impedance of a capacitor?

31

The complex impedance of a capacitor is $-j/\omega C$

Here is the circuit and its phasor diagram:

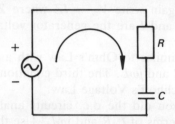 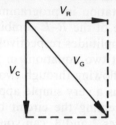

Taking the resistor voltage as a reference as we have above we can write:

$$V_G = V_R + V_C = IR - Ij/\omega C$$

In this case, since the V_C phasor is in the direction of the $-y$-axis, we write V_C as $-Ij/\omega C$. As before, we use bold type for complex phasors. It is therefore as if the current I was flowing through a complex impedance $-j/\omega C$.

Remembering that $j^2 = -1$, can you re-write the expression for the complex impedance of a capacitor to include a term $j\omega$?

32

$-j/\omega C = 1/j\omega C$

Since $j^2 = -1$, we can divide both sides of this expression by j to obtain:

$$j = -1/j \quad \text{and hence} \quad -j = 1/j$$

We can therefore re-write $-j/\omega C$ as $1/j\omega C$. We have, in effect, 'moved the j down to be next to the ω'.

The expressions we now have for the complex impedances of an inductor and a capacitor are thus the same as the real impedances except for the fact that the ω is preceded by a j. Attaching the j to the ω in this way turns out to be a very useful notation for some analysis we shall be doing in a later programme. It is as if we were assigning the 'imaginary' property to the frequency. We often speak of the analysis of circuits using this notation as 'working in the *complex frequency domain*'.

33

GENERALISED COMPLEX FREQUENCY DOMAIN CIRCUIT ANALYSIS

The results we have derived above have come from some fairly simple circuits. The real power of complex number notation or j-notation comes from the following statement:

> However complicated the circuit, we can assign to all inductors a
> complex impedance $j\omega L$ and to all capacitors a complex impedance
> $1/j\omega C$. All resistors still have a real resistance R. With this
> notation we can then apply all the usual rules and theorems of
> d.c. circuit theory to circuits containing reactive components.

To justify this statement fully requires analysis which is beyond the scope of this text. For the moment we will analyse some more circuits to see how the technique can be applied. Before doing this, however, there is one more thing we must be aware of. To check this, can you answer the following question?

What are the dimensions of the terms $j\omega L$ and $1/j\omega C$?

34

$$\boxed{\text{Both terms have dimensions of resistance}}$$

We saw in programme 4 that the terms ωL and $1/\omega C$ both have dimensions of resistance. The number j, although imaginary, still has the dimensions of a pure number. In other words it is dimensionless. Multiplying or dividing a quantity by it will not therefore change the dimensions of that quantity. Expressions such as $R + j\omega L$ and $R + 1/j\omega C$ are thus dimensionally consistent. They too have dimensions of resistance. They too are complex impedances. They are not complex phasors, but complex phasors can be multiplied by them to produce other complex phasors. Used in this way they are sometimes known as '*complex impedance operators*'.

A current phasor when multiplied by a complex impedance operator is changed into a voltage phasor. This is exactly what is happening in the equation $V = I(R + j\omega L)$. When dealing with this kind of equation, we conventionally choose the phase angle of the current phasor to be zero. The modulus of the complex impedance multiplied by the amplitude of the current then gives us the amplitude of the voltage. The argument of the complex impedance gives us the relative phase angles of the voltage and the current.

35

Here is a problem for you to try:

A voltage generator giving a sine wave output with an amplitude of 5 volts at a frequency of $(1/2\pi)$ kHz is connected in series with a resistor of 1 kΩ and an inductor. The current through the resistor is found to have an amplitude of 3 milliamps. What is the inductance of the inductor and what is the amplitude of the voltage across it? What is the phase shift between the generator voltage and the current drawn from it?

36

> The inductance of the inductor is 1.33 H
> The amplitude of the voltage across the inductor is 4 V
> The generator voltage leads the current by an angle arctan 1.33 = 53.13°

Here is the working in detail:

$$V_G = I(R + j\omega L) = 3 \times 10^{-3}(1000 + j1000 \times L) = 3(1 + jL)$$

$$|V_G| = 5 = 3|1 + jL| = 3\sqrt{(1 + L^2)}$$

$$\sqrt{(1 + L^2)} = 5/3 \text{ so } 1 + L^2 = 25/9 \text{ and } L^2 = 25/9 - 1 = 16/9 \text{ so } L = 1.33 \text{ H}$$

$$V_L = jI\omega L = j3 \times 10^{-3} \times 1000 \times 4/3 = j4 \text{ so } V_L = 4 \text{ V}$$

$$\phi = \arctan \omega L/R = \arctan 1000 \times 1.33/1000 = \arctan 1.33 = 53.13°$$

Here is another problem involving a circuit with more than two components:

Find the complex impedance **Z** of the circuit below and, from it, deduce the impedance Z. Remember: *the* impedance Z is the modulus of the complex impedance **Z**. Notice that we use a bold capital **Z** for complex impedance and a normal capital Z for impedance as previously defined. It is important to remember, however, that **Z** is an impedance operator and NOT a phasor.

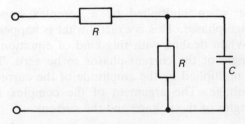

37

$$Z = \frac{R(2 + j\omega CR)}{(1 + j\omega CR)} \qquad Z = R\sqrt{\left(\frac{4 + \omega^2 C^2 R^2}{1 + \omega^2 C^2 R^2}\right)}$$

Assigning an impedance $1/j\omega C$ to the capacitor, we can write down the complex impedance of the circuit directly. It is that of a resistor R in series with a parallel combination of another resistor R and a capacitor C.

We have $$\mathbf{Z} = R + \frac{R \times 1/j\omega C}{R + 1/j\omega C} = R + \frac{R}{1 + j\omega CR} = \frac{R(2 + j\omega CR)}{(1 + j\omega CR)}$$

To find the impedance Z we multiply both numerator and denominator of the complex impedance $\mathbf{Z}$ by their complex conjugates and take the square root.

Can you now find the phase shift between the output voltage of a sinusoidal voltage generator connected to the circuit and the current drawn from this generator? Does the voltage lead or lag the current?

38

The phase shift is $\phi = \arctan \dfrac{-\omega CR}{2 + \omega^2 C^2 R^2}$ voltage lagging current

To find the phase shift between current and voltage we can use the fact that $\mathbf{V} = \mathbf{IZ}$ and, as usual, choose the phase angle of $\mathbf{I}$ to be zero. The required result is then obtained by finding the phase angle $\mathbf{Z}$. To do this we first take the expression for $\mathbf{Z}$ which we obtained in frame 37. We then have two choices in the way in which we can evaluate the phase angle. One way is to multiply both numerator and denominator of the expression for $\mathbf{Z}$ by the conjugate of the denominator. This leaves the numerator as a complex number but makes the denominator a real number. This way is shown here:

We have $$\mathbf{Z} = R\frac{(2 + j\omega CR)(1 - j\omega CR)}{(1 + j\omega CR)(1 - j\omega CR)} = R\frac{(2 + \omega^2 C^2 R^2 - j\omega CR)}{1 + \omega^2 C^2 R^2}$$

We then have $$\phi = \arctan\frac{\text{Im } \mathbf{Z}}{\text{Rl } \mathbf{Z}} = \arctan\frac{-\omega CR}{1 + CR} \div \frac{2 + \omega^2 C^2 R^2}{1 + \omega^2 C^2 R^2}$$

$$= \arctan\frac{-\omega CR}{2 + \omega^2 C^2 R^2}$$

Now, $\mathbf{V} = \mathbf{IZ}$ so, if we choose the phase angle of $\mathbf{I}$ to be zero then the phase angle of $\mathbf{V}$ will be the same as the phase angle of $\mathbf{Z}$. The voltage thus leads or lags the current depending on whether the phase angle of $\mathbf{Z}$ is positive or negative. In this case the phase angle is negative so the voltage lags the current.

39

As we saw in frame 13, an alternative way of finding the phase angle of the quotient of two complex numbers is to express them in exponential form. To proceed with this method we first return to the expression for Z, the complex impedance, that we derived in frame 37. If we put both numerator and denominator into exponential form, the result we discovered in frame 13 then shows us that the phase angle of the resulting number is just the phase angle of the numerator minus the phase angle of the denominator. Can you complete the expression below? Express ϕ in terms of the inverse tangents of the phase angles of the complex numbers in the numerator and the denominator of the expression for Z.

$$Z = \frac{R\,(2 + j\omega CR)}{(1 + j\omega CR)} \text{ so } \phi = \cdots\cdots\cdots\cdots\cdots\cdots$$

40

$$\boxed{\phi = \arctan \omega CR/2 - \arctan \omega CR}$$

We can form each individual tangent by remembering that, for a complex number $a + jb$ with phase angle ϕ, $\tan \phi = b/a$.

We can use the rules of trigonometry to show that this answer and the one we obtained in frame 38 are the same.

Now, $\tan \phi = \tan (\phi_1 - \phi_2)$ where ϕ_1 and ϕ_2 are the phase angles of the numerator and denominator respectively.

$$\text{But } \tan (\phi_1 - \phi_2) = \frac{\tan \phi_1 - \tan \phi_2}{1 + \tan \phi_1 \times \tan \phi_2} = \frac{\omega CR/2 - \omega CR}{1 + \omega^2 C^2 R^2/2}$$

$$= \frac{-\omega CR/2}{1 + \omega^2 C^2 R^2/2} = \frac{-\omega CR}{2 + \omega^2 C^2 R^2}$$

Of the two methods, the one we have used in this frame is probably the better when components and frequency have known values and we want to find the numerical value of the phase angle. The method we used in frame 38 is sometimes useful when we want to find a relationship between the component values and frequency to produce a particular result. We will look at such a problem in the next frame. You should, in any case, make sure you understand and can apply both methods.

41

RESONANCE

We wish to find the impedance of the circuit in the diagram below and determine the condition for this circuit to be *resonant*. A circuit is said to be resonant or to exhibit the property of *resonance* when the voltage across it and the current through it are in phase. We have seen in earlier frames that the only *component* for which this condition is true is a resistor. So, *at resonance, the impedance of a reactive circuit appears purely resistive*.

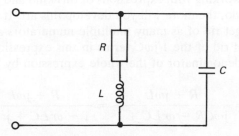

If we imagine an alternating voltage generator of output **V** connected to the input terminals of the circuit so that an alternating current **I** is drawn and we denote the equivalent impedance of the circuit by **Z**, we can write

$$V = IZ \quad \text{or} \quad V/I = Z$$

In frames 18 and 19 we found that, when two complex numbers having the same arguments were divided, the result was a real number. So, if V and I have the same arguments (which is what is meant by being in phase) then their quotient must be a real number. But the quotient of V and I is Z so, if we express Z in j-notation form and find the condition for it to be real, we will have solved the problem.

Now, using j-notation, can you write down an expression for the impedance of this circuit? Try to write down the impedance directly. Remember that we have an expression for the impedance of two impedances in parallel (it is the same as for two resistors in parallel but with the R's replaced by Z's). Consider the capacitor as one impedance, Z_1, and the series combination of the inductor and the resistor as 'the other impedance', Z_2. It is quite alright to consider more than one component as 'an impedance' as we saw in frame 37. From now on, when we are using j-notation, 'an impedance' is just another complex number. In fact, in the expression we have above, $V = IZ$, we are aiming to combine all three components in this circuit into an impedance, **Z**.

So, can you write an expression for **Z**?

42

$$Z = \frac{(R + j\omega L) \times (1/j\omega C)}{R + j\omega L + (1/j\omega C)}$$

Using the expression $Z = Z_1 \times Z_2/(Z_1 + Z_2)$ and setting $Z_2 = (1/j\omega C)$ and $Z_1 = (R + j\omega L)$ we get the result above. We now have to use algebraic manipulation on this expression to find the condition that it should be real.

There is an art in working with expressions of this kind and you will find that, the more problems you do, the more will you develop this art. It is usually worthwhile first of all to try to get rid of as many 'multiple numerators and denominators' as possible. We can get rid of the $1/j\omega C$ terms in this expression by multiplying the numerator and the denominator of the whole expression by $j\omega C$. We then have:

$$Z = \frac{R + j\omega L}{j\omega CR - \omega^2 LC + 1} = \frac{R + j\omega L}{1 - \omega^2 LC + j\omega CR}$$

We now have two alternative ways of tackling the problem. We can express Z as a complex number with separate real and imaginary parts and set the imaginary part to zero. Alternatively we can write expressions for the phase angles of the numerator and denominator and make them equal.

If we want to use the first method what is the first step? Give your answer in words and then write an expression to carry out what you suggest.

43

Multiply numerator and denominator by the complex conjugate of the denominator.

$$Z = \frac{(R + j\omega L)(1 - \omega^2 LC - j\omega CR)}{(1 - \omega^2 LC + j\omega CR)(1 - \omega^2 LC - j\omega CR)}$$

We now want a condition that the imaginary part of Z shall be zero. We can save some effort by making the following observations: the *denominator* will necessarily be *real and positive* so will not affect the signs of any terms in the numerator. Thus, since the condition we want relies only on the value of the *imaginary* part of the number and this is to be zero, all we need do is evaluate the *imaginary* part of the *numerator* and set this to zero.

Can you write an expression for the imaginary part of the numerator?

$$\boxed{\text{Im num } (\mathbf{Z}) = \omega L(1 - \omega^2 LC) - \omega CR^2}$$

To obtain this expression, we just have to multiply the real parts by the imaginary parts of both brackets in the numerator. All we have to do now is set the above expression to zero and we will have a condition for Im $\mathbf{Z}$ to be zero and so for $\mathbf{Z}$ to be real. We will find that doing this gives us a certain value for ω.

What is this value?

$$\boxed{\omega = \sqrt{\left(\frac{1}{LC} - \frac{R^2}{L^2}\right)}}$$

Here is the working: $\omega L (1 - \omega^2 LC) - \omega CR^2 = 0$ so $\omega L (1 - \omega^2 LC) = \omega CR$. $\omega = 0$ is plainly one solution but this means zero frequency (in other words direct voltage) so can be discounted. Since we are assuming that ω is non-zero we can cancel by it to obtain, with a little rearrangement:

$$\omega^2 LC = 1 - \frac{CR^2}{L} \quad \text{so} \quad \omega = \sqrt{\left(\frac{1}{LC} - \frac{R^2}{L^2}\right)}$$

This value of ω is called the resonant frequency of the circuit and the circuit is said to 'resonate' at this frequency. Notice that it is a value determined solely by the circuit components so, for a given set of components, the circuit built with them would resonate at a fixed frequency.

Now consider the solution using the other method. Let us recall the expression for $\mathbf{Z}$ that we arrived at in frame 42:

$$\mathbf{Z} = \frac{R + j\omega L}{1 - \omega^2 LC + j\omega CR}$$

If we now write expressions for the phase angles of the numerator and denominator and equate them, we should get the same result as we have above. All we need do, in fact, is calculate the tangents of the phase angles and equate these. Can you do this?

46

$$\omega L/R = \omega CR/(1 - \omega^2 LC)$$

In each case the tangent of the phase angle is obtained by dividing the imaginary part of the number by its real part. Cross multiplying the above expression gives us the same expression as we had in frame 45 so the result is indeed the same.

Now move on to the next frame for some more examples for you to try on your own.

47

REVISION QUESTIONS

1. If $Z_1 = R + j\omega L$ and $Z_2 = 1/j\omega C$ (with ω, R, L and C real as usual), find values of ω which make the following quantities real:

$$Z_1 + Z_2 \quad \text{and} \quad \frac{1}{Z_1} + \frac{1}{Z_2}$$

2. Calculate the amplitude of the voltage developed across the the circuit in the diagram below when a current $i = I \sin \omega t$ flows through it. What is the phase shift between the current and the voltage. Give your answer as the inverse tangent of the phase angle.

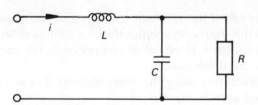

3. An alternating voltage generator is connected in series with an inductor, L, and a resistor, R_1, so that a current is drawn from the generator. What value of resistor R_2 can be connected in parallel with the inductor so that the amplitude of the current drawn from the generator is not altered?
4. Calculate the resonant frequency of the circuit in question 2 above. Substitute this value of frequency into an expression for Z, the impedance of the circuit, to find the value of the impedance at this frequency.

ANSWERS TO REVISION QUESTIONS

1. $Z_1 + Z_2 = R + j\omega L + 1/j\omega C = R + j\omega L - j/\omega C = R + j(\omega L - 1/\omega C)$

For this quantity to be real the imaginary part must be zero.

Thus $\omega L - 1/\omega C = 0$ so $\omega^2 = 1/LC$ and $\omega = 1/\sqrt{(LC)}$

$$\frac{1}{Z_1} + \frac{1}{Z_2} = \frac{1}{R + j\omega L} + j\omega C = \frac{R - j\omega L}{R^2 + \omega^2 L^2} + j\omega C = \frac{R}{R^2 + \omega^2 L^2} - \frac{j\omega L}{R^2 + \omega^2 L} + j\omega C$$

Again the imaginary part must be zero

so $\quad -\omega L/(R^2 + \omega^2 L^2) + \omega C = 0 \quad$ and $\quad \omega L = \omega C(R^2 + \omega^2 L^2)$

Cancelling by ω, since we are looking for a non-zero value, and rearranging:

$\omega^2 L^2 = L/C - R^2 \quad$ so $\quad \omega^2 = 1/LC - R^2/L^2 \quad$ and $\quad \omega = \sqrt{(1/LC - R^2/L^2)}$

2. In complex notation $V = IZ$ where Z is the complex impedance of the circuit.

The voltage amplitude is given by $|V| = V = |I| \times |Z| = I|Z|$

$$Z = j\omega L + \frac{R \times (1/j\omega C)}{R + 1/j\omega C} = j\omega L + \frac{R}{1 + j\omega CR}$$

(*Note*: The expression $Z = R/(1 + j\omega CR)$ for the impedance of a resistor and capacitor in parallel is worth remembering.)

$$Z = \frac{j\omega L - \omega^2 LCR + R}{1 + j\omega CR} = \frac{R(1 - \omega^2 LC) + j\omega L}{1 + j\omega CR} \quad \text{so} \quad Z = \sqrt{\left\{ \frac{R^2(1 - \omega^2 LC)^2 + \omega^2 L^2}{1 + \omega^2 C^2 R^2} \right\}}$$

$$\text{Thus } V = I\sqrt{\left(\frac{R^2(1 - \omega^2 LC)^2 + \omega^2 L^2}{1 + \omega^2 C^2 R^2} \right)}$$

With the usual convention that the phase of I can be taken as zero, we can find the phase difference between current and voltage by calculating the phase angle of the impedance Z. To express this phase angle in terms of its inverse tangent we must write Z as a complex number with identifiable real and imaginary parts. We therefore multiply numerator and denominator of the basic expression for Z by the complex conjugate of the denominator.

$$Z = \frac{[R(1 - \omega^2 LC) + j\omega L](1 - j\omega CR)}{(1 + j\omega CR)(1 - j\omega CR)} = \frac{R(1 - \omega^2 LC) + \omega^2 LCR + j[\omega L - \omega CR^2(1 - \omega^2 LC)]}{1 + \omega^2 C^2 R^2}$$

$$= \frac{R + j[\omega L - \omega CR^2(1 - \omega^2 LC)]}{1 + \omega^2 C^2 R^2}$$

So $\quad \phi = \arctan[(\omega L/R) - \omega CR(1 - \omega^2 LC)]$

3. It always helps to have a diagram, so we will draw one. Since a circuit and a modification to it are involved, we will draw them both. We can then calculate the complex impedance of each. The amplitude of the current will be determined by the modulus of the complex impedance, so we will calculate this for the two cases and equate the two expressions to find R_2.

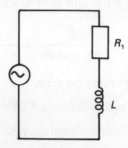 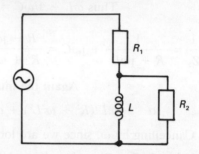

For the left-hand circuit we have $\quad Z = R_1 + j\omega L \quad$ so $\quad Z^2 = R_1^2 + \omega^2 L^2$

For the right-hand circuit we have $\; Z = R_1 + j\omega L R_2/(j\omega L + R_2)$

$$= (R_1 R_2 + j\omega L R_1 + j\omega L R_2)/(j\omega L + R_2)$$

So $\quad Z^2 = (R_1^2 R_2^2 + \omega^2 L^2 (R_1 + R_2)^2/R_2^2 + \omega^2 L^2)$

Equating impedances for the two circuits and multiplying by the denominator of the right-hand side, we have:

$$(R_1^2 + \omega^2 L^2)(R_2^2 + \omega^2 L^2) = R_1^2 R_2^2 + \omega^2 L^2 (R_1^2 + 2R_1 R_2 + R_2^2)$$

$$R_1^2 R_2^2 + \omega^2 L^2 R_1^2 + \omega^2 L^2 R_2^2 + \omega^4 L^4 = R_1^2 R_2^2 + \omega^2 L^2 R_1^2 + 2\omega^2 L^2 R_1 R_2 + \omega^2 L^2 R_2^2$$

So $\quad \omega^4 L^4 = 2\omega^2 L^2 R_1 R_2 \quad$ and thus $\quad R_2 = \omega^2 L^2/R_1$

4. In question 2 above we found an expression for Z as a complex number with separate real and imaginary parts. At the resonant frequency of the circuit, Z must be real. The imaginary part of Z must therefore be zero.

Now $\quad Z = \dfrac{R(1 - \omega^2 LC) + j\omega L}{1 + j\omega CR} = \dfrac{R + j[\omega L - \omega CR^2 (1 - \omega^2 LC)]}{1 + \omega^2 C^2 R^2}$

Setting the imaginary part of the numerator to zero (we can ignore the denominator since it is real and positive) we have:

$$\omega L - \omega CR^2 (1 - \omega^2 LC) = 0 \quad \text{so} \quad \omega^2 LC = 1 - L/CR^2 \quad \text{and}$$

$$\omega = \sqrt{\left(\frac{1}{LC} - \frac{1}{C^2 R^2}\right)}$$

Substituting this value back into the expression for Z we have:

$$Z = \frac{R}{1 + \omega^2 C^2 R^2} = \frac{R}{1 + C^2 R^2 \left[\dfrac{1}{LC} - \dfrac{1}{C^2 R^2} \right]} = \frac{R}{1 + \dfrac{C^2 R^2}{LC} - 1}$$

So
$$Z = \frac{R}{\dfrac{C^2 R^2}{LC}} = \frac{LCR}{C^2 R^2} = \frac{L}{CR} = Z \text{ since } Z \text{ is real}$$

49

TRANSFER FUNCTIONS

In designing circuits, engineers frequently need to connect simple circuits together to make more complicated circuits. It is therefore often useful to know how a current or a voltage at the output of a circuit depends on the current or voltage at the input. Such output/input relationships are called *transfer functions*: they describe how information (voltages or currents) will be *transferred* from the input of the circuit to its output. When such circuits contain reactive elements, j-notation analysis provides a very convenient way of evaluating these transfer functions.

To start with a simple example, we will look again at a circuit we have analysed before in a different context. The circuit shown below left consists of a capacitor and a resistor connected in series with an alternating voltage generator. Re-drawing the circuit but not altering it electrically in any way, we can represent it in a form often called a 'two-port network'.

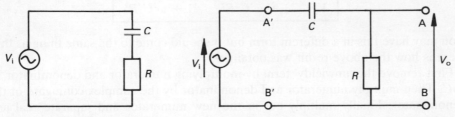

We have added terminals to the circuit to denote points between which we wish to make measurements (in a practical circuit we could connect an oscilloscope to these terminals). Terminals A′ and B′ are regarded as the input terminals or '*input port*'. Terminals A and B are regarded as the output terminals or '*output port*'.

We are interested in finding the ratio of the output voltage to the input voltage. This quantity is called the *voltage transfer function* of the circuit. Since it is the ratio of two quantities of the same kind (two voltages) it is dimensionless. Using j-notation for the impedance of the capacitor, the circuit can be analysed as a kind of '*a.c. potential divider*'.

Can you write down an expression for the ratio V_o/V_i?

50

$$\frac{V_o}{V_i} = \frac{R}{R + \dfrac{1}{j\omega C}}$$

We can obtain this result by using the 'potential divider rule' we developed in programme 2 for d.c. circuits. Here is the circuit we analysed in frames 71 and 72 of programme 2 and the result we found for it:

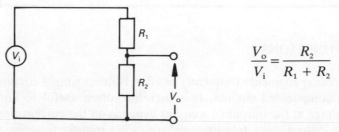

$$\frac{V_o}{V_i} = \frac{R_2}{R_1 + R_2}$$

In the expression in the box above, the normal capital V's are replaced by bold capital V's to denote the change from d.c. to a.c. signals and the use of j-notation. R_2 is replaced by R and R_1 by $1/j\omega C$.

Can you now manipulate this expression for V_o/V_i into the form $a + jb$? That is, express it as a complex number with separate real and imaginary parts.

51

$$\frac{V_o}{V_i} = \frac{\omega^1 C^2 R^2}{1 + \omega^2 C^2 R^2} + \frac{j\omega CR}{1 + \omega^2 C^2 R^2}$$

You may have this in a different form but it should come to the same thing as this. Here is how the above result was obtained.

First remove the 'unwieldy' term by multiplying numerator and denominator by $j\omega C$. Then multiply numerator and denominator by the complex conjugate of the denominator. Finally multiply out in the new numerator and separate real and imaginary parts. So we have:

$$\frac{V_o}{V_L} = \frac{R}{R + \dfrac{1}{j\omega C}} = \frac{j\omega CR}{j\omega CR + 1} = \frac{j\omega CR\,(-\,j\omega CR + 1)}{\omega^2 C^2 R^2 + 1}$$

$$= \frac{\omega^2 C^2 R^2}{1 + \omega^2 C^2 R^2} + \frac{j\omega CR}{1 + \omega^2 C^2 R^2}$$

What is the phase angle ϕ of V_o/V_i?

$$\phi = \arctan \frac{\text{Im}\ (V_o/V_i)}{\text{Rl}\ (V_o/V_i)} = \arctan \frac{\omega CR}{\omega^2 C^2 R^2} = \arctan \frac{1}{\omega CR}$$

We will now consider what information this phase angle gives us. Remember that V_o and V_i are complex phasors. So the phase angle of their ratio tells us the phase difference between them. If we once again take one phasor, V_i, as a reference and let it lie along the real axis it will represent a voltage $V \sin \omega t$. Since we have shown above that the ratio V_o/V_i is a complex number, say z, we can write $V_o = V_i \times z$. We use a small z here because capital Z's are conventionally kept to represent impedances. We do not need to make this z a bold letter but should realise that it, too, should strictly be regarded as a phasor operator. We also note that this small z is dimensionless whereas Z has dimensions of resistance.

Since we have chosen V_i as a reference phasor, we can write:

$$V_i = V\underline{/0} = V \quad \text{so} \quad V_o = Vz$$

If we can express z in exponential form as $z = Ke^{j\phi}$ where, as in the case we are considering at present, K and ϕ are determined by circuit components and input signal frequency, we have:

$$V = KVe^{j\phi}$$

So v_o, the time-varying function represented by the phasor V_o is completely specified by the amplitude and frequency of v_2, the time-varying *input signal* and by the modulus and argument (phase angle) of the complex number z. A diagram will once again help in the understanding of this. Since, in the example above, the phase angle of z is positive, V_o leads V_i. The diagram below thus serves to define the relationship between V_o and V_i.

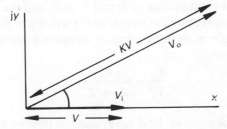

Since the V_o phasor represents a sinusoidally varying voltage, v_o, derived from v_i, we can write $v_o = KV \sin (\omega t + \phi)$.

What are the values of K and ϕ?

53

$$K = \omega CR/\surd(1 + \omega^2 C^2 R^2) \quad \phi = \arctan(1/\omega CR)$$

ϕ is the angle we found in the previous frame. K is the modulus of V_o/V_i. This is easily derived from the second expression given in the calculation for V_o/V_i in frame 51.

THE GENERALISED a.c. POTENTIAL DIVIDER

The circuit analysed in the previous few frames was easy to represent as an 'a.c. potential divider' which then made it easy to analyse using rules we established when working with d.c. circuits. We have seen in earlier frames how, using j-notation, combinations of components can be regarded as 'complex impedances'. We can define such combinations as complex impedances Z_1, Z_2 etc. In circuit analysis we can often simplify calculations by combining these two ideas. Consider the following example.

We want to find a condition for the output voltage of the circuit in the diagram shown below left to be in phase with the input voltage. This circuit is called a Wien Bridge after its inventor, and is widely used in laboratory oscillators – instruments to produce sinusoidally varying output voltages.

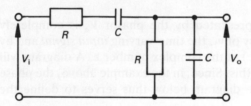 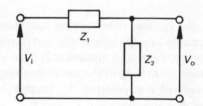

By defining the series combination of R and C as Z_1 and the parallel combination of R and C as Z_2, we can redraw the circuit as shown above right. We can then use the potential divider rule in its more general complex form as:

$$\frac{V_o}{V_i} = \frac{Z_2}{Z_1 + Z_2}$$

The format is exactly the same as the d.c. version but now we have Z_1 and Z_2 instead of R_1 and R_2.

Can you write down an expression for V_o/V_i?
Do not try to simplify it at this stage.

$$\frac{V_o}{V_i} = \frac{\dfrac{R/j\omega C}{R + 1/j\omega C}}{\dfrac{R/j\omega C}{R + 1/j\omega C} + R + 1/j\omega C}$$

The numerator is just the expression for a resistor and capacitor in parallel – the two components to the right of the circuit diagram. They comprise Z_2. The denominator repeats this expression and adds to it the expression for a resistor and capacitor in series – the two components to the left of the circuit diagram which comprise Z_1. To simplify this expression we can first multiply the numerator and denominator of the terms representing the parallel components by $j\omega C$. This gives:

$$\frac{V_o}{V_i} = \frac{\dfrac{R}{1 + j\omega CR}}{\dfrac{R}{1 + j\omega CR} + R + 1/j\omega C}$$

We can now multiply numerator and denominator of the whole expression by $1 + j\omega CR$ to give:

$$\frac{V_o}{V_i} = \frac{R}{R + (1 + 1/j\omega CR)(1 + j\omega CR)} = \frac{R}{R + R + 1/j\omega C + j\omega CR + R}$$

$$= \frac{R}{3R + j(\omega CR - 1/\omega C)}$$

We now need to find a condition for this expression to be real. This is the condition for the two phasors V_o and V_i to have zero phase difference. We could multiply numerator and denominator by the complex conjugate of the denominator to make the denominator real as we have before. We can save a lot of work however if we recognise that, since the numerator is already real, all we have to do is find a condition for the denominator to be real too. The whole expression must then be real. What is this condition?

55

$$\omega = 1/CR$$

If the j term is zero then $\omega CR = 1/\omega C$ so $\omega^2 = 1/C^2R^2$ and $\omega = 1/CR$

Since, at this value of ω, the j term in the expression for V_o/V_i is zero it is easy to see that $V_o/V_i = R/3R = 1/3$. So the output amplitude is one-third of the input amplitude.

56

THEVENIN'S THEOREM IN j-NOTATION

You may remember how, in programme 2, we found that, by using Thevenin's Theorem for circuits containing resistors and direct voltage and/or current generators, we could reduce any circuit with output terminals A and B to a single voltage generator in series with a single resistor. We can develop a similar theorem for circuits containing reactive elements and alternating voltage and/or current generators. Here is a simple example to start with:

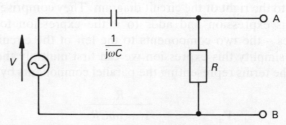

If we now want to connect loads to the terminals A and B it would be convenient to have the circuit represented in a simpler form. For d.c. circuits, the *Thevenin equivalent voltage generator* was given by calculating the *open-circuit output voltage*. The same is true for a.c. circuits analysed using j-notation. So the generator, which we will call V_T can be derived from the voltage transfer function. From frame 50 we have:

$$V_o/V_i = R/(R + 1/j\omega C) \quad \text{but} \quad V_o = V_T \quad \text{so} \quad V_T = V_i R/(R + 1/j\omega C)$$

In the d.c. case we also had a Thevenin equivalent resistance. Its value, for circuits with only independent generators, was that of the resistance seen 'looking back into the output terminals with all voltage generators short-circuited and all current generators open-circuited'. We have a directly comparable property for reactive circuits but now we must think in terms of a '*Thevenin equivalent impedance*, Z' calculated in the same way.

What is this impedance for the circuit above?

57

$$\boxed{Z = R/(1 + j\omega CR)}$$

This is the impedance of the resistor and the capacitor in parallel. As we did with the d.c. case, it will help to re-draw the circuit with the generator 'shorted out' to check this result. Can you do this?

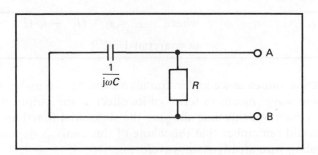

It is now easier to see that, for this circuit, both the resistor and the capacitor are connected directly between the output terminals. We can now talk of the '*impedance seen looking back into the output terminals*'.

Using a small rectangular box to represent an impedance as we did in frame 53, can you now draw the Thevenin equivalent circuit for the circuit in frame 56, giving the values for V_T and Z_T?

59

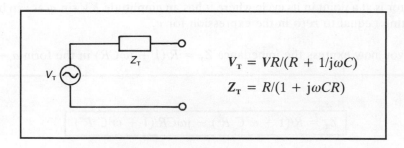

$$V_T = VR/(R + 1/j\omega C)$$

$$Z_T = R/(1 + j\omega CR)$$

The diagram looks just like the d.c. version except that the generator is now shown as an alternating generator and the resistor replaced by a generalised impedance. The values of V_T and Z_T are those we found in frames 56 and 57. It is worth considering what the expressions for the Thevenin equivalent generator and impedance mean in real terms. We saw in frame 52 that, having defined V_i as $V \underline{/0}$, an expression of the form we now have for V_o could be written in the form $V_o = KV_i e^{i\phi}$. Thevenin's theorem now states that, in terms of the effect it has at the output terminals, a generator with these properties can replace the real generator at the input to the circuit.

How would you write the expression for the Thevenin equivalent generator, V_T in the time domain in terms of K and ϕ? Give values for K and ϕ.

60

$$v_T = KV \sin(\omega t + \phi) \quad \text{where} \quad K = R/\sqrt{(R^2 + \omega^2 C^2)} \quad \text{and}$$
$$\phi = \arctan 1/\omega CR$$

These are the same values as we had in frames 52 and 53. To understand what this 'replacement sine wave' means in terms of its effect at the output it will again be useful to draw a diagram, this time showing the sinusoidal functions as well as the phasors. We should remember that the whole of this analysis depends on the fact that we are dealing with steady-state waveforms.

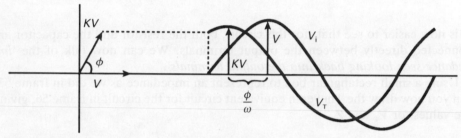

As we discovered in programme 4, the time $t = 0$ defines only the time at which we start taking an interest in the waveforms and is not in any sense absolute. A phase difference simply means then that, at the time $t = 0$, the replacement generator is at a point in its cycle where it has an amplitude $KV \sin \phi$ as can be seen by putting t equal to zero in the expression for v_T.

Can you now express the impedance $Z_T = R/(1 + j\omega CR)$ in the form $a + jb$?

61

$$Z_T = R/(1 + \omega^2 C^2 R^2) - j\omega CR/(1 + \omega^2 C^2 R^2)$$

To get the expression above, we multiply numerator and denominator of the expression for Z_T by the conjugate of the denominator.

$$\text{So } Z_T = \frac{R}{1 + j\omega CR} = \frac{R(1 - j\omega CR)}{1 + \omega^2 C^2 R^2} = \frac{R}{1 + \omega^2 C^2 R^2} - \frac{j\omega CR}{1 + \omega^2 C^2 R^2}$$

Notice that the expression for Z_T has a positive real (or resistive) part and a negative imaginary (or reactive) part. Since these two parts are added together they act as if they were in series. The Thevenin equivalent impedance could, at a given frequency, ω, be interpreted as a series combination of a resistor R' and a capacitor C' (because the reactive part is negative).

Can you work out expressions for R' and C' at the generator frequency ω?

$$R' = R/(1 + \omega^2 C^2 R^2) \quad C' = (1 + \omega^2 C^2 R^2)/\omega^2 C R^2$$

If we imagine Z_T to be made up of a resistor R' in series with a capacitor C', we can write $Z_T = R' + 1/j\omega C' = R' - j/\omega C'$, so:

$$R' - \frac{j}{\omega C'} = \frac{R}{1 + \omega^2 C^2 R^2} - \frac{j\omega C R}{1 + \omega^2 C^2 R^2}$$

Equating real parts and imaginary parts, we have:

$$R' = \frac{R}{1 + \omega^2 C^2 R^2} \quad \text{and} \quad \frac{1}{\omega C'} = \frac{\omega C R}{1 + \omega^2 C^2 R^2} \quad \text{so} \quad C' = \frac{1 + \omega^2 C^2 R^2}{\omega^2 C R^2}$$

We can always express the Thevenin equivalent impedance as a resistive term and a reactive term. The resistive term will always be positive (or zero) because, for real, passive components, there is no such thing as a negative resistance. The reactive term may be positive (in which case it appears inductive) or negative (in which case it appears capacitive).

We saw in programme 2 that the real power of the Thevenin equivalent circuit was the way it simplified the analysis of complicated circuits having a component (which we called the load) across which we wanted to find the voltage or through which we wanted to find the current. We were able to reduce the complicated circuit to a single generator in series with a single resistor so that the voltage across the load could then be calculated by using the potentiometer rule and the current could be calculated from Ohm's Law. The same thing is true about Thevenin's theorem in j-notation so, in most cases, it is sufficient to leave the equivalent impedance just as an impedance Z_T and not split it up into real and imaginary parts. Both the equivalent voltage generator and the equivalent impedance are used as a means to an end: that of making further calculations on the circuit simpler.

Referring back to the d.c. version of Thevenin's theorem in programme 2 if necessary, can you now write down a version which would be applicable to circuits containing reactive elements?

63

> Thevenin's theorem states that any circuit consisting of alternating voltage and/or current generators together with some combination of impedances and having a pair of output terminals, A and B, may be replaced at those terminals by a single alternating voltage generator in series with a single impedance. The output voltage of the generator is the open-circuit voltage of the original circuit. The value of the impedance is given by the ratio of the open-circuit voltage to the short-circuit current of the original circuit. For circuits with only independent generators, this is the same as the impedance which would be seen looking back into the output terminals if all voltage generators were replaced by short-circuits and all current generators by open-circuits.

We have obtained the above theorem by taking the d.c. version given earlier and simply replacing the word *direct* by the word alternating and the word resistance by the word *impedance*. If we have a circuit containing more than one alternating generator of whatever kind, there is an important restriction we must make to the above theorem. Can you think what it is?

64

> All generators must give outputs at the same frequency.

If this were not so, we would not be justified in replacing all inductors by impedances $j\omega L$ and all capacitors by impedances $1/j\omega C$. When writing down this theorem in future then for reactive circuits with alternating generators, we must add the words 'all of which give outputs at the same frequency' after the word generators in the second line.

By analogy with what we found in programme 3 we should now be able to write a dual theorem to Thevenin's theorem which we call Norton's theorem. This will allow us to represent any system of generators and impedances by a single current generator I_N in parallel with a single impedance Z_N.

Without writing the theorem out in full, can you draw a generalised Norton equivalent circuit and say what the value of the current generator I_N and impedance Z_N will be?

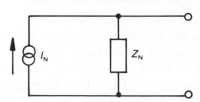

The current generator is the current that would be measured
in a short-circuit connected between the output terminals of
the circuit to be simplified. The impedance is the same as
that calculated for the Thevenin equivalent circuit.

If the Thevenin equivalent circuit has already been derived then, just as we found
for d.c. circuits, the Norton equivalent current generator can be found by dividing
the Thevenin equivalent voltage generator by the Thevenin equivalent impedance.
We will now see how to use these very powerful theorems to analyse a number of
circuits.

In frame 52 we found that the phase angle of the circuit to the left below was
$\phi = \arctan(1/\omega CR)$. The maximum value that this phase angle can assume is $\pi/2$ or
$90°$. This will be the value in the limiting condition that $\omega = 0$. We would like to
devise a circuit using sub-circuits of this kind to give a phase shift of π or $180°$ from
input to output.

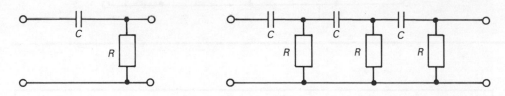

With two such circuits connected one after the other we could only hope to
achieve this when ω was zero. With three such circuits we should be able to find a
non-zero value of ω which will give us the required phase shift. Like the Wien
bridge, such circuits are used in the construction of oscillators. So we will analyse
the circuit to the right above to see what implications there are for the values of C,
R and ω. We will first establish what the required condition implies in terms of the
input/output voltage ratio.

If we let the input voltage be $v_i = V \sin \omega t$, what expression can we write for the
output voltage?

66

$$v_o = KV \sin (\omega t + \pi)$$

We must assume that the amplitude will be subject to a scaling factor K. We can also refer to K as an 'attenuation factor' since it is reasonable to assume from our previous work that v_o will be less than v_i. To attenuate means to make smaller. We put a positive sign for π because we know that the output of a single circuit leads the input, so it is reasonable to assume that the output of three such circuits in series will do so too.

If $\quad v_o = KV \sin (\omega t + \pi) \quad$ then $\quad v_o = -KV \sin \omega t$

or $\quad v_o = -v_i \quad$ so $\quad v_o/v_i = -K$

This relationship must apply to the phasor representation too. That is $V_o/V_i = -K$ so, if we express V_o/V_i in terms of C, R and $j\omega$, we want the condition that this expression shall be real and negative so the j term must be zero. We will apply Thevenin's theorem to the circuit in stages.

Can you re-draw the circuit with the part to the left of the broken line shown below replaced by its Thevenin equivalent? Give values for the equivalent voltage generator and impedance.

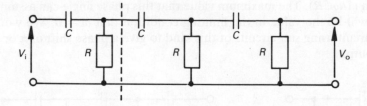

67

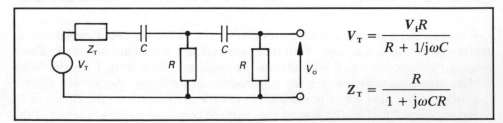

$$V_T = \frac{V_i R}{R + 1/j\omega C}$$

$$Z_T = \frac{R}{1 + j\omega CR}$$

The values are the ones we derived in frame 52.

68

We can now apply Thevenin's theorem again to the left of the broken line shown in the diagram below.

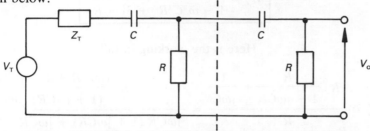

Can you re-draw the circuit again to show how it will look after this second application of Thevenin's theorem? Call the new Thevenin equivalent generator and impedance V_T' and Z_T' and write expressions for V_T' and Z_T' in terms of V_T and Z_T. Do not try to simplify them further at this stage.

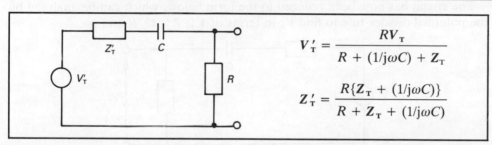

69

$$V_T' = \frac{RV_T}{R + (1/j\omega C) + Z_T}$$

$$Z_T' = \frac{R\{Z_T + (1/j\omega C)\}}{R + Z_T + (1/j\omega C)}$$

We apply the potential divider rule to the circuit to the left of the broken line in frame 68 to calculate V_T'. We calculate the impedance looking back into the output terminals with V_T shorted out to find Z_T'. If we now substitute the expressions for V_T and Z_T from the beginning of frame 67 into the expression for V_T' we have:

$$V_T' = \frac{R^2 V_i}{\left(R + \dfrac{1}{j\omega C}\right)\left(R + \dfrac{1}{j\omega C} + \dfrac{R}{1 + j\omega CR}\right)}$$

$$= \frac{R^2 V_i}{\left(\dfrac{j\omega CR + 1}{j\omega C}\right)\left(\dfrac{j\omega CR(1 + j\omega CR) + (1 + j\omega CR) + j\omega CR}{j\omega C(1 + j\omega CR)}\right)}$$

$$= \frac{-\omega^2 C^2 R^2 V_i}{(j\omega CR + 1)(1 + j\omega CR) + j\omega CR} = \frac{-\omega^2 C^2 R^2 V_i}{1 - \omega^2 C^2 R^2 + 3j\omega CR}$$

Can you now work out the expression for Z_T' in the same way?

70

$$Z'_T = \frac{R(1 + 2j\omega CR)}{1 - \omega^2 C^2 R^2 + 3j\omega CR}$$

Here is the working in full.

$$Z'_T = \frac{R \dfrac{R}{1 + j\omega CR} + \dfrac{1}{j\omega C}}{R + \dfrac{R}{1 + j\omega CR} + \dfrac{1}{j\omega C}} = \frac{R \dfrac{(j\omega CR + 1 + j\omega CR)}{(1 + j\omega CR)(j\omega C)}}{\dfrac{j\omega CR(1 + j\omega CR) + j\omega CR + 1 + j\omega CR}{(1 + j\omega CR)(j\omega C)}}$$

$$= \frac{R(1 + 2j\omega CR)}{1 - \omega^2 C^2 R^2 + 3j\omega CR}$$

The circuit has now been reduced to the form below, which can be analysed by the potential divider rule to find V_o in terms of V'_T, Z'_T, C, R and $j\omega$.

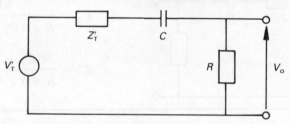

Can you write down the expression for V_o?

71

$$V_o = \frac{R V'_T}{R + 1/j\omega C + Z'_T}$$

We can now substitute for V'_T and Z'_T in this expression and then find V_o/V_i. We can then deduce under what conditions V_o/V_i will be real and negative. Do not forget to do a dimensional check on everything you write down. Since, in the expressions above, we have a term V_o on the left of the expression, then the right-hand side must have 'dimensions' of voltage too. All other terms must therefore 'balance out' dimensionally. Notice that terms such as ωCR, $\omega^2 C^2 R^2$ and so on are dimensionless!

Bearing these points in mind, can you now write down the full expression for V_o/V_i and reduce it to a quotient of two quotients?

$$\frac{V_o}{V_i} = \frac{\dfrac{-\omega^3 C^3 R^3}{1 - \omega^2 C^2 R^2 + 3j\omega CR}}{R + \dfrac{1}{j\omega C} + \dfrac{R(1 + 2j\omega CR)}{1 - \omega^2 C^2 R^2 + 3j\omega CR}} = \frac{\dfrac{-\omega^3 C^3 R^3}{1 - \omega^2 C^2 R^2 + 3j\omega CR}}{\dfrac{(1 + j\omega CR)(1 - \omega^2 C^2 R^2 + 3j\omega CR) + j\omega CR(1 + 2j\omega CR)}{j\omega C(1 - \omega^2 C^2 R^2 + 3j\omega CR)}}$$

We now want to simplify this expression and find a condition for it to be real. If you are not used to dealing with these 'four-decker' fractions, it may help you to think

of them as follows. Suppose we have a fraction $\dfrac{\dfrac{a}{b}}{\dfrac{c}{d}}$. We can think of this as two

fractions a/b divided by c/d which can therefore be re-written as a/b multiplied by d/c. So we can write:

$$\frac{\dfrac{a}{b}}{\dfrac{c}{d}} = \frac{ad}{bc}$$

We could re-organise any four-decker fraction we get in this way before trying to simplify it. However, to save a bit of work, we can note that any common factors of a and c will cancel, as will any common factors of b and d. (We can still, of course, cancel common factors between a and b and between c and d.) We will then be left with a simple fraction made up of what is left of ad divided by what is left of bc.

Can you now turn the expression for V_o/V_i above into a simple fraction?

$$\frac{V_o}{V_i} = \frac{-j\omega^3 C^3 R^3}{(1 + j\omega CR)(1 - \omega^2 C^2 R^2 + 3j\omega CR) + j\omega CR(1 + 2j\omega CR)}$$

Referring to frame 72, the whole of b cancels with part of d. The $j\omega C$, which is all that is left of d, is then multiplied by a to give the numerator above. b has been cancelled so the denominator above is just c.

We can now multiply out in the denominator and collect up real and imaginary terms to obtain:

$$\frac{V_o}{V_i} = \frac{-j\omega^3 C^3 R^3}{1 - 6\omega^2 C^2 R^2 + j(5\omega CR - \omega^3 C^3 R^3)}$$

Can you now find a value of ω for which V_o/V_i is real?

74

$$\omega = 1/\sqrt{6CR}$$

For the expression in frame 73 to be real, the *real* part of the denominator must be zero. This will leave only *imaginary* terms in both numerator and denominator. The j's will therefore cancel leaving a real result. For the real part to be zero we must have $1 - 6\omega^2C^2R^2 = 0$, giving ω the above value.

With this value of ω, what is the value of V_o/V_i?

75

$$\frac{V_o}{V_i} = -\frac{1}{29}$$

Here is the working:

$$\frac{V_o}{V_i} = \frac{-j\omega^3C^3R^3}{j(5\omega CR - \omega^3C^3R^3)} = \frac{-\omega^2C^2R^2}{5 - \omega^2C^2R^2} = \frac{-1/6}{5 - 1/6} = \frac{-1/6}{29/6} = -\frac{1}{29}$$

We will now use Norton's theorem to solve a problem.

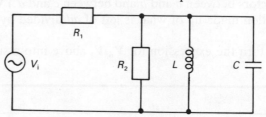

Using j-notation, we will find an expression for the current in the capacitor in the circuit above in terms of the input voltage. We will then determine the frequency at which the capacitor current is 90° out of phase with the generator voltage and write an expression in the time domain for the current at this frequency. If we regard the two resistors and the inductor as a two-port network, the current/voltage ratio we are setting out to calculate, that is, I_o/V_i is called the *transconductance* of the network.

If we regard the capacitor as a load, we can disconnect it and apply Norton's theorem to what is left of the circuit. To apply Norton's theorem we must make a modification to the part of the circuit that remains when the capacitor has been disconnected.

Can you re-draw the circuit with this modification made?

76

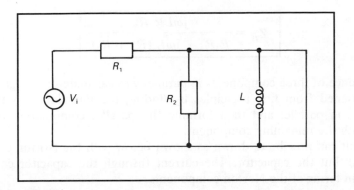

Since, in Norton's theorem, we have to calculate the current flowing in a *short-circuit* between the output terminals, we must *connect* this short-circuit when we *disconnect* the load. In this case we are regarding the capacitor as the load. The current we calculate will be I_N, the Norton equivalent current generator.

If the voltage generator is V_i, what is the value of the Norton generator?

77

$$I_N = V_i/R_1$$

Since R_2 and L are by-passed by the short-circuit, all the current in R_1 flows through the short-circuit. There is no voltage across the short-circuit, so all the generator voltage V_i is across R_1.

The Norton equivalent impedance is the impedance looking back into the output terminals with the short-circuit removed from between them again and with the voltage generator shorted out as well, as shown below.

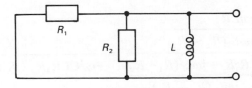

What is value of the Norton equivalent impedance?

78

$$Z_N = \frac{j\omega L R_1 R_2}{R_1 R_2 + j\omega L (R_1 + R_2)}$$

The impedance of three components in parallel was calculated in programme 2. It can be obtained from first principles by finding the impedance of two of the components in parallel and then forming the parallel combination of this impedance with the remaining component.

The circuit can now be re-drawn as shown below with the Norton components replacing all but the capacitor. The current through the capacitor can then be calculated in terms of the Norton components.

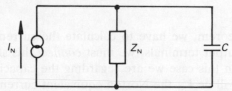

What is the current through the capacitor?

79

$$I_o = \frac{I_N Z_N}{Z_N + 1/j\omega C}$$

This result comes directly from the current splitter rule. The rest of the working is very similar to other problems we have solved already. We can now substitute for the values of I_N and Z_N found in frames 77 and 78 to give:

$$I_o = \frac{\dfrac{V_i}{R_1} \times \dfrac{j\omega L R_1 R_2}{R_1 R_2 + j\omega L (R_1 + R_2)}}{\dfrac{j\omega L R_1 R_2}{R_1 R_2 + j\omega L (R_1 + R_2)} + \dfrac{1}{j\omega C}}$$

Hence:

$$\frac{I_o}{V_i} = \frac{\dfrac{j\omega L R_2}{R_1 R_2 + j\omega L (R_1 + R_2)}}{\dfrac{-\omega^2 CLR_1 R_2 + R_1 R_2 + j\omega L (R_1 + R_2)}{j\omega C [R_1 R_2 + j\omega L (R_1 + R_2)]}} = \frac{-\omega^2 CLR_2}{-\omega^2 CLR_1 R_2 + R_1 R_2 + j\omega L (R_1 + R_2)}$$

Now, for what value of ω will there be a 90° phase shift between I_o and V_i?

$$\boxed{\omega = \sqrt{(1/LC)}}$$

For a 90° phase shift between input and output, the ratio I_o/V_i must be *imaginary*. Since the numerator is real, the denominator must be imaginary. This is true when:

$$-\omega^2 CLR_1R_2 + R_1R_2 = 0 \quad \text{so} \quad \omega^2 = 1/CL \quad \text{and} \quad \omega = \sqrt{(1/CL)}$$

What is the current at this frequency?

$$\boxed{\text{If } v_i = V \sin \omega t \quad \text{then} \quad i_o = \frac{V}{Z} \cos \omega t \quad \text{where} \quad Z = \frac{\omega L (R_1 + R_2)}{R_2}}$$

Since no expression is given for v_i in the question, we can choose it to be $V \sin \omega t$ to give the simplest form for the reference phasor. Substituting the value of ω found above into the expression for I_o, we get:

$$I_o = -V_iR_2/j\omega L (R_1 + R_2) = jV_iR_2/\omega L (R_1 + R_2)$$

The amplitude of i_o is the modulus of this expression. Since the j term is positive, the phase shift is $+\pi/2$ but $\sin (\omega t + (\pi/2)) = \cos \omega t$ hence the result at the beginning of the frame.

To conclude the examples in this programme we will use Thevenin's theorem to solve one more problem. We will calculate the current in the 10 kΩ resistor in the circuit below if the voltage generator gives an output with an amplitude of 40 volts at a frequency at $100/\pi$ kHz. This problem has numbers in it so that we do not forget that, in real circuit design, we shall ultimately be dealing with component and frequency values rather than just symbols.

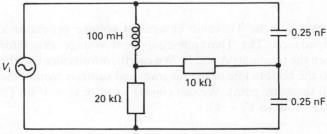

Try to solve this problem yourself before turning the page for the answer.

82

> Writing the voltage as $v = 40 \sin (200 \times 10^3 t)$ volts,
> the current is $-1 \cos (200 \times 10^3 t)$ milliamps

Here is the working in full. Although this may not seem, at first sight, the kind of problem to which one might easily apply Thevenin's theorem, it helps to recall the way in which we applied it to problems in programme 3. To find the current through or voltage across a load, we first analyse the circuit with the load removed to find the Thevenin equivalent of the circuit minus the load. In this problem we can regard the 10 kΩ resistor as a load, so we first re-draw the circuit without this resistor. Since we know the frequency, we can now calculate the values of the complex impedances of the inductor and the capacitors. These values have been marked on the diagram.

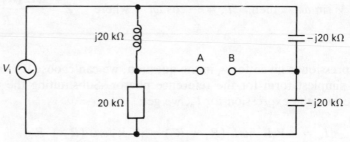

Can you do the working to confirm the values shown on the diagram? Notice that all components are marked in kΩ.

83

> Since $f = 100/\pi$ kHz and $\omega = 2\pi f$, then $\omega = 200 \times 10^3$
>
> $Z_i = j\omega L = j200 \times 10^3 \times 100 \times 10^{-3} = j20,000 = j20$ kΩ
>
> $Z = 1/j\omega C = 1/j200 \times 10^3 \times 0.25 \times 10^{-9} = 1/j0.05 \times 10^{-3} = -j20$ kΩ

We can now calculate the Thevenin equivalent voltage generator and Thevenin equivalent impedance. The Thevenin equivalent voltage generator will be the voltage between the terminals A and B. We can therefore calculate the voltage at A with respect to the bottom line of the diagram and subtract from it the voltage at B with respect to the same point. We can *choose* to write $v_i = V \sin (200 \times 10^3 t)$ or $V_i = V\underline{/0}$ but $V = 40$ so $V_i = 40$.

Now, can you calculate V_A and V_B and say what V_T is in complex form.

$$V_A = \frac{20 \times 40}{20 + j20} = 40\,\frac{1}{(1+j)} = \frac{40\,(i-j)}{2} = 20\,(1-j)\ \text{V}$$

$V_B = V_i/2$ by inspection, since the two capacitors form
an a.c. potential divider with equal impedances, so
$$V_B = 40/2 = 20\ \text{V}$$

So $V_T = V_A - V_B = 20 - j20 - 20 = -j20\ \text{V}$

The next thing to do is calculate Z_T, the Thevenin equivalent impedance. We can do this by looking back into the output terminals. To do this it will help to draw a diagram of the circuit with the voltage generator shorted out. You draw the diagram and calculate Z_T. Work in kΩ.

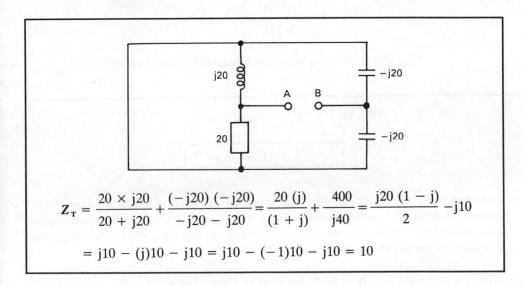

$$Z_T = \frac{20 \times j20}{20 + j20} + \frac{(-j20)\,(-j20)}{-j20 - j20} = \frac{20\,(j)}{(1+j)} + \frac{400}{j40} = \frac{j20\,(1-j)}{2} - j10$$

$$= j10 - (j)10 - j10 = j10 - (-1)10 - j10 = 10$$

With the generator shorted out, the path from terminal A to terminal B is first via the resistor *in parallel with* the inductor, since the top and bottom lines of the diagram are now effectively the same point. To get to B we must now go through both capacitors *in parallel*. These two parallel combinations are in series. The calculations above show this. The equivalent impedance thus has a real value of 10 kΩ at this frequency.

We now have both components of the Thevenin equivalent circuit so can draw the circuit with the load connected back in. You do this.

86

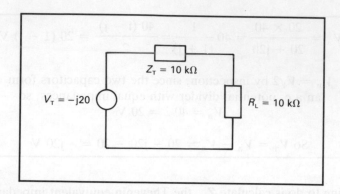

Just as we found with resistive circuits in programme 3, the circuit has been greatly simplified. It is now a simple matter to calculate the current i in complex form. By Ohm's Law we have:

$$I = \frac{-\mathrm{j}20 \text{ V}}{20 \text{ k}\Omega} = -\mathrm{j} \text{ mA}$$

Can you now write the time function for the current?

87

$$\boxed{i = -1 \cos (200 \times 10^3 t)}$$

The term $(-\mathrm{j})$ implies an amplitude of unity for the current and a phase *lag* of $\pi/2$ compared with the voltage input. Since we have calculated all resistances in kilohms and all voltages in volts, the units of current are milliamps. We can convert this into an answer in the time domain as follows:

If $v = 40 \sin (200 \times 10^3 t)$ then

$$i = 1 \sin (200 \times 10^3 t - \pi/2)$$

$$= -1 \cos (200 \times 10^3 t)$$

That completes the material to be covered in this programme. Now check through the following summary and revision exercises, and then try the test questions.

88

SUMMARY

1. In applying j-notation to circuit analysis, all inductors can be replaced by a *complex impedance* $j\omega L$ and all capacitors by a *complex impedance* $1/j\omega C$, where L and C are the values of the components and ω is the frequency of all generators in the circuit.

2. If an alternating voltage generator whose output is represented by a *complex phasor V* causes an alternating current which can be represented by a complex phasor *I* to flow through a complex impedance Z, the following relationships apply:

$$V = IZ$$

The modulus, $|Z|$, of Z gives the ratio of the amplitudes of V and I.

The argument, ϕ, of Z gives the phase shift between V and I.

3. If, in point 2 above, the current is represented in the time domain by the expression $i = I \sin \omega t$, then the voltage can be represented by the expression $v = IZ \sin (\omega t + \phi)$. If ϕ is *positive*, the voltage is said to *lead* the current. If ϕ is *negative*, the voltage is said to *lag* the current.

4. A circuit containing resistors, capacitors and inductors is said to be *resonant* at a certain frequency if its impedance at that frequency is wholly resistive. Its *complex impedance* will therefore have a *zero imaginary part*.

5. The *transfer functions* of circuits containing reactive components can be calculated very conveniently using j-notation. Calculating voltage and current transfer functions often reduces to applying the potentiometer or current splitter rules in the *complex frequency domain*.

6. All circuit laws and theorems derived for resistive circuits apply to reactive circuits analysed using j-notation. In particular, Thevenin's and Norton's theorems can be applied provided all generators in the circuit being analysed have outputs at the same frequency. The *Thevenin and Norton equivalent circuits* are quoted as having *output impedances* rather than output resistances, and the equivalent *generators* in general *have different phases* from those they replace.

7. The algebraic expressions produced when analysing circuits using j-notation are often quite complicated. The *dimensions* of all terms involved in the expressions *should* therefore *be checked frequently* to minimise the possibility of error.

89

1.

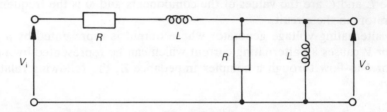

The circuit above is excited by an alternating voltage generator of variable frequency. Write an expression for the voltage transfer function of the circuit and find a value of frequency at which the output voltage is in phase with the input voltage. What is the output/input voltage amplitude ratio at this frequency?

2.

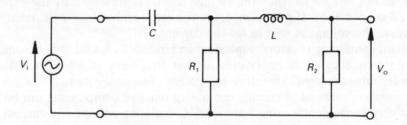

Reduce the circuit above to a simpler form by applying Thevenin's theorem to the generator, the capacitor and the resistor R_1, and hence find a value of frequency at which the voltage across the resistor R_2 is in phase with the generator voltage. What is the output/input voltage amplitude ratio at this frequency?

3. Using the simplified version of the circuit in problem 2 above, derive a Norton equivalent circuit for the generator, the capacitor, the resistor R_1 and the inductor in the original circuit. If the resistor R_2 was replaced by a second capacitor C, what current would flow through this capacitor? Leave your answer in j-notation form.

ANSWERS TO REVISION QUESTIONS

1.

$$\frac{V_o}{V_i} = \frac{\dfrac{R \times j\omega L}{R + j\omega L}}{\dfrac{R \times j\omega L}{R + j\omega L} + R + j\omega L} = \frac{j\omega LR}{j\omega LR + R^2 + 2j\omega LR - \omega^2 L^2}$$

$$= \frac{j\omega LR}{R^2 - \omega^2 L^2 + 3j\omega LR}$$

V_o is in phase with V_i when $R^2 - \omega^2 L^2 = 0$ because, with this condition, the numerator and denominator are then both imaginary so the j's cancel making the voltage transfer function real.

$$\text{When} \quad R^2 - \omega^2 L^2 = 0 \quad \text{then} \quad \omega = R/L$$

$$\text{At this value of } \omega \quad \frac{V_o}{V_i} = \frac{j\omega LR}{3j\omega LR} = \frac{1}{3}$$

2.

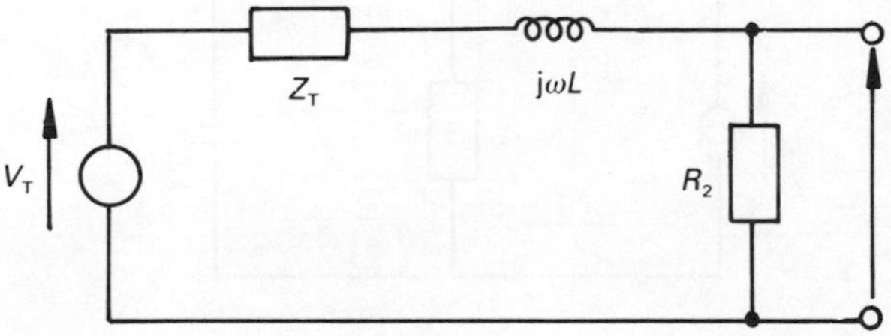

$$V_T = \frac{V_i R_1}{R_1 + 1/j\omega C} = \frac{j\omega C R_1 V_i}{1 + j\omega C R_1} \quad Z_T = \frac{R_1 (1/j\omega C)}{R_1 + 1/j\omega C} = \frac{R_1}{1 + j\omega C R_1}$$

$$\text{So} \quad V_o = \frac{R_2}{R_2 + j\omega L + R_1/(1 + j\omega C R_1)} \times \frac{j\omega C R_1 V_i}{1 + j\omega C R_1}$$

$$= \frac{j\omega C R_1 R_2 V_i}{R_2 + j\omega L + j\omega C R_1 R_2 - \omega^2 L C R_1 + R_1}$$

$$\text{and} \quad \frac{V_o}{V_i} = \frac{j\omega C R_1 R_2}{R_1 + R_2 - \omega^2 L C R + j\omega L + j\omega C R_1 R_2}$$

V_o is in phase with V_i when $R_1 + R_2 - \omega^2 LCR_1 = 0$ so $\omega^2 = \dfrac{R_1 + R_2}{LCR_1}$

With this condition $\dfrac{V_o}{V_i} = \dfrac{\omega CR_1R_2}{\omega L + \omega CR_1R_2} = \dfrac{CR_1R_2}{L + CR_1R_2}$

ANSWERS TO REVISION QUESTIONS

3. The simplified circuit and the new load are shown below.

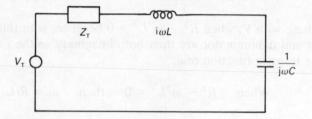

They must be transformed to the following form:

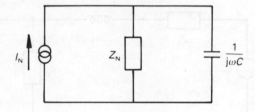

To find I_N, the capacitor must be replaced by a short-circuit. Then:

$$I_N = \frac{V_T}{Z_T + j\omega L} = \frac{\dfrac{j\omega CR_1 V_i}{1 + j\omega CR}}{\dfrac{R_1}{1 + j\omega CR_1} + j\omega L} = \frac{j\omega CR_1 V_i}{R_1 - \omega^2 LCR_1 + j\omega L}$$

$$Z_N = Z_T + j\omega L = \frac{R_1}{1 + j\omega CR_1} + j\omega L = \frac{R_1 - \omega^2 LCR_1 + j\omega L}{1 + j\omega CR_1}$$

The current in the capacitor I is given by

$$I_c = \cfrac{Z_N \times I_N}{Z_N + \cfrac{1}{j\omega C}} = \cfrac{\cfrac{R_1 - \omega^2 LCR_1 + j\omega L}{1 + j\omega CR_1} \times \cfrac{j\omega CR_1 V_i}{R_1 - \omega^2 LCR_1 + j\omega L}}{\cfrac{R_1 - \omega^2 LCR_1 + j\omega L}{1 + j\omega CR_1} + \cfrac{1}{j\omega C}}$$

$$= \cfrac{\cfrac{j\omega CR_1 V_i}{1 + j\omega CR_1}}{\cfrac{j\omega C\,(R_1 - \omega^2 LCR_1 + j\omega L) + 1 + j\omega CR_1}{j\omega C\,(1 + j\omega CR_1)}}$$

$$= \cfrac{-\omega^2 C^2 R_1 V_i}{1 - \omega^2 LC + j\,(2\omega CR - \omega^2 LC^2 R_1)}$$

TEST ON PROGRAMME 5

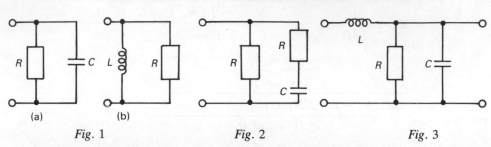

Fig. 1   *Fig.* 2   *Fig.* 3

1. Write down the input impedances of the two circuits in figure 1, (a) in the form $Z = x + jy$ and (b) in the form $Z = re^{j\theta}$.
2. Find the complex impedance and hence the impedance of the circuit in figure 2, and the phase shift between an alternating voltage input to the circuit and the current which would be drawn from a generator supplying it.
3. At what value of ω is the output voltage of the circuit in figure 3, 90° out of phase with the input voltage? Is the phase difference a lead or a lag?

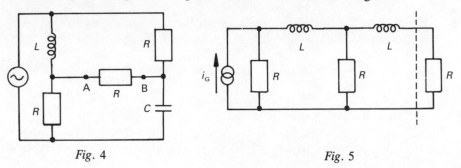

Fig. 4   *Fig.* 5

4. For what relationship between the component values would there be no current in the resistor R connected between A and B in the circuit in figure 4? Give your answer in terms of quantities having dimensions of time. If these conditions were not met, use Thevenin's theorem to find a frequency at which the current in this resistor is in phase with the generator voltage and say what the amplitude of this current is.
5. Writing the generator current in the circuit in figure 5 as $i = I \sin \omega t$, find the current in the resistor at the right-hand end of the diagram. (Use Norton's theorem to replace the components to the left of the broken line by an equivalent circuit, then analyse the resulting circuit.) Find a frequency at which the current is 90° out of phase with the generator current and write an expression in the time domain for the current at this frequency.

FURTHER QUESTIONS ON PROGRAMME 5

1. Find the roots of the equations $x^2 + 4x + 13 = 0$ and $x^2 - 6x + 13 = 0$. Give the roots in Cartesian form.

2. Express the answers to question 1(a) in polar form and 1(b) in exponential form, and plot them on an Argand diagram.

3. Plot the numbers $3e^{j\pi/6}$ and $3e^{j\pi/3}$ on an Argand diagram. If these numbers represent voltages expressed as complex phasors, determine their sum and show this too on your diagram. Plot a second Argand diagram with the lagging voltage represented as a phasor on the real axis, and show that all the amplitude and phase relationships are preserved.

4. Electronic circuit designers usually express alternating signals in terms of their voltage or current amplitudes (as has been done in this programme). Thus an alternating voltage with an amplitude of 10 volts could be represented in the form $v = 10 \sin \omega t$. The reasons for this convention relate to the limitations imposed by fixed power supplies on electronic circuit design.

   Electrical power engineers, on the other hand, prefer to describe alternating voltages and currents in terms of their r.m.s. values since these relate directly to the power carried by the waveforms. They refer to such voltages and currents *on the assumption* that the values quoted are r.m.s. values. Thus a *'100 volt a.c. supply'* is automatically taken by a power engineer to mean a supply whose *r.m.s. value is 100 volts*. Such a supply could be represented in the form $v = (100\sqrt{2}) \sin \omega t$.

   Power engineers nevertheless use phasor diagrams and j-notation to describe the voltages and currents with which they deal, making the lengths of phasors and the equivalent quantities in j-notation equal to the r.m.s. values of the voltages and currents they are being used to represent.

   Explain why this convention still leads to correct answers, the answers now being obtained directly as r.m.s. values.

5. Two impedances which can be represented as having complex values $(8 - j7)$ ohms and $(5 + j6)$ ohms are connected in parallel across a 100 volt a.c. supply as understood by a power engineer in question 4 above. Calculate the total (r.m.s.) current drawn from the supply and its phase relative to the applied voltage.

6. A 50 mH inductor is connected in parallel with a 100 Ω resistor. This parallel connection is connected in series with a 10 µF capacitor and a 10 Ω resistor. Calculate: (a) the complex impedance of the circuit at a frequency of $(1/2\pi)$ kHz; (b) the complex impedance at a frequency of $(2/\pi)$ kHz; (c) a value of frequency at which the circuit appears purely resistive; and (d) the impedance of the circuit at the frequency found in (c) above.

7. The circuit in question 6 above is energised by a voltage generator with an output of amplitude 3 V at a frequency of $(1/\pi)$ kHz. What is the amplitude of the current in the inductor and what is its phase relative to the generator?

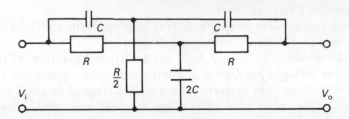

8. Using nodal analysis or the complex form of the star–delta transformation developed in further question 1 in programme 3, find a frequency at which the output of the above circuit is zero for any input V_i. What is the output at very high frequency and at very low frequency?

9. Determine the input impedance of the above circuit at the frequency at which the voltage output is zero and hence deduce the phase difference between the applied voltage and the current drawn at this frequency.

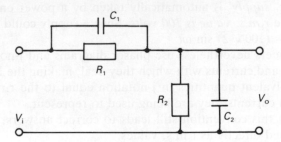

10. If the values of R_1, R_2 and C_2 are known the voltage output of the circuit above can be made independent of frequency by suitable choice of C_1. Calculate a value of C_1 to give this output/input relationship. In this form the circuit is known as a '*compensated attenuator*'. If $R_2 = 1$ MΩ and $C_2 = 22$ pF (typical values for the input impedance of an oscilloscope), design 2:1, 5:1 and 10:1 compensated attenuators for the oscilloscope, all of which still offer an input impedance of 1 MΩ.

Programme 6

FREQUENCY AND PHASE RESPONSE PLOTTING

INTRODUCTION

We have seen, in programme 5, how to use complex numbers to produce models of circuits which enable their steady-state response to sinusoidal driving functions to be analysed. A particularly important aspect of this theory is the application of the methods of analysis to the derivation of the 'frequency response' and 'phase response' of circuits. These two responses are a measure of how the input/output amplitude ratio and output phase relative to input phase change over a wide range of frequencies.

How a circuit responds to signals of different frequencies is of importance in many branches of circuit analysis and design. An audio amplifier of the kind used in domestic sound reproduction equipment has to give an output which is acceptable to a listener over the range of frequencies capable of being heard by the human ear. Radar signals (which are generated at much higher frequencies) must be gathered and processed by suitable equipment and reliably reconstructed so that the information they carry can be decoded to reveal the position of the object being monitored. It can be shown (but will not be covered in this text) that a waveform of *any* shape can be 'decomposed' into a sum of sinusoidal waveforms of different frequencies. The subject of Fourier Analysis covers this topic. How a circuit responds to the range of frequencies having a signficant component in the decomposition of a given waveform determines how well that circuit can handle that waveform.

In this programme you will learn how to manipulate into a form suitable for presentation as frequency and phase responses the complex number relationships produced by analysing circuits with sinusoidal inputs. You will see how logarithmic plots are widely used in presenting this information and will find that most of the important features of the responses can quickly be ascertained by straight-line plots which can be approximated to the complete responses.

All the terms used above will be fully explained as the programme progresses.

SYSTEM FUNCTIONS

In programme 5 we encountered many functions of the form V_o/V_i, V_o/I_i and so on, where terms such as V_o, V_i and I_i are complex functions of ω. In fact, as we saw, wherever ω occurs in any such function it is always preceded by j, so we can consider all functions as being functions, not just of ω, but of $j\omega$. Ratios of the form V_o/V_i, V_o/I_i and so on are called '*system functions*'. A system function is the ratio of a particular '*response*' of a circuit to a given stimulus. If the circuit shown here, for example, had an input stimulus V_i where V_i was the complex phasor representation of a sinusoidal voltage, we could deduce expressions for I_i, V_o and I_o which are the responses of the circuit to the stimulus V_i. Can you write an expression for V_o/V_i?

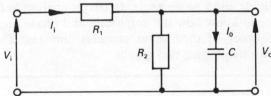

$$\frac{V_o}{V_i} = \frac{R_2}{R_1 + R_2 + j\omega C R_1 R_2}$$

Treating the circuit as a potential divider we can write:

$$\frac{V_o}{V_i} = \frac{R_2 \cdot \dfrac{1}{j\omega C}}{\dfrac{R_2 \cdot \dfrac{1}{j\omega C}}{R_2 + \dfrac{1}{j\omega C}} + R_1} = \frac{\dfrac{R_2}{j\omega C}}{\dfrac{R_2}{j\omega C} + R_1 R_2 + \dfrac{R_1}{j\omega C}} = \frac{R_2}{R_1 + R_2 + j\omega C R_1 R_2}$$

This ratio is a measure of how the input voltage is affected as it is 'transferred' to the output. It is called the '*voltage transfer function*'.

What are the dimensions of the voltage transfer function?

3

The voltage transfer function is dimensionless

Since it is a *ratio* of two *voltages*, the function must be dimensionless. It is just one of a number of system functions of the circuit. In a later programme we shall examine the general idea of system functions in more detail. In this programme, however, we are going to examine some particularly important properties of a restricted range of system functions: the voltage and current transfer functions.

Voltage and current transfer functions are dimensionless ratios of the input and output voltages and input and output currents respectively. Using complex notation they can be expressed as functions of $j\omega$ which, as we have seen, have associated with them an amplitude and a phase angle. In circuit analysis and design it is often of great importance to know how the amplitude and phase angle of these ratios change as the frequency of their input stimulus changes. This relationship is conventionally shown by plotting two graphs.

4

DEFINITIONS

1. The graph of amplitude against frequency is known as '*the frequency response*'.

2. The graph of phase angle against frequency is known as '*the phase response*'.

Frequency and phase responses are traditionally plotted in a particular way and the function of $j\omega$ is manipulated into a particular form in order to facilitate this. The expression we obtained for V_o/V_i in the previous frame was:

$$\frac{V_o}{V_i} = \frac{R_2}{R_1 + R_2 + j\omega CR_1R_2}$$

Can you manipulate this expression so that it is given in terms of an '*attenuation ratio*' $A_0 = \dfrac{R_2}{R_1 + R_2}$ and a frequency term $\omega_0 = \dfrac{R_1 + R_2}{CR_1R_2}$? (Check that ω_0 is indeed a frequency!)

5

$$\boxed{\frac{V_o}{V_i} = \frac{A_0}{1 + j\omega/\omega_0}}$$

Starting from the original expression, we have:

$$\frac{V_o}{V_i} = \frac{R_2}{R_1 + R_2 + j\omega CR_1R_2} = \left(\frac{R_2}{R_1 + R_2}\right) \cdot \frac{1}{\left(1 + \dfrac{j\omega CR_1R_2}{R_1 + R_2}\right)} = \frac{A_0}{1 + j\omega/\omega_0}$$

where $A_0 = R_2/(R_1 + R_2)$ and $\omega_0 = (R_1 + R_2)/CR_1R_2$

We note that a term with dimensions of frequency such as ω_0 can arise as the reciprocal of a term of the form CR. Since $R_1R_2/(R_1 + R_2)$ has dimensions of R, the product of C with this term does indeed have dimensions of frequency.

The expression for V_o/V_i is now in the classic form for deriving the frequency and phase responses of the circuit. Notice that it contains an attenuation term $R_2/(R_1 + R_2)$ which is a dimensionless ratio of circuit component values. We always look for a term of this kind (which may often simply be unity). It also contains a frequency dependent term $(1 + j\omega/\omega_0)$. Again, we always look for terms of this kind. That is, terms of the form $j\omega/\omega_0$ or $j\omega_0/\omega$ which may appear on their own or may be added to 1. It is very important to realise that *only* terms of this kind are acceptable. If the terms are not of the form $j\omega/\omega_0$ or $j\omega_0/\omega$ or are added to any number other than 1, then the expression is not in the right form.

6

PLOTTING THE FREQUENCY RESPONSE

As defined in frame 4, the frequency response is obtained by plotting the amplitude of the complex number representing the voltage ratio V_o/V_i against frequency. The *amplitude* of this number is the modulus of the complex number which represents the ratio of the *amplitudes* of the sinusoidal signals $v_i = V_i \sin \omega t$ and $v_o = V_o \sin(\omega t \pm \phi)$. We write this as $|V_o/V_i| = V_o/V_i$. Make sure you understand the slightly different meanings of the word 'amplitude' in the above description.

To plot the frequency response we examine the ratio V_o/V_i at the extremes of the frequency range and at significant points between them.

Can you write the expression for $|V_o/V_i|$ and say
what its values are when $\omega \to 0$ and when $\omega \to \infty$?

7

$$\left| \frac{V_o}{V_i} \right| = \frac{V_o}{V_i} = \frac{A_0}{\left(1 + \dfrac{\omega^2}{\omega_0^2} \right)^{1/2}}$$

As $\omega \to 0$ $\quad \dfrac{V_o}{V_i} \to A_0$ $\quad$ As $\omega \to \infty$ $\dfrac{V_o}{V_i} \to 0$

$$\frac{V_o}{V_i} = \left| \frac{V_o}{V_i} \right| = \left(\frac{A_0}{1 + j\dfrac{\omega}{\omega_0}} \cdot \frac{A_0}{1 - j\dfrac{\omega}{\omega_0}} \right)^{1/2} = \frac{A_0}{\left(1 + \dfrac{\omega}{\omega_0} \right)^{1/2}}$$

When $\omega \to 0$, the term in ω in the denominator tends to zero, so $\dfrac{V_o}{V_i} \to A_0$.

When $\omega \to \infty$, the term in ω in the denominator tends to ∞, so $\dfrac{V_o}{V_i} \to 0$.

The only other significant value of ω in this expression is $\omega = \omega_0$. What is the value of V_o/V_i when $\omega = \omega_0$?

8

$$\frac{V_o}{V_i} = \frac{A_0}{\sqrt{2}}$$

Here is a graph of V_o/V_i against ω:

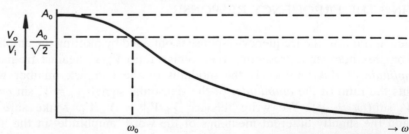

Because we are plotting from very low to very high frequencies, the graph is very asymmetrical. Most of the changes in V_o/V_i in which we are interested take place over a relatively short range of the frequency scale. To produce graphs on which the information of interest is more conveniently displayed it has become customary to use logarithmic scales for the plotting of frequency responses. We will spend the next few frames studying these.

9

LOGARITHMIC FREQUENCY SCALES

It is common practice, when carrying out a theoretical analysis of a circuit, to use the angular frequency ω and to plot this on the frequency axis as we have done in frame 8. When experimental or design work is being done, however, it is more usual to work with the frequency f where $\omega = 2\pi f$. This makes little difference to the general shape of the graphs when plotted linearly or logarithmically but should be kept in mind to avoid numerical errors. We shall discuss the technique using the angular frequency ω.

When logarithmic plotting is used the horizontal axis is laid out with values of $\log \omega$ rather than with values of ω. Since frequency and phase response plots are so important in amplifier and control system design, 'logarithmic graph paper' is widely available commercially. The major divisions on such paper correspond to the logarithms of multiples of 10. Multiples of 10 are called decades. Here is a logarithmic scale showing such major divisions:

0.001	0.01	0.1	1	10	100	1000	ω
-3	-2	-1	0	1	2	3	$\log \omega$

Notice how the values of ω and their corresponding logarithms are arranged on the axis and complete the following sentence:

> Equal multiples on the ω scale result
> in equal . . . . on the log ω scale.

10

> Equal multiples on the ω scale result
> in equal *increments* on the log ω scale.

The scale above shows only multiples of 10. The same statement is true, however, whatever starting point is used. The values 2, 20, 200 and so on are spaced the same distance apart as the values 1, 10, 100 and so on.

It is also important to notice what happens on the logarithmic scale for values of frequency less than unity. Here is another sentence for you to complete:

> When $\omega = 0$, the log ω scale is at . . . .

11

> When $\omega = 0$ the log ω scale is at *minus infinity*.

When $\omega < 1$ the equal multiples become equal sub-multiples as measured from right to left so, on a finite logarithmic scale, the value corresponding to $\omega = 0$ is never reached. By definition, in fact, log $(0) = -\infty$. The net effect of logarithmic plotting on the frequency scale is to compress the frequency range for values of frequency greater than unity and to expand it for values less than unity.

THE DECIBEL SCALE

A logarithmic scale is also conventionally used on the vertical axis for plotting the frequency response of a circuit. This depends on a unit of measurement called the *decibel* which is usually abbreviated as dB. The decibel is strictly defined in terms of power ratios as follows:

> Given two powers P_1 and P_2, they are said to differ by n decibels where $n = 10 \log_{10} P_1/P_2$.
>
> If $P_1 = 10P_2$ then $n = 10$. P_1 is said to 'show a power gain of 10 dB over P_2' or 'to be 10 dB up on P_2'.
>
> If $P_1 = P_2/10$ then $n = -10$. P_1 is said to 'show a power loss of 10 dB over P_2' or 'to be 10 dB down on P_2'.

What power gains or losses correspond to power ratios $P_1 = 2P_2$ and $P_1 = P_2/2$? Give your answers to the nearest whole number.

12

> $P_1 = 2P_2$ represents a power gain of 3 dB. P_1 is 3 dB up on P_2
> $P_1 = P_2/2$ represents a power loss of 3 dB. P_1 is 3 dB down on P_2

$\log_{10}2 = 0.3010$ so $10 \log_{10}2 = 3.01$. The decimal part is conventionally ignored and a ratio of 2:1 is regarded as a $+3$ dB difference.

$\log_{10}(0.5) = \bar{1}.6990 = -0.3010$ so $10 \log_{10}(0.5) = -3.01$. The decimal part is again ignored and a ratio of 0.5:1 is regarded as a -3 dB difference.

Decibels can also be used to describe voltage ratios, as we shall see in the next frame.

13

LOGARITHMIC VOLTAGE RATIO SCALES

If a power P is dissipated in a resistor R due to a voltage V developed across it, then $P = V^2/R$. If two powers P_1 and P_2 are dissipated in identical resistors of value R (or at different times in the same resistor) then we have:

$$P_1 = \frac{V_1^2}{R} \quad \text{and} \quad P_2 \, \frac{V_2^2}{R} \quad \text{hence} \quad \frac{P_1}{P_2} = \frac{V_1^2}{V_2^2}$$

$$\text{So Gain or Loss in dB} = 10 \log_{10}\left(\frac{P_1}{P_2}\right) = 10 \log_{10}\left(\frac{V_1^2}{V_2^2}\right) = 20 \log_{10}\left(\frac{V_1}{V_2}\right)$$

Thus, if two electrical quantities are said to differ by n dB, this can be intepreted as a certain power ratio P_1/P_2 where $n = 10 \log_{10}(P_1/P_2)$ or a certain voltage ratio V_1/V_2 where $n = 20 \log_{10}(V_1/V_2)$. This definition is often used in practice even if the two voltages are not developed across equal resistors.

A particularly important example is when two voltages differ by a factor $\sqrt{2}$. What is the difference in dB between two voltages V_1 and V_2 when $V_1 = \sqrt{2}V_2$?

14

$$\boxed{\text{When } V_1 = \sqrt{2}V_2, \text{ then } V_1 \text{ is 3 dB up on } V_2}$$

$$\text{Since } n \text{ dB} = 20 \log_{10} \frac{V_1}{V_2}, \text{ then } n = 20 \log_{10} \sqrt{2} = \frac{20}{2}\log_{10}2$$

$$= 10 \log_{10}2 = 10 \times 0.3 = 3$$

Similarly, if two voltages differ by a factor of $1/\sqrt{2}$, then their difference can be expressed as -3 dB. The smaller is 3 dB down on the larger.

We encountered this case in frames 7 and 8. For the circuit analysed in these frames we found that the output/input voltage ratio at low frequencies could be given a value of A_0. At a value of frequency ω_0 the output/input ratio had dropped to $A_0/\sqrt{2}$. For a constant input voltage amplitude therefore the ratio of output voltages was $1/\sqrt{2}$ and both output voltages were, of course, developed in the same resistor; the resistor R_2. For the same input voltage amplitude, then, we can say that the output voltage at the frequency ω_0 is 3 dB down on the output voltage at low frequencies.

We will now use these ideas to plot on logarithmic scales the quantities we used to obtain the frequency response plotted on linear scales in frame 8. Look out for the scale expansion and compression for values less than and greater than 1.

15

THE LOGARITHMIC FREQUENCY RESPONSE PLOT

To obtain the logarithmic frequency response, the horizontal frequency scale is divided into decades logarithmically. The vertical scale is for the ratio V_o/V_i expressed in decibels. That is, the values plotted are of $20 \log_{10} V_o/V_i$. Major intervals are again usually given in decades. Here is the graph we first plotted in frame 8 re-plotted on logarithmic scales:

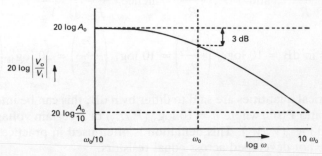

Because of the scale compression and expansion, changes on the graph are now much smoother. This change to a smoothly varying graph permits the use of a rapid curve sketching technique. The technique assumes the graph to be *defined by its asymptotes* and is so widely used that graphs plotted in this way are given a special name. They are called *Bode plots* after the man who first used them.

16

BODE PLOTS – ASYMPTOTICALLY DEFINED FREQUENCY RESPONSE GRAPHS

Definition

An asymptote to a graph is a tangent to the graph which meets it at infinity.

We have already seen that, to plot frequencies which might vary from zero to very high values, we require a log frequency scale which varies from minus infinity to plus infinity.

When voltage amplitude ratios are measured we again find that, as the amplitude ratio approaches zero, the decibel scale approaches minus infinity.

In the graph above, the horizontal line through $20 \log A_0$ is an asymptote to the graph at minus infinity on the frequency scale. The right-hand part of the graph also has an asymptote which meets it at plus infinity on the frequency scale and minus infinity on the decibel scale. We will confirm this by determining the equations of these asymptotes.

17

If we let $V_o/V_i = A$, the equation from which the graph is to be derived is:

$$\frac{V_o}{V_i} = A = \left| \frac{A_0}{1 + j\dfrac{\omega}{\omega_0}} \right| = \sqrt{\left(\frac{A_0}{1 + \dfrac{\omega^2}{\omega_0^2}} \right)}$$

As $\omega \to 0$, the j term becomes very small. When the modulus of $(1 + j\omega/\omega_0)$ is taken, therefore, the term ω^2/ω_0^2 which results is also very small. If ω is small enough, this term can be ignored with respect to 1. As $\omega \to 0$, therefore, $A \to A_0$. But, as $\omega \to 0$, $\log \omega \to -\infty$. When $\log \omega = -\infty$, then $A = A_0$. The 'point' with co-ordinates $(20 \log A_0, -\infty)$ therefore lies on the graph. But a plot of $20 \log_{10} A$ against $\log \omega$ when $A = A_0$, a constant, is simply a horizontal straight line. It is the broken line shown on the graph in frame 15. Now complete the following statement:

> The line through $20 \log A$ meets the graph only when $\log \omega = -\infty$.
> It is therefore, by definition, an . . . . to the graph.

18

> It is an *asymptote* to the graph.

The line satisfies the definition given in frame 16, so the assertion made at the end of that frame is justified. Remember that a tangent to a graph is a line which meets it at only one point. In the case of an asymptote, that point must have at least one co-ordinate which is infinite. It is thus a rather special kind of tangent but is, nonetheless, still a tangent.

We will now turn our attention to the other part of the graph. As $\omega \to \infty$, the j term becomes very large. When the modulus of $(1 + j\omega/\omega_0)$ is taken, therefore, the term ω^2/ω_0^2 which results is also very large. If ω is large enough, the 1 can be ignored with respect to the term ω^2/ω_0^2. With this condition then:

$$A = A_0\omega_0/\omega \quad \text{and so} \quad 20 \log A = 20 \log A_0 + 20 \log \omega_0 - 20 \log \omega$$

Remember that the logarithms of quantities which are multiplied and divided add and subtract respectively.

Now, bearing in mind that we are plotting $20 \log A$ against $\log \omega$, can you re-write this expression so that it can be clearly identified as a straight line of the general form $y = mx + c$. What are y and x and what are the values of m and c?

19

$$20 \log A = -20 \log \omega + 20 \log A_0 + 20 \log \omega_0$$
$$y = 20 \log A \quad x = \log \omega \quad m = -20 \quad c = 20 \log A_0 + 20 \log \omega_0$$

A little care is needed in interpreting the information contained in this equation. The variable ω is a frequency and thus has the dimension T^{-1}. The function $\log \omega$ could be represented by a power series which would therefore include terms having increasing powers of T^{-1}. $\log \omega$ can therefore have no meaningful physical interpretation and the equation appears to be dimensionally inconsistent. The same problem occurs with the term $\log \omega_0$ contained in the constant term. The problem is resolved, however, by the existence of this term $\log \omega_0$ in the same equation as $\log \omega$. When forming expressions from which logarithmic plots can be made, you will find that terms such as $\log \omega$ and $\log \omega_0$ will always occur in pairs and that one of them will always be negative. If the two terms are taken together, the *difference of their logarithms* is the same as the logarithm of their *ratio* which is, of course, a dimensionless quantity. We thus have a slightly modified rule for analysing logarithmic equations for dimensional consistency: the terms whose logarithms are taken must either be dimensionless or must occur in pairs of opposite sign. (The terms A and A_0 are ratios of voltages so are dimensionless.)

We now want to establish that this line is an asymptote to the graph and see how it appears on the diagram. Can you say, first of all, where it meets the line $20 \log A = 20 \log A_0$? Remember, $20 \log A$ is our y co-ordinate.

20

The two lines meet in the point $(20 \log A_0, \log \omega_0)$

The y co-ordinate of the point of intersection must, of course, be $20 \log A_0$. To determine the x co-ordinate we solve the equations of the two lines simultaneously, equating the two y terms. Thus:

$$20 \log A_0 = -20 \log \omega + 20 \log A_0 + 20 \log \omega_0$$

$20 \log A_0$ cancels on both sides so

$$0 = -20 \log \omega + 20 \log \omega_0 \quad \text{and therefore} \quad 20 \log \omega = 20 \log \omega_0 \quad \text{so} \quad \omega = \omega_0$$

We will now determine the slope of the line as it appears on the graph. It is often expressed in terms of 'decibels per decade'. Can you do this? Calculate how many decibels the y co-ordinate changes when the frequency changes from ω_0 to $10\omega_0$, that is, by one decade.

21

> The slope of the line is 20 dB per decade.

When $\omega = \omega_0$ we know that $A = A_0$, so the y co-ordinate is 20 log A_0 dB

If we let $A = A_1$ when $\omega = 10\omega_0$ we have:

$$20 \log A_1 = -20 \log 10\ \omega_0 + 20 \log A_0 + 20 \log \omega_0$$

As suggested in frame 19 for checking the dimensions, we can combine the two terms in log ω_0 and 10 log ω_0, so:

$$20 \log A_1 = 20 \log A_0 + 20(\log \omega_0 - \log 10\ \omega_0) = 20 \log A_0 + 20 \log(\omega_0/10\omega_0)$$

$$= 20 \log A_0 + 20 \log(0.1) = 20 \log A_0 + 20(-1) = 20 \log A_0 - 20$$

Thus, when $\omega = 10\omega_0$, the y co-ordinate is 20 log A_1 which is 20 dB less than 20 log A_0. So, for a change in frequency by a factor of 10 (one decade), the change in attenuation is 20 dB. The slope of the line can thus be expressed as 20 dB per decade.

22

We must now establish that the line is an asymptote. From the equation for the line in frame 19 we see that, if ω is allowed to assume the value $+\infty$, then the first term of the right-hand side assumes the value $-\infty$. The other two (constant) terms can thus be ignored. For the term on the left-hand side (20 log A) to be infinite and negative, A must be zero. The 'point' $(-\infty, +\infty)$ therefore lies on the line and, for these values, $A = 0$. But, when we first plotted the graph non-logarithmically in frames 7 and 8, we found that A was 0 when ω was at plus infinity. The 'point' $(-\infty, +\infty)$ therefore also lies on the graph. Hence the line meets the graph at infinity and so is an asymptote (in this case both the co-ordinates are infinite, one being $+\infty$ and the other $-\infty$).

Can you now re-draw the graph showing the curve and both its asymptotes? To enable you to put some scales on the diagram, assume that R_1, R_2 and C have such values that $A_0 = 0.1$ and $\omega_0 = 10$ radians. Plot 20 log A vertically and log ω horizontally. Take care to choose scales for your axes which show up important features of the graph.

23

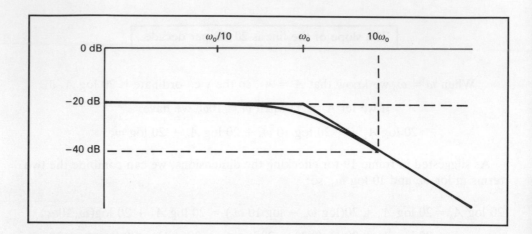

The statement was made in frame 15 that the curve can be assumed to be defined by its asymptotes. The diagram above shows how this can be justified. The horizontal asymptote is an acceptable approximation to the graph for values of log frequency from minus infinity to ω_0. The sloping asymptote is an acceptable approximation to the graph for values of log frequency from ω_0 to plus infinity. We will now investigate how much the straight line approximation differs from the actual graph.

24

THE SIGNIFICANCE OF THE FREQUENCY ω_0

From the calculations done in frame 14 we see that the actual graph is '3dB down on the approximate one' when $\omega = \omega_0$. The frequency ω_0 is often called the '3dB point' or '3dB frequency' of the graph. From the shape of the approximate graph it is also called the 'corner point', 'corner frequency', 'break point' or 'break frequency'. Calculations done in frames 12 and 13 show that, at $\omega = \omega_0$, since the voltage ratio is $1:\sqrt{2}$, the power ratio is 1:2. The frequency ω_0 is thus also sometimes known as the 'half-power point' or 'half-power frequency'. It is plainly the most significant point in defining the approximate graph. If a function of ω reduces to a form with only one corner frequency, then the approximate graph can be drawn without further calculation simply by drawing the two asymptotes.

It is interesting to discover what the differences between the actual and approximate graphs are for values of frequency of $2\omega_0$ and $\omega_0/2$. Can you deduce these values? Give answers to the nearest full decibel.

> The actual graph is 1 dB down on the approximate one at both frequencies

When $\omega = \omega_0/2$ the attenuation given by the approximate graph is $20 \log A_0$, that is, the value on the horizontal straight line. The value on the actual graph is given by:

$$20 \log A = 20 \log \frac{A_0}{\sqrt{\left(1 + \dfrac{\omega^2}{\omega_0^2}\right)}} = 20 \log \frac{A_0}{\sqrt{\left(1 + \dfrac{1}{4}\right)}} = 20 \log A_0 - 20 \log 1.25$$

$$= 20 \log A_0 - 20(0.0485) = 20 \log A_0 - 0.97 \approx 20 \log A - 1$$

That is, the actual graph is 1 dB down on the approximate one.

When $\omega = 2\omega_0$ we first use the same method as in frame 21 to find the value on the approximate graph – the sloping asymptote. If $A = A_2$ when $\omega = 2\omega_0$:

$$20 \log A_2 = 20 \log A_0 + 20(\log \omega_0 - \log 2\omega_0) = 20 \log A_0 + 20 \log \omega_0/2\omega_0$$

$$= 20 \log A_0 + 20 \log(0.5) = 20 \log A_0 + 20(-0.301) \approx 20 \log A_0 - 6$$

So, if frequency changes by a factor of 2 (this is called an octave), then the attenuation changes by 6 dB. The slope of the line may also thus be described as 6 dB per octave.

The value on the actual graph is:

$$20 \log A = 20 \log \left(\frac{A_0}{\sqrt{\left(1 + \dfrac{\omega^2}{\omega_0^2}\right)}} \right) = 20 \log \left(\frac{A_0}{\sqrt{(1+4)}} \right) = 20 \log A_0 - 20 \log\sqrt{5}$$

$$= 20 \log A_0 - 20(0.3495) = 20 \log A_0 - 6.99 \approx 20 \log A - 7$$

Again, the actual graph is 1 dB down on the approximate one.

Now, here is an example for you to try on your own. First, derive the transfer function V_o/V_i of the circuit given here. Then, put it into a suitable form for plotting the frequency response and, finally, plot the response showing both the actual graph and its asymptotic approximation.

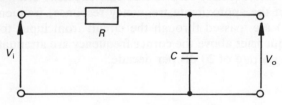

26

Here is the circuit to be analysed again:

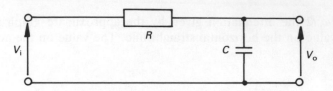

And here is the working of the problem:

$$\frac{V_o}{V_i} = \frac{\dfrac{1}{j\omega C}}{R + \dfrac{1}{j\omega C}} = \frac{1}{1 + j\omega CR} = \frac{1}{1 + j\dfrac{\omega}{\omega_0}} \quad \text{where } \omega_0 = \frac{1}{CR}$$

The expression for V_o/V_i is thus of exactly the same mathematical form as that in frame 5 but with $A = 1$ and with $\omega_0 = 1/CR$. The frequency response must therefore also be of the same shape except that the horizontal asymptote is now the line $20 \log A = 0$ (since $\log 1 = 0$). The horizontal asymptote is thus the log frequency axis.

The equation for the sloping asymptote is obtained by allowing ω to become very large in the expression for $|V_o/V_i|$. Thus:

$$20 \log A = 20 \log(\omega_0/\omega) = 20 \log \omega_0 - 20 \log \omega = -20 \log \omega + 20 \log \omega_0$$

Taking $20 \log A$ as the y co-ordinate and $\log \omega$ as the x co-ordinate, this is a straight line of the general form $y = mx + c$ where $m = -20$ and $c = +20 \log \omega_0$.

It meets the other asymptote (the x-axis) when $A = 1$ (so $20 \log A = 0$) and $\omega = \omega_0$.

When $\omega = 10\omega_0$, the attenuation in decibels is

$$20 \log A = 20 \log \omega_0 - 20 \log 10\omega_0 = 20 \log(\omega_0/10\omega_0) = 20 \log(0.1) = -20$$

As for the previous example, the slope may be expressed as 20 dB per decade.

The shape of the frequency response of this circuit is often described as 'low pass'. In terms of the approximate frequency response, frequencies less than ω_0 (low frequencies) are 'passed through the circuit from input to output' with no attenuation. Frequencies above the corner frequency are attenuated by an amount which increases at a rate of 20 dB per decade.

Here is a diagram of the frequency response:

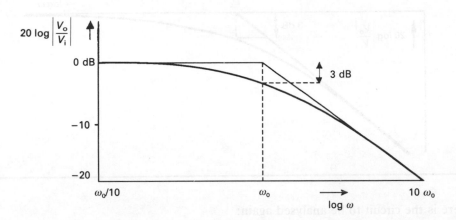

The low-pass frequency response is characteristic of circuits which have a resistor such as R 'in the signal path through the circuit' and a capacitor such as C 'across the signal path'. Broadly speaking, electrical signals can be thought to flow through the circuit from left to right.

The first circuit we analysed can also be spoken of as low pass. In fact, by applying Thevenin's theorem to the two resistors, it can be reduced to the same form as the one we have just analysed. The frequency response is the same shape as the one for the circuit we have just analysed except that low-frequency signals are passed from input to output with attenuation caused *by the resistive components* in the circuit. It is the horizontal section at low frequencies with the 'roll-off' at high frequencies which is the characteristic feature of a low-pass response.

Here is another circuit for you to analyse. Can you plot the frequency response of this circuit together with its asymptotic approximation? First obtain the transfer function and then reduce it to a form containing only one j-term. The analysis is then similar to that we have just done.

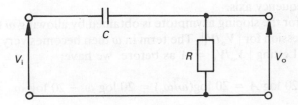

27

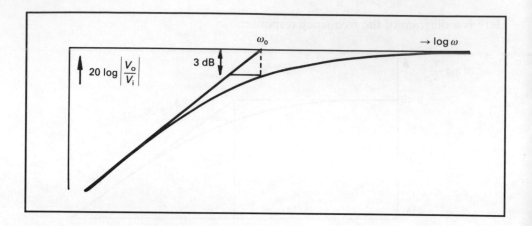

Here is the circuit to be analysed again:

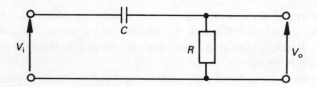

And here is the working of the problem:

$$\frac{V_o}{V_i} = \frac{R}{R + \dfrac{1}{j\omega C}} = \frac{1}{1 + \dfrac{1}{j\omega CR}} = \frac{1}{1 + \dfrac{\omega_0}{j\omega}} = \frac{1}{1 - j\dfrac{\omega_0}{\omega}} \quad \text{where } \omega_0 = \frac{1}{CR}$$

The expression for V_o/V_i is thus of a similar mathematical form to the one in frame 26 but with the ω term negative and appearing as ω_0/ω rather than ω/ω_0. If ω becomes very large the ω_0/ω term is negligibly small compared with 1 and the expression for V_o/V_i reduces to $1 \times 20 \log 1 = 0$, so the horizontal asymptote is again the log frequency axis.

The equation for the sloping asymptote is obtained by allowing ω to become very small in the expression for $|V_o/V_i|$. The term in ω then becomes very large and the 1 can be ignored. Letting $|V_o/V_i| = A$ as before, we have:

$$20 \log A = 20 \log(\omega/\omega_0) = 20 \log \omega - 20 \log \omega_0$$

Taking $20 \log A$ as the y co-ordinate and $\log \omega$ as the x co-ordinate, this is a straight line of the general form $y = mx + c$ where $m = +20$ and $c = -20 \log \omega_0$.

The straight line $20 \log A = 20 \log \omega - 20 \log \omega_0$ meets the other asymptote (the axis) when $A = 1 (20 \log A = 0)$ and $\omega = \omega_0$.

When $\omega = \omega_0/10$ the attenuation in decibels is

$$20 \log A = 20 \log \omega_0/10 - 20 \log \omega_0 = 20 \log(\omega_0/10\omega_0) = 20 \log(0.1) = -20$$

As for the previous examples, the slope may be expressed as 20 dB per decade, but in this case it is positive.

The shape of the frequency response of this circuit is often described as 'high pass'. In terms of the approximate frequency response, frequencies greater than ω_0 (high frequencies) are 'passed through the circuit from input to output' with no attenuation. Frequencies below the corner frequency are attenuated by an amount which increases at a rate of 20 dB per decade as frequency gets smaller.

The high-pass frequency response is characteristic of circuits which have a capacitor such as C 'in the signal path through the circuit' and a resistor such as R 'across the signal path'. Again, electrical signals can be thought to flow through the circuit from left to right. It is the horizontal section at high frequencies with the 'roll-off' at low frequencies which is the characteristic feature of a high-pass response.

We have so far established, then, a number of the ideas involved in producing frequency and phase response graphs for a circuit.

We have seen how to manipulate the expressions obtained for the transfer functions of such circuits into a form which simplifies the task of plotting the responses.

We have seen the benefit of using logarithmic scales for the axes of the frequency response.

We have observed that certain circuit configurations give characteristic frequency responses and have plotted two different kinds: a 'low-pass' response and a 'high-pass' response.

The next frame contains a summary of the results obtained so far.

28

SUMMARY

1. If a circuit has a given input stimulus of the form v_i or i_i, where v_i and i_i are sinusoidally varying quantities, and an output voltage v_o or output current i_o can be identified which has appeared as a 'response' to the input stimulus then, using complex phasor notation:

   V_o/V_i is called the voltage transfer function of the circuit

   I_o/I_i is called the current transfer function of the circuit

2. When these transfer functions are derived using j-notation, they can be expressed as dimensionless functions of $j\omega$ of the general form $A(j\omega)$. The function $A(j\omega)$ may include a dimensionless ratio A_0 (which will be derived from circuit components) together with terms of the form $j\omega/\omega_0$ or $j\omega_0/\omega$ which may appear alone or as terms $(1 \pm j\omega/\omega_0)$ or $(1 \pm j\omega_0/\omega)$. The ω_0's will also be derived from circuit components.

3. The frequency response of the circuit is defined as the graph of the amplitude of the complex number A against frequency. The amplitude of A is the ratio of voltage or current amplitudes of the input stimulus and the output response.

4. The phase response of the circuit is defined as the graph of the phase angle of the complex number A against frequency. The phase angle of A is the phase difference between the input stimulus and the output response.

5. Logarithmic scales are widely used in the plotting of frequency and phase responses because they present the important information about the transfer functions in a more useful way than is obtained with linear scales. Logarithmic scales are usually laid out in decades (multiples of 10 of the variable being plotted). Equal multiples of the variable being plotted result in equal increments on the logarithmic scale.

6. The decibel (dB) is a logarithmic unit used in the measurement of power ratios, voltage ratios or current ratios.

   If two powers, P_1 and P_2, differ by n dB then $n = 10 \log P_1/P_2$

   If two voltages, V_1 and V_2, differ by n dB then $n = 20 \log V_1/V_2$

   If two currents, I_1 and I_2, differ by n dB then $n = 20 \log I_1/I_2$

   A voltage or current ratio of 10:1 is a difference of 20 dB

   A voltage or current ratio of $\sqrt{2}$:1 is a difference of 3 dB

7. If the frequency response of a circuit is plotted logarithmically (a voltage transfer function would be plotted as 20 log V_o/V_i against log ω, for example) then the resulting graph may be approximated to by its asymptotes. An asymptote is a tangent to the graph which meets it at infinity. A graph approximated in this manner is called a Bode plot or Bode diagram.

8. Bode plots of functions of the form $(1 \pm j\omega/\omega_0)$ are characterised by horizontal asymptotes and sloping asymptotes which meet at 'corner frequencies'. The slope of such asymptotes is described as '20 dB per decade or '6 dB per octave'. Since the accurate graph and the approximate graph show a difference of 3 dB at the corner frequencies, they are also known as '3 dB points'.

9. A Bode plot which exhibits a horizontal section at low frequencies and a section which 'rolls off at 20 dB per decade with increasing frequency' at frequencies greater than the corner frequency is called a 'low-pass' response. A Bode plot which exhibits a horizontal section at high frequencies and a section which 'rolls off at 20 dB per decade with decreasing frequency' at frequencies less the corner frequency is called a 'high-pass' response.

29

REVISION QUESTIONS

Here are two more circuits for you to analyse. Derive their transfer functions and then plot the frequency responses of these transfer functions. Since no component values are given, you cannot plot numerical values for frequency and amplitude ratios. Choose scales which show the essential features of the graphs. Say whether they are high-pass or low-pass responses. Circuit 1 is another voltage transfer function, circuit 2 is a current transfer function. Manipulate these transfer functions into forms which contain only a single term of the form $(1 + j\omega/\omega_0)$ or $(1 + j\omega_0/\omega)$.

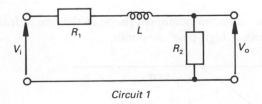

Circuit 1

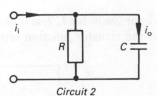

Circuit 2

ANSWERS TO REVISION QUESTIONS

Circuit 1

$$\frac{V_o}{V_i} = \frac{R_2}{R_1 + R_2 + j\omega L} = \frac{R_2}{(R_1 + R_2)\left(1 + \dfrac{j\omega L}{R_1 + R_2}\right)} = \frac{A_0}{1 + j\dfrac{\omega}{\omega_0}}$$

where $A_0 = \dfrac{R_2}{R_1 + R_2}$ and $\omega_0 = \dfrac{R_1 + R_2}{L}$

Note that the factor taken out of the denominator of the original expression for V_o/V_i MUST be $(R_1 + R_2)$ so that the bracket including the $j\omega$ term begins with 1.

The expression for V_o/V_i is of exactly the same mathematical shape as that in frame 5. The transfer function thus represents a 'low-pass' response.

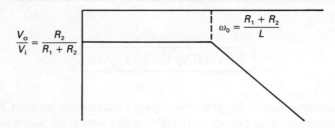

$$\frac{V_o}{V_i} = \frac{R_2}{R_1 + R_2}$$

$$\omega_0 = \frac{R_1 + R_2}{L}$$

Circuit 2

$$\frac{I_o}{I_i} = \frac{R}{R + \dfrac{1}{j\omega C}} = \frac{1}{1 + \dfrac{1}{j\omega CR}} = \frac{1}{1 + \dfrac{\omega_0}{j\omega}} = \frac{1}{1 - j\dfrac{\omega_0}{\omega}} \qquad \text{where} \qquad \omega_0 = \frac{1}{CR}$$

The expression for I_o/I_i is thus of the same mathematical shape as the one in frame 27 so the transfer function represents a 'high-pass' response.

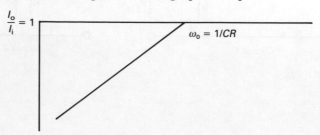

$$\frac{I_o}{I_i} = 1$$

$$\omega_0 = 1/CR$$

THE ADDITION OF GRAPHS

Here is the high-pass $C-R$ circuit again:

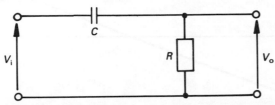

An alternative way of analysing the expression for V_o/V_i throws an interesting light on the way in which such functions can be manipulated. Starting from the original expression for V_o/V_i, we can proceed as follows:

$$\frac{V_o}{V_i} = \frac{R}{R + \dfrac{1}{j\omega C}} = \frac{j\omega CR}{j\omega CR + 1} = \frac{j\omega CR}{1 + j\omega CR} = \frac{\dfrac{j\omega}{\omega_0}}{1 + j\dfrac{\omega}{\omega_0}} \quad \text{where} \quad \omega_0 = \frac{1}{CR}$$

So
$$\left|\frac{V_o}{V_i}\right| = \frac{V_o}{V_i} = \frac{\dfrac{\omega}{\omega_0}}{\sqrt{\left(1 + \dfrac{\omega^2}{\omega_0^2}\right)}}$$

and
$$20 \log \frac{V_o}{V_i} = 20 \log \frac{\omega}{\omega_0} + 20 \log \frac{1}{\sqrt{\left(1 + \dfrac{\omega^2}{\omega_0^2}\right)}}$$

If we let $A = 20 \log \dfrac{V_o}{V_i}$, $A_1 = 20 \log \dfrac{\omega}{\omega_0}$ and $A_2 = 20 \log \dfrac{1}{\sqrt{\left(1 + \dfrac{\omega^2}{\omega_0^2}\right)}}$

$$\text{Then } A = A_1 + A_2$$

We can plot separate graphs of A_1 against log ω and A_2 against log ω, and then add the graphs together to obtain the graph of A against log ω. Looking back to frame 26, however, we see that A_2 is the function we have already plotted in that frame. Can you plot A_1, A_2 and hence A? Since no numerical values are given, again you must choose suitable scales for the graphs so that important features are shown up. We have not plotted a graph of a function such as A before, so you will need to give this one some thought. You will find that it is, in fact, even simpler than the ones we have plotted so far.

32

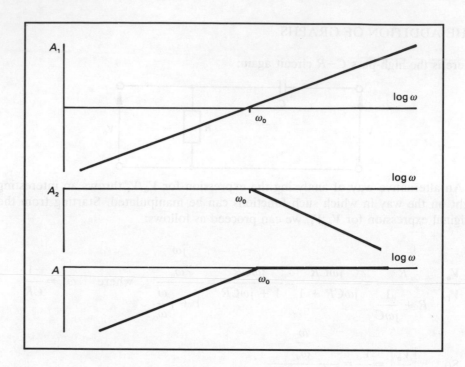

$$A_1 = 20 \log \frac{\omega}{\omega_0} = 20 \log \omega - 20 \log \omega_0$$

When $\omega = \omega_0$ then $A_1 = 0$ so the graph of A_1 against log ω is a straight line of slope 20 cutting the line $A = 0$ when $\omega = \omega_0$.

The graph of A_2 against log ω can be copied from frame 26. It can be approximated by a horizontal straight line on which $A_2 = 0$ from log $\omega = -\infty$ to log $\omega = \log \omega_0$ and a line of slope -20 from log $\omega = \log \omega_0$ to log $\omega = +\infty$.

Adding the two graphs together results in a graph which has a slope of $+20$ from log $\omega = -\infty$ to log $\omega = \log \omega_0$ and a slope of zero (the slopes of $+20$ and -20 cancel each other out) from log $\omega = \log \omega_0$ to log $\omega = +\infty$. This is the same graph as we obtained in frame 27 (as, of course, it must be because we are plotting the same function). We have simply plotted it a different way.

The important point to notice about this piece of analysis is that, if a function of $j\omega$ can be represented as the *product* of two separate functions, then the graph of the function can be formed as the *sum* of the two separate logarithmic graphs. The result follows from the fact that the logarithm of the product of two terms is the sum of the logarithms of the terms.

33

The principle established in the previous frame can be extended to any transfer function which can be represented as the product of two or more terms. Provided the terms have been suitably manipulated (that is, they are of the form $j\omega/\omega_0$, $j\omega_0/\omega$, $(1 \pm j\omega/\omega_0)$ or $(1 \pm j\omega_0/\omega)$), then the graph of their product is obtained by plotting a graph of each term separately and then adding all the graphs together. A slight modification to the principle is often easier to implement. If a term appears in the denominator of the original function then its graph can be *subtracted* from the graph of any terms in the numerator. This follows from the fact that $\log(1/x) = -\log x$. If there is also a constant of the form A_0 then a term $20 \log A_0$ is added to the final result. Here is an example to establish these ideas.

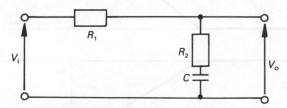

Can you write down the voltage transfer function of this circuit and manipulate it into a suitable form for plotting?

$$\frac{V_o}{V_i} = \frac{1 + j\omega/\omega_1}{1 + j\omega/\omega_2} \quad \text{or} \quad \frac{V_o}{V_i} = \frac{R_2}{R_1 + R_2}\left(\frac{1 - j\omega_1/\omega}{1 - j\omega_2/\omega}\right)$$

$$\text{where } \omega_1 = 1/CR_2 \quad \text{and} \quad \omega_2 = 1/C(R_1 + R_2)$$

Either of the above forms is correct. Which you get depends on how you manipulate the basic expression for V_o/V_i. Here is how they are obtained:

$$\frac{V_o}{V_i} = \frac{R_2 + 1/j\omega C}{R_1 + R_2 + 1/j\omega C} = \frac{1 + j\omega CR_2}{1 + j\omega C(R_1 + R_2)} \quad \text{or} \quad \frac{R_2(1 + 1/j\omega CR_2)}{(R_1 + R_2)(1 + 1/j\omega C(R_1 + R_2))}$$

The first of the two alternatives is obtained by multiplying throughout the numerator and denominator of the original expression by $j\omega C$. The second is obtained by taking out a factor of R_2 in the numerator and a factor of $(R_1 + R_2)$ in the denominator. The results follow when the substitutions for ω_1 and ω_2 are made and the fact that $1/j = -j$ is used. Can you now plot the frequency response from the first alternative expression?

35

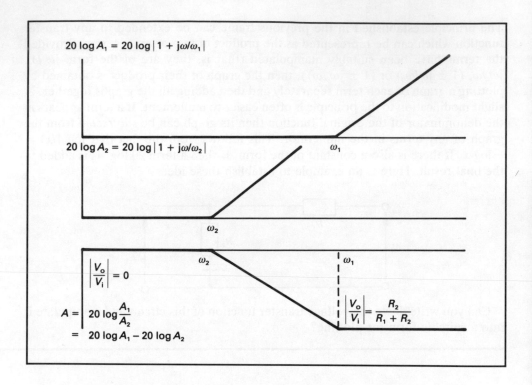

Both terms are of the form $(1 + j\omega/\omega_0)$. In an expression such as this, if $\omega << \omega_0$ the expression reduces to 1 so, for $\omega < \omega_0$, the graph is a horizontal straight line along the axis. If $\omega >> \omega_0$ the expression reduces to ω/ω_0 so, as in frame 32, when $\omega > \omega_0$ the graph is a sloping line of gradient $+20$ cutting the axis when $\omega = \omega_0$.

In this example the two graphs are the same shape. One cuts the axis when $\omega = \omega_1$ and the other when $\omega = \omega_2$.

Now, $\omega_2 < \omega_1$ since $1/C(R_1 + R_2) < 1/CR_2$ and the graph with the corner point at ω_2 is subtracted from the graph with the corner point at ω_1.

When $\omega < \omega_2$, therefore, the combined graph is along the axis. From $\omega = \omega_2$ to $\omega = \omega_1$ the subtracted graph causes the combined graph to roll off at 20 dB per decade as frequency increases. When $\omega > \omega_1$ the two slopes cancel and the graph is horizontal again but at the value it has reached on the subtracted graph when $\omega = \omega_1$.

By comparison with frame 32, the equation of the subtracted graph when $\omega > \omega_2$ is $A = 20 \log \omega/\omega_2$. But, since this graph *is* subtracted, the combined value is $0 - 20 \log \omega/\omega_2 = 20 \log \omega_2/\omega$. (Remember: $\log(1/x) = -\log x$.) Putting $\omega = \omega_1$ in this expression thus gives $A = 20 \log \omega_2/\omega_1 = 20 \log R_2/(R_1 + R_2)$. The combined graph is thus as shown above.

Here is an alternative way of tackling the same problem. We start from one of the two alternative expressions for V_o/V_i. We will use the first.

$$\text{We have} \quad \frac{V_o}{V_i} = \frac{1 + j\omega/\omega_1}{1 + j\omega/\omega_2}$$

$$\text{where} \quad \omega_1 = 1/CR_2 \quad \text{and} \quad \omega_2 = 1/C(R_1 + R_2)$$

Since $R_1 + R_2 > R_2$ and these terms appear in the denominators of the expressions for ω_1 and ω_2, then $\omega_2 < \omega_1$. When $\omega << \omega_2$ then it is certainly true that $\omega << \omega_1$. If ω is small enough to satisfy both these inequalities then the j terms in the expression for V_o/V_i can be ignored in comparison with the real terms (the 1's). Strictly, we should take the modulus of the expression for V_o/V_i before comparing terms but, as long as it is understood that that is what we are doing, we can make comparisons by looking at the components of the complex terms.

$$\text{So, when } \omega \text{ is very small,} \quad \left|\frac{V_o}{V_i}\right| = 1$$

When $\omega >> \omega_1$ then it is certainly true that $\omega >> \omega_2$. If ω is large enough to satisfy both these inequalities then the real terms in the expression for V_o/V_i (the 1's) can be ignored in comparison with the j terms. Again we should strictly take the modulus of the expression for V_o/V_i before comparing terms, but can once more make comparisons by looking at the components of the complex terms.

$$\text{So, when } \omega \text{ is very large,} \quad \left|\frac{V_o}{V_i}\right| = \left|\frac{j\omega/\omega_1}{j\omega/\omega_2}\right| = \frac{\omega_2}{\omega_1} = \frac{1/C(R_1 + R_2)}{1/CR_2} = \frac{R_2}{R_1 + R_2}$$

If we take 'small' ω to be from zero (log $\omega = -\infty$) to ω_2 and 'large' ω to be from ω_1 to $+\infty$ and plot $20 \log |V_o/V_i|$ for these ranges and then join the ends of the two lines thus produced, we obtain directly the 'combined' graph from frame 35. Remember that this is only an approximation to the accurate graph.

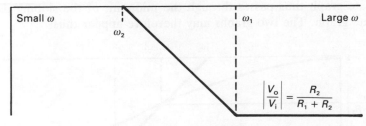

One point on the accurate graph is worth investigating further. Can you evaluate the accurate value of $|V_o/V_i|$ when $\omega = \sqrt{(\omega_1\omega_2)}$?

37

$$\boxed{\text{When } \omega = \surd(\omega_1\omega_2) \text{ then } \left|\frac{V_o}{V_i}\right| = \surd\left(\frac{R_2}{R_1 + R_2}\right)}$$

We have $\quad \dfrac{V_o}{V_i} = \dfrac{1 + j\omega/\omega_1}{1 + j\omega/\omega_2} = \dfrac{1 + j(\surd(\omega_1\omega_2))/\omega_1}{1 + j(\surd(\omega_1\omega_2))/\omega_2} = \dfrac{1 + j\surd(\omega_2/\omega_1)}{1 + j\surd(\omega_1/\omega_2)}$

So $\quad \left|\dfrac{V_o}{V_i}\right| = \surd\left(\dfrac{1 + \omega_2/\omega_1}{1 + \omega_1/\omega_2}\right) = \surd\left(\dfrac{(\omega_1 + \omega_2)/\omega_1}{(\omega_1 + \omega_2)/\omega_2}\right)$

$$= \surd\left(\frac{\omega_2}{\omega_1}\right) = \surd\left(\frac{R_2}{R_1 + R_2}\right)$$

Now, $\surd(\omega_1\omega_2)$ is, by definition, the geometric mean of ω_1 and ω_2 and $\surd\{R_2/(R_1 + R_2)\}$ is the geometric mean of 1 and $R_2/(R_1 + R_2)$. Thus the ratio $|V_o/V_i|$ at the geometric mean of the corner frequencies is the geometric mean of the voltage ratios at the two individual frequencies. The significance of this discovery becomes apparent when we take logs. Can you describe log $\surd(\omega_1\omega_2)$ in terms of the logs of the two individual frequencies?

38

$$\boxed{\log \surd(\omega_1\omega_2) \text{ is the arithmetic mean of } \log \omega_1 \text{ and } \log \omega_2}$$

$$\log \surd(\omega_1\omega_2) = (\log \omega_1\omega_2)/2 = (\log \omega_1 + \log \omega_2)/2$$

which is, by definition, the arithmetic mean.

Similarly 20 log $\surd\{R_2/(R_1 + R_2)\}$ is the arithmetic mean of 20 log 1 and 20 log $R_2/(R_1 + R_2)$.

So, on the graph of 20 log $|V_o/V_i|$ against log ω, the point whose co-ordinates are 20 log $\surd\{R_2/(R_1 + R_2)\}$ and log $\surd(\omega_1\omega_2)$ is half way down the sloping part of the approximate graph. But, as we have seen, this point lies *on* the accurate graph. The accurate graph thus passes through the midpoint of the sloping part of the approximate graph. The two graphs may therefore appear thus:

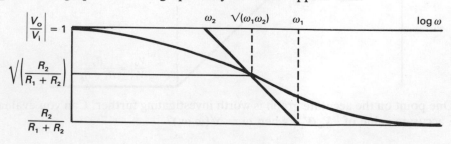

39

When, as in this graph, there is more than one corner frequency, some care is needed in deciding by how much the accurate graph differs from the approximate one at the break points. We can observe that the difference in attenuation on the two horizontal parts of the graph depends on the values of R_1 and R_2. Since the analysis carried out in the previous few frames was purely algebraic, the general shape of the frequency response will be as shown in frame 38 whatever the values of R_1 and R_2. If, for example, the values of R_1 and R_2 were such that the difference in attenuation on the two horizontal lines was no more than 6 dB, then it would plainly not be correct to call the corner frequencies 3 dB points. The centre of the sloping line which is also a point on the accurate graph would, in fact, be the point at which the attenuation had fallen by 3 dB from its low-frequency value.

We shall state without proof that it is not until values of R_1 and R_2 are chosen such that ω_1 is approximately two decades greater than ω_2 (that is, $\omega_1 = 100\omega_2$) that the corner points can be described as 3 dB points with any degree of accuracy. The difference between high- and low-frequency attenuation ratios would thus be approximately 40 dB. Derivation of the graph as in frame 35 shows that the slope of the line is 20 dB per decade or 6 dB per octave whatever the difference between the attenuation ratios.

40

PHASE RESPONSE GRAPHS

So far we have concentrated solely on frequency response graphs. When we are designing audio systems (radios, tape recorders and so on) we are usually concerned only with the frequency response of the system. If we wish to design pulse amplifiers or control systems, however, it is often essential to know how the relative phase of the input and output signals varies as frequency changes. We will start by analysing again the high-pass circuit.

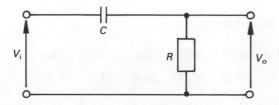

Can you write an expression for the relative phase difference between input and output voltages? You may remember from programme 5 that it is the phase angle of the voltage transfer function.

41

> The phase difference between input and output voltages is $\arctan(\omega_0/\omega)$
> where $\omega_0 = 1/CR$

$$\frac{V_o}{V_i} = \frac{R}{R + \dfrac{1}{j\omega C}} = \frac{1}{1 + \dfrac{1}{j\omega CR}} = \frac{1}{1 + \dfrac{\omega_0}{j\omega}} = \frac{1}{1 - j\dfrac{\omega_0}{\omega}} = \frac{1 + j\dfrac{\omega_0}{\omega}}{1 + \dfrac{\omega_0^2}{\omega^2}}$$

The phase angle of V_o/V_i is $\arctan\left\{\dfrac{\mathrm{Im}(V_o/V_i)}{\mathrm{Rl}(V_o/V_i)}\right\}$

$= \arctan(\omega_0/\omega)$ where $\omega_0 = 1/CR$ hence the result.

We now want to see how this phase difference changes as frequency changes. To do this we will plot a graph of the phase angle against frequency.

What is the phase difference at very low frequency, at very high frequency and at the corner frequency? Give your answers in degrees.

42

> When $\omega \to 0$ $\arctan(\omega_0/\omega) \to 90°$
> When $\omega \to \infty$ $\arctan(\omega_0/\omega) \to 0$
> When $\omega = \omega_0$ $\arctan(\omega_0/\omega) \to 45°$

If $\arctan(\omega_0/\omega) = \phi$ then, when $\omega \to 0$, $\tan\phi \to \infty$ so $\phi \to \pi/2 = 90°$

Similarly, when $\omega \to \infty$, $\tan\phi \to 0$ so $\phi \to 0$

and, when $\omega = \omega_0$, $\tan\phi = 1$ so $\phi = \pi/4 = 45°$

Here are some more values:

ω	$\omega_0/10$	$\omega_0/4$	$\omega_0/2$	$2\omega_0$	$4\omega_0$	$10\omega_0$
ϕ	84.3°	76.0°	63.4°	26.6°	14.0°	5.7°

Now you plot a graph to display the variation illustrated by the above values. Look carefully at the range of values listed and choose suitable axes for your graph. Remember that we want to compare this information with that given on the frequency response. What do you notice about the values of the phase angles for values of frequency above and below the corner frequency?

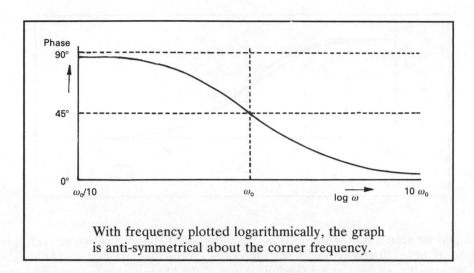

43

With frequency plotted logarithmically, the graph
is anti-symmetrical about the corner frequency.

Since we want to compare the information on the graph with that on the frequency
response, it is sensible to choose a logarithmic scale for frequency. ϕ can be plotted
on a linear vertical scale. This is the way phase responses are normally plotted.

If we look carefully at the values of ϕ in the table for given values of frequency,
we can see that the values of ϕ for frequencies of $n\omega_0$ are the complements of the
values for ω_0/n. This is true for all values of n. (The complement of an angle ϕ is
$(90° - \phi)$). Multiples or sub-multiples of frequency above and below the corner
frequency thus lead to equal increments or decrements in ϕ. This property leads to
the logarithmic 'anti-symmetry' of the graph about the corner frequency. We shall
find that this anti-symmetry is characteristic of all phase responses for tranfer
functions having a single corner frequency.

Phase responses are also often represented by linear approximations. For the
high-pass circuit just analysed the following observations may be made from the
table of values in frame 42:

1. When $\omega < \omega_0/10$ the phase shift from input to output is approximately constant
   at 90°.
2. When $\omega > 10\omega_0$ the phase shift from input to output is approximately constant at
   0°.
3. When $\omega_0/10 < \omega < 10\omega_0$ the phase shift from input to output falls approximately
   linearly from 90° to 0°.

Can you now re-draw the phase response for the high-pass circuit using these
approximations? Superimpose the accurate response onto the approximate response for comparison.

44

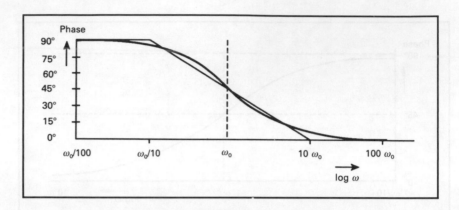

As may be seen from the two graphs, the difference between the two responses is about 6° at $\omega_0/10$ and at $10\omega_0$ while the values on the two graphs coincide at ω_0.

What is the gradient of the sloping section of the phase response in degrees per decade?

45

The gradient of the sloping section is 45° per decade

From $\omega_0/10$ to $10\omega_0$ is two decades and, over this region, the phase changes by 90°, so the slope is 90° over two decades or 45° per decade.

Here is one of the circuits whose frequency response we described as low pass. Can you derive the expression for its phase response and then plot it on a suitable graph. Plot both accurate and approximate responses again for comparison. How does the low-pass phase response compare with the high-pass phase response we have just examined?

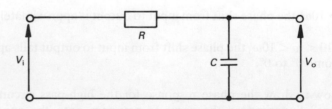

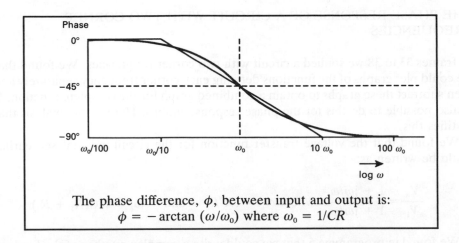

The phase difference, ϕ, between input and output is:
$$\phi = -\arctan(\omega/\omega_0) \text{ where } \omega_0 = 1/CR$$

$$\frac{V_o}{V_i} = \frac{\dfrac{1}{j\omega C}}{R + \dfrac{1}{j\omega C}} = \frac{1}{1 + j\omega CR} = \frac{1}{1 + \dfrac{j\omega}{\omega_0}} = \frac{1 - j\dfrac{\omega}{\omega_0}}{1 + \dfrac{\omega^2}{\omega_0^2}}$$

The phase angle of V_o/V_i is arctan $\left\{ \dfrac{\text{Im}(V_o/V_i)}{\text{Rl}(V_o/V_i)} \right\}$

$= \arctan(-\omega/\omega_0 = -\arctan(\omega/\omega_0)$ where $\omega_0 = 1/CR$ hence the result.

Since tan ϕ for this low-pass circuit is minus the reciprocal of tan ϕ for the high-pass circuit, values of ϕ for a range of values of ω for this circuit can be obtained from the table for the high-pass circuit. Here are some corresponding values of ω and ϕ for the low-pass circuit:

ω	0	$\omega_0/10$	$\omega_0/4$	$\omega_0/2$	ω_0	$2\omega_0$	$4\omega_0$	$10\omega_0$	∞
ϕ	0	$-5.7°$	$-14.0°$	$-26.6°$	$-45.0°$	$-63.4°$	$-76.0°$	$-84.3°$	$-90.0°$

Comparing the two circuits we see that, in the high-pass circuit, high-frequency inputs appear at the output with no attenuation and no phase shift. Low-frequency inputs appear at the output attenuated and *leading* the input by a phase angle of up to 90°. The relative phase angle between output and input is positive.

In the low-pass circuit, low-frequency inputs appear at the output with no attenuation and no phase shift. High-frequency inputs appear at the output attenuated and *lagging* the input by a phase angle of up to 90°. The relative phase angle between output and input is negative.

47

THE PHASE RESPONSE OF A CIRCUIT WITH TWO CORNER FREQUENCIES

In frames 33 to 38 we studied a circuit with two corner frequencies. We found that we could plot graphs of the functions defining each corner frequency separately and then subtract these graphs to obtain a combined graph for the complete function. It is also possible to do this for the phase response graphs. Here is the analysis that justifies this.

We found that the voltage transfer function for the circuit we analysed earlier could be written as:

$$\frac{V_o}{V_i} = \frac{1 + j\omega/\omega_1}{1 + j\omega/\omega_2} \quad \text{where} \quad \omega_1 = 1/CR_2 \quad \text{and} \quad \omega_2 = 1/C(R_1 + R_2)$$

We found in programme 5 that we could write a complex number of the kind we now have to represent V_o/V_i in polar form thus:

$$\frac{V_o}{V_i} = \frac{1 + j\omega/\omega_1}{1 + j\omega/\omega_2} = \frac{r_1 e^{j\phi_1}}{r_2 e^{j\phi_2}} = \frac{r_1}{r_2} e^{j(\phi_1 - \phi_2)}$$

where r_1 and ϕ_1 are the modulus and argument of $1 + j\omega/\omega_1$

and r_2 and ϕ_2 are the modulus and argument of $1 + j\omega/\omega_2$

Here $r_1 = \sqrt{(1 + \omega^2/\omega_1^2)}$ $\quad r_2 = \sqrt{(1 + \omega^2/\omega_2^2)}$ $\quad \phi_1 = \arctan(\omega/\omega_1)$

$$\phi_2 = \arctan(\omega/\omega_2)$$

Plots of $20 \log r_1$ against $\log \omega$ and $20 \log r_2$ against $\log \omega$ are the two separate frequency responses. Plots of $\arctan(\omega/\omega_1)$ against $\log \omega$ and $\arctan(\omega/\omega_2)$ against $\log \omega$ are the two separate phase responses. We have already seen that frequency response graphs can be subtracted. The above analysis confirms this since $20 \log(r_1/r_2) = 20 \log r_1 - 20 \log r_2$. The analysis also shows that the phase responses can be subtracted since $\phi = \phi_1 - \phi_2$ where ϕ is the combined phase difference and ϕ_1 and ϕ_2 are the two separate phase differences.

We already have some phase response graphs for functions very similar to those above. They are plotted from tables of values of ω which are multiples or sub-multiples of the corner frequencies. By comparison with these results, can you plot the two separate phase response graphs for the transfer function analysed above and hence the combined function? Take care! The separate phase responses in this case are not quite the same as those we have already studied. Do not worry too much about exact values. It is the general shape of the graphs that we are interested in at present. Assume, however, that ω_1 is more than two decades above ω_2. That is $\omega_1 > 100\omega_2$. Plot both the accurate and approximate phase responses.

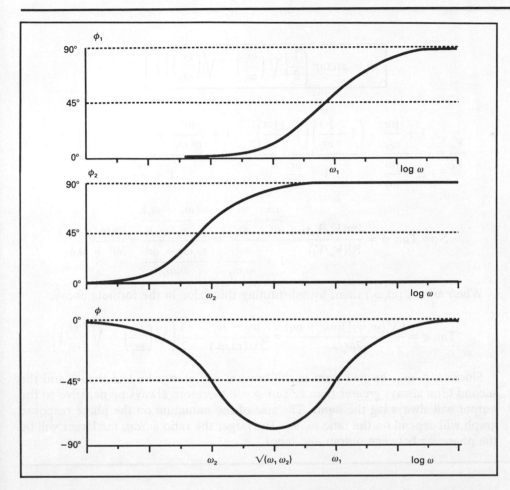

48

The two separate graphs are the phase responses corresponding to the functions $(1 + j\omega/\omega_1)$ and $(1 + j\omega/\omega_2)$. So $\phi_1 = \arctan(\omega/\omega_1)$ and $\phi_2 = \arctan(\omega/\omega_2)$. By comparison with the other phase responses studied so far we can see that both these responses will show zero phase shift at very low frequencies (the imaginary terms are negligible compared with the 1's), $+90°$ phase shift at very high frequencies (the imaginary terms are positive and tending to infinity) and $+45°$ phase shift when $\omega = \omega_1$ and $\omega = \omega_2$ respectively. Since $\omega_2 < \omega_1$ and ϕ_2 is subtracted from ϕ_1, the combined phase response must be negative for all values of ω.

Plainly, the combined phase response graph has a minimum between the two corner frequencies. From the anti-symmetrical shapes of the two separate graphs it seems reasonable to assume that this minimum occurs halfway between these frequencies on the logarithmic scale. This is, in fact, so and could be proved by calculus. The frequency at this minimum is thus $\sqrt{(\omega_1\omega_2)}$.

Can you derive an expression for the value of the phase angle at this frequency expressed in terms of the ratio of the corner frequencies. It is quite a difficult calculation so, if you have trouble, turn to the next frame to see how it is done.

49

$$\phi = \arctan\left[\frac{1}{2}\left\{\sqrt{\left(\frac{\omega_2}{\omega_1}\right)} - \sqrt{\left(\frac{\omega_1}{\omega_2}\right)}\right\}\right]$$

$$\frac{V_o}{V_i} = \frac{1 + \dfrac{j\omega}{\omega_1}}{1 + \dfrac{j\omega}{\omega_2}} = \frac{\left(1 + \dfrac{j\omega}{\omega_1}\right)\left(1 - \dfrac{j\omega}{\omega_2}\right)}{1 + \dfrac{\omega^2}{\omega_2^2}} = \frac{1 + \dfrac{\omega^2}{\omega_1\omega_2} + j\left(\dfrac{\omega}{\omega_1} - \dfrac{\omega}{\omega_2}\right)}{1 + \dfrac{\omega^2}{\omega_2^2}}$$

Now $\text{Tan } \phi = \dfrac{\text{Im}(V_o/V_i)}{\text{Rl}(V_o/V_i)} = \dfrac{\dfrac{\omega}{\omega_1} - \dfrac{\omega}{\omega_2}}{1 + \dfrac{\omega^2}{\omega_1\omega_2}} = \dfrac{\dfrac{\omega(\omega_2 - \omega_1)}{\omega_1\omega_2}}{\dfrac{\omega_1\omega_2 + \omega^2}{\omega_1\omega_2}} = \dfrac{\omega(\omega_2 - \omega_1)}{\omega^2 + \omega_1\omega_2}$

When $\omega = \sqrt{(\omega_1\omega_2)}$ then, by substituting this value in the formula above:

$$\text{Tan } \phi = \frac{(\sqrt{\{\omega_1\omega_2\}})(\omega_2 - \omega_1)}{2\omega_1\omega_2} = \frac{\omega_2 - \omega_1}{2\sqrt{(\omega_1\omega_2)}} = \frac{1}{2}\left\{\sqrt{\left(\frac{\omega_2}{\omega_1}\right)} - \sqrt{\left(\frac{\omega_1}{\omega_2}\right)}\right\}$$

Since $\omega_1 > \omega_2$, the first term in the bracket will always be less than 1 and the second term always greater than 1. Tan ϕ will therefore always be negative so the output will always lag the input. The size of the minimum on the phase response graph will depend on the ratio ω_1/ω_2. The larger the ratio ω_1/ω_2, the larger will be the phase lag between output and input.

50

THE BANDPASS CIRCUIT

Another circuit which, in its simplest form, has two corner frequencies is the so-called bandpass circuit. We will analyse a circuit of this kind and see how it earns its name. Here is the circuit:

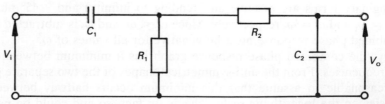

Can you write an expression for the voltage transfer function and reduce it to a form which has unity as its numerator? The analysis can be simplified by first applying Thevenin's theorem to the components C_1 and R_1.

$$\frac{V_o}{V_i} = \frac{1}{1 + \dfrac{C_2R_2}{C_1R_1} + \dfrac{C_2}{C_1} + j\omega C_2R_2 - \dfrac{j}{\omega C_1R_1}}$$

Applying Thevenin's theorem to the components C_1 and R_1 would reduce the circuit to the form shown here where V' and Z' are to be determined:

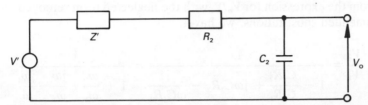

V' is the open-circuit voltage of the 'a.c. potential divider' made up of C_1 and R_1 and Z' is the 'impedance looking back at R_1 and C_1' with V_i replaced by a short-circuit, so:

$$V' = \frac{R_1 V_i}{R_1 + \dfrac{1}{j\omega C_1}} = \frac{j\omega C_1 R_1 V_i}{1 + j\omega C_1 R_1} \quad \text{and} \quad Z' = \frac{\dfrac{R_1}{j\omega C_1}}{R_1 + \dfrac{1}{j\omega C_1}} = \frac{R_1}{1 + j\omega C_1 R_1}$$

V_o can be written down by applying the potential divider rule to V', Z', R_2 and C_2 to give:

$$V_o = \frac{\dfrac{1}{j\omega C_2}}{\left(\dfrac{1}{j\omega C_2} + R_2 + \dfrac{R_1}{1 + j\omega C_1 R_1}\right)} \cdot \frac{j\omega C_1 R_1 V_i}{(1 + j\omega C_1 R_1)} \quad \text{and hence}$$

$$\frac{V_o}{V_i} = \frac{\dfrac{C_1 R_1}{C_2}}{\dfrac{1}{j\omega C_2} + \dfrac{C_1 R_1}{C_2} + R_2 + j\omega C_1 R_1 R_2 + R_1} = \frac{1}{\dfrac{1}{j\omega C_1 R_1} + 1 + \dfrac{C_2 R_2}{C_1 R_1} + j\omega C_2 R_2 + \dfrac{C_2}{C_1}}$$

$$\frac{V_o}{V_i} = \frac{1}{1 + \dfrac{C_2 R_2}{C_1 R_1} + \dfrac{C_2}{C_1} + j\omega C_2 R_2 - \dfrac{j}{\omega C_1 R_1}}$$

Now let us assume that $C_2 << C_1$ so that the term C_2/C_1 in the denominator can be neglected. (If this is not the case, the following analysis will be an approximation to the true situation. How approximate it is will depend on the relative values of C_2 and C_1.) If we write $\omega_1 = 1/C_1 R_1$ and $\omega_2 = 1/C_2 R_2$, we can manipulate the terms in the denominator into a form from which frequency and phase response graphs can be plotted. Can you do this?

52

$$\boxed{\frac{V_o}{V_i} = \frac{1}{\left(1 + j\dfrac{\omega}{\omega_2}\right)\left(1 - j\dfrac{\omega_1}{\omega}\right)}}$$

Starting from the expression for V_o/V_i with the neglected term removed and making the recommended substitutions, we have:

$$\frac{V_o}{V_i} = \frac{1}{1 + \dfrac{C_2 R_2}{C_1 R_1} + j\omega C_2 R_2 - \dfrac{j}{\omega C_1 R_1}} = \frac{1}{1 + \dfrac{\omega_1}{\omega_2} + \dfrac{j\omega}{\omega_2} - \dfrac{j\omega_1}{\omega}}$$

which can be factorised into $\dfrac{V_o}{V_i} = \dfrac{1}{\left(1 + \dfrac{j\omega}{\omega_2}\right)\left(1 - \dfrac{j\omega_1}{\omega}\right)}$

Remember that, to express a function in a suitable form for plotting frequency and phase responses, we try to break it down into products of terms of the form $(1 + j\omega/\omega_0)$ and so on. We can often anticipate the kind of terms to expect from the mathematical analysis by looking at the relative sizes of components in the circuit. We will do this in the next frame.

53

If we knew initially that $C_1 \gg C_2$, we could analyse the circuit approximately as follows. Assume that C_1 has no effect at high frequencies (it 'looks like' a short-circuit). This leaves R_1 across the signal source V_i so it has no effect on the current drawn by the rest of the circuit which thus determines the high-frequency response. Only C_2 and R_2 therefore have any effect so we expect a simple low-pass response with a corner frequency when $\omega = \omega_2 = 1/C_2 R_2$.

If we assume that C_2 has no effect at low frequencies (it 'looks like' an open-circuit) then the voltage V_o will be the same as the voltage across R_1. R_2 thus has no effect and the low-frequency response is determined solely by C_1 and R_1. We therefore expect a simple high-pass response with a corner frequency when $\omega = \omega_1 = 1/C_1 R_1$.

The above assumptions in effect imply that $\omega_2 > \omega_1$. With these assumptions can you plot the frequency and phase responses of the voltage transfer function? Once again, do not worry about exact scales. It is the general shape of the responses which is of interest. Assume, however, that $\omega_2 \gg 100\omega_1$. That is, the difference between the two corner frequencies is much greater than two decades. Plot both accurate and approximate responses.

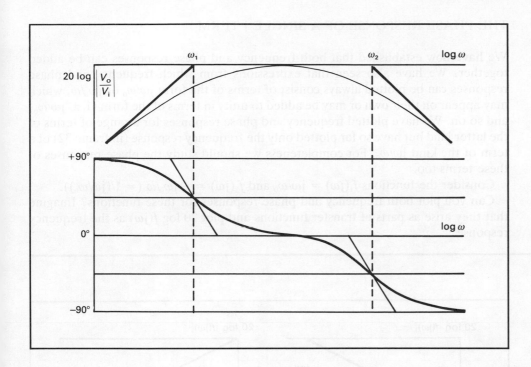

With a little rearrangement the expression for V_o/V_i can be written as the product of two terms whose frequency responses we have already analysed in frames 26 and 27 and whose phase responses we have analysed in frames 40 to 46. The overall frequency and phase responses of the present circuit can therefore be obtained, as we have seen, by adding together the separate responses of the product terms.

At very low frequencies ($\omega << \omega_1$) the output is attenuated with respect to the input and leads the input by up to 90°. At very high frequencies ($\omega >> \omega_2$) the output is attenuated with respect to the input and lags the input by up to 90°. For frequencies between ω_1 and ω_2 ($\omega_1 < \omega < \omega_2$) the input 'passes through' to the output with no attenuation and no phase shift. This range of frequencies is called the '*passband*' of the circuit or the '*midband*' region of the frequency response. The circuit is called a '*bandpass circuit*'.

This kind of frequency and phase response is very commonly a design require-ment of amplifier circuits. '*Audio amplifiers*', for example, are designed to pass signals having frequencies in the '*audible range*'. For people with good hearing this means frequencies from about 25 Hz to about 25 kHz. To allow for component tolerances, 3 dB point design values of 10 Hz and 100 kHz may well be aimed for. This represents a passband four decades wide.

55

THE PHASE RESPONSE OF A SINGLE j TERM

We have now established that both frequency and phase responses can be added together. We have also seen that expressions from which frequency and phase responses can be plotted always consist of terms of the form $j\omega/\omega_0$ or $j\omega_0/\omega$, which may appear on their own or may be added to unity in terms of the form $(1 \pm j\omega/\omega_0)$ and so on. We have plotted frequency and phase responses for a range of terms of the latter kind but have so far plotted only the frequency response (in frame 32) of a term of the kind $j\omega/\omega_0$. For completeness we should study the phase responses of these terms too.

Consider the functions $f_1(j\omega) = j\omega/\omega_0$ and $f_2(j\omega) = -j\omega_0/\omega \; (= 1/(j\omega/\omega_0))$.

Can you plot both frequency and phase responses for these functions? Imagine that they arise as parts of transfer functions and plot $20 \log f(j\omega)$ as the frequency response.

56

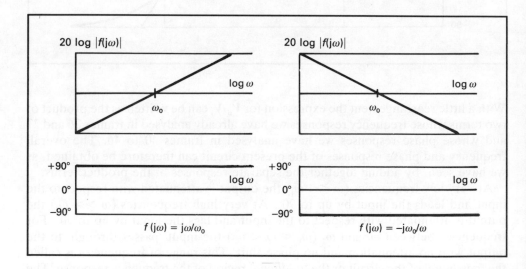

The frequency response of $f(j\omega) = j\omega/\omega_0$ can be copied from frame 32. By comparison the response of $f(j\omega) = -j\omega_0/\omega$ can be seen to take high values when the first takes low values and vice versa. The negative sign has no effect when the modulus is taken.

Since $\tan \phi = \text{Im}\{f(j\omega)\}/\text{Rl}\{f(j\omega)\}$ where ϕ is the phase angle and $\text{Rl}\{f(j\omega)\}$ is zero in both cases, $\tan \phi$ is infinite in both cases. Thus the phase graphs are everywhere 90°, the sign of the angle depending on the sign of the infinity, positive when $f(j\omega) = j\omega/\omega_0$ and negative when $f(j\omega) = -j\omega_0/\omega$.

57

We can add or subtract the phase responses of single j-terms to the phase responses of terms of the form $(1 \pm j\omega/\omega_0)$ in just the same way as we can add or subtract frequency responses. In frame 31 we wrote the voltage transfer function of the simple high-pass $C–R$ circuit in the following form:

$$\frac{V_o}{V_i} = \frac{\dfrac{j\omega}{\omega_0}}{1 + \dfrac{j\omega}{\omega_0}}$$

Can you show how the phase response of this expression can be plotted as the difference of the phase responses of the numerator and the denominator?

58

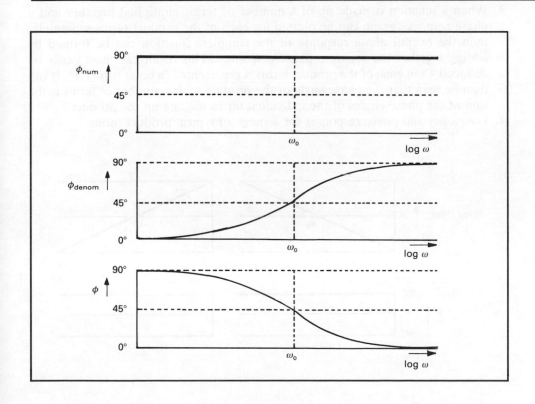

The phase response of the numerator is everywhere +90°. The phase response of the denominator varies from zero at low frequencies to +90° at high frequencies, so the difference between these two gives the net response above.

SUMMARY

1. When a function is made up of a number of terms multiplied together and a frequency response graph can be plotted for each of the product terms separately, then the overall frequency response of the complete function can be formed by adding together the separate frequency responses. This result follows because the vertical axis is logarithmic and the logarithm of the product of any number of terms is the sum of the logarithms of the terms.

2. If a frequency value ω lies halfway between two frequencies ω_1 and ω_2 on the logarithmic frequency scale then its value is $\omega = \sqrt{(\omega_1\omega_2)}$. The arithmetic mean of the logarithms of the two frequencies is the logarithm of their geometric mean. If attenuation is also plotted logarithmically on the vertical scale then the attenuation at the 'logarithmic halfway point' is the geometric mean of the attenuation values at the two endpoints.

3. When a function is made up of a number of terms multiplied together and a phase response graph can be plotted for each of the product terms separately, then the overall phase response of the complete function can be formed by adding together the separate phase responses. This result can most easily be deduced when each of the product terms is represented in polar form $re^{j\phi}$. It can then be seen that the phase angle of the product of any number of terms is the sum of the phase angles of the individual terms making up the product.

4. Frequency and phase responses for a range of typical product terms:

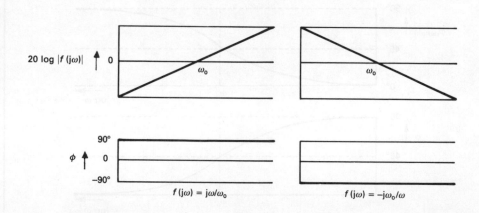

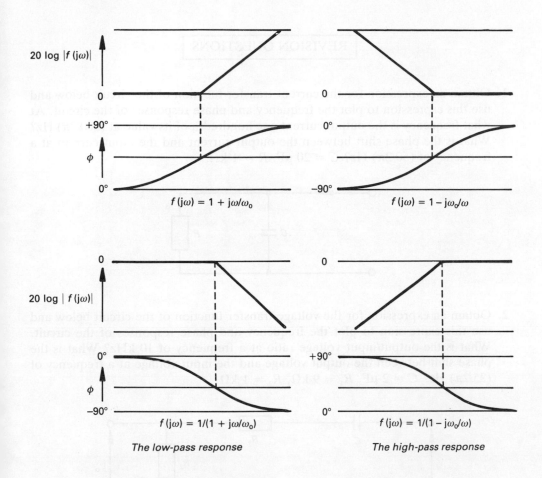

$$20 \log |f(j\omega)|$$

$$f(j\omega) = 1 + j\omega/\omega_0$$

$$f(j\omega) = 1 - j\omega_0/\omega$$

$$f(j\omega) = 1/(1 + j\omega/\omega_0)$$

$$f(j\omega) = 1/(1 - j\omega_0/\omega)$$

The low-pass response

The high-pass response

All functions whose frequency and phase responses are to be plotted are broken down into products of terms such as those plotted above. It follows that all frequency and phase response graphs can be derived by some combination of those above added or subtracted as necessary.

REVISION QUESTIONS

1. Obtain an expression for the current transfer function of the circuit below and use this expression to plot the frequency and phase responses of the circuit. At what frequency is the output current one hundredth of its value at $(500/2\pi)$ Hz? What is the phase shift between the output current and the input current at a frequency of $(50/2\pi)$ Hz? $C = 20$ μF, $R = 1$ kΩ.

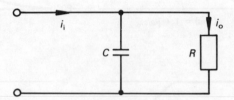

2. Obtain an expression for the voltage transfer function of the circuit below and use this expression to plot the frequency and phase responses of the circuit. What is the output/input voltage ratio at a frequency of 10 kHz? What is the phase shift between the output voltage and the input voltage at a frequency of $(25/2\pi)$ Hz? $C = 2$ μF, $R_1 = 9$ kΩ, $R_2 = 1$ kΩ.

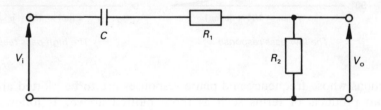

3. Derive the transfer function and plot the frequency and phase responses for the circuit below. What is the value of the greatest phase shift between input and output? At what frequency does this greatest value occur? $R_1 = 9.9$ kΩ, $R_2 = 100$ Ω, $L = 100$ mH.

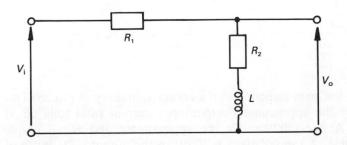

4. In the circuit below $C_2 \gg C_1$. By considering the relative sizes of the two capacitors and their effects at high and low frequencies, try to predict the shape of the frequency and phase responses of this circuit before carrying out exact calculations. Confirm your answer by obtaining an expression for the current transfer function. What approximation must be made to put it into a form which makes plotting the frequency and phase responses a straightforward process of adding or subtracting standard known responses?

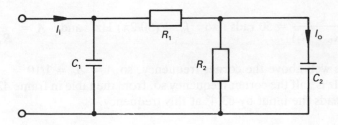

61

1.

$$\frac{I_o}{I_i} = \frac{\dfrac{1}{j\omega C}}{R + \dfrac{1}{j\omega C}} = \frac{1}{1 + j\omega CR} = \frac{1}{1 + \dfrac{j\omega}{\omega_0}} \quad \text{where } \omega_0 = \frac{1}{CR} = 50 \text{ rads}$$

This is a low-pass response with a corner frequency at $(50/2\pi)$ Hz. Above this frequency the approximate output/input current ratio rolls off at 20 dB per decade. Above $(500/2\pi)$ Hz the approximate and actual graphs are indistinguishable. A ratio of 100:1 is 40 dB so the output is $(1/100)$th of its value at $(500/2\pi)$ Hz at a frequency two decades higher, that is $(50/2\pi)$ kHz.
$(50/2\pi)$ Hz is the corner frequency so the output lags the input by 45° at this frequency.

2.

$$\frac{V_o}{V_i} = \frac{R_2}{R_1 + R_2 + \dfrac{1}{j\omega C}} = \frac{R_2}{(R_1 + R_2)\left(1 + \dfrac{1}{j\omega C(R_1 + R_2)}\right)} = \frac{A}{1 + \dfrac{\omega}{j\omega_0}} = \frac{A}{1 - \dfrac{j\omega}{\omega_0}}$$

This is a high-pass response with a corner point at $\omega = \omega_0$ where

$$\omega_0 = \frac{1}{C(R_1 + R_2)} = 50 \text{ rads} \quad \text{so} \quad f_0 = (50/2\pi) \text{ Hz} \quad \text{and} \quad A = \frac{R_2}{R_1 + R_2} = \frac{1}{10}$$

10 kHz is well above the corner frequency, so $A = A_0 = 1/10 = -20$ dB.
$(25/2\pi)$ Hz is half the corner frequency so, from the table in frame 42, the output voltage leads the input by 63.4° at this frequency.

3.

$$\frac{V_o}{V_i} = \frac{R_2 + j\omega L}{R_1 + R_2 + j\omega L} = \frac{R_2}{R_1 + R_2} \cdot \frac{\left(1 + \dfrac{j\omega L}{R_2}\right)}{\left(1 + \dfrac{j\omega L}{R_1 + R_2}\right)} = A_0 \cdot \frac{\left(1 + \dfrac{j\omega}{\omega_1}\right)}{\left(1 + \dfrac{j\omega}{\omega_2}\right)}$$

$$\text{where} \quad A_0 = \frac{R_2}{R_1 + R_2}, \quad \omega_1 = \frac{R_2}{L} \quad \text{and} \quad \omega_2 = \frac{R_1 + R_2}{L}$$

$$\text{So } A_0 = 0.01 \quad \omega_1 = 1000 \text{ rads} \quad \omega_2 = 100{,}000 \text{ rads}$$

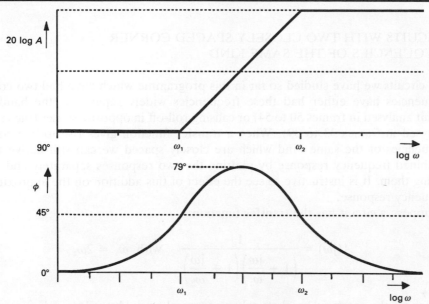

The greatest phase lead of arctan $\dfrac{1}{2}\left\{\sqrt{\left(\dfrac{\omega_2}{\omega_1}\right)} - \sqrt{\left(\dfrac{\omega_1}{\omega_2}\right)}\right\}$ occurs when, $\omega = \sqrt{(\omega_1\omega_2)}$

So $\phi = 79°$ when $f = (50/\pi)$ kHz

4. Since $C_2 \gg C_1$, assume frequency is high enough for C_2 to be regarded as a short-circuit. The high-frequency response will then be determined by C_1 and R_1 (all the current in R_1 will flow through the (short-circuit) C_2). C_1 and R_1 thus give a high-pass response with a single corner point at $\omega_1 = 1/C_1R_1$. Now assume frequency is low enough for C_1 to be regarded as an open-circuit. All of I_i thus flows through R_1 and then divides between C_2 and R_2 which thus determine the low-frequency response. This is a simple low-pass circuit with a single corner point at $\omega = 1/C_2R_2$. The circuit thus has the frequency and phase response of a simple bandpass circuit.

$$\frac{I_o}{I_i} = \frac{R_2}{\left(R_2 + \dfrac{1}{j\omega C_2}\right)} \cdot \frac{\dfrac{1}{j\omega C_1}}{\left(\dfrac{1}{j\omega C_1} + R_1 + \dfrac{\dfrac{R_2}{j\omega C_2}}{R_2 + \dfrac{1}{j\omega C_2}}\right)} = \frac{j\omega C_2 R_2}{1 + j\omega C_2 R_2} \cdot \frac{1}{1 + j\omega C_1 R_1 + \dfrac{j\omega C_2 R_2}{1 + j\omega C_2 R_2}}$$

$$= \frac{j\omega C_2 R_2}{(1 + j\omega C_2 R_2)(1 + j\omega C_1 R_1) + j\omega C_1 R_2} = \frac{1}{\left(1 + \dfrac{1}{j\omega C_2 R_2}\right)(1 + j\omega C_1 R_1) + \dfrac{C_1}{C_2}}$$

$$= \frac{1}{\left(1 - \dfrac{j\omega_2}{\omega}\right)\left(1 + \dfrac{j\omega}{\omega_1}\right)} \quad \text{if } \frac{C_1}{C_2} \text{ is neglected}$$

62

CIRCUITS WITH TWO CLOSELY SPACED CORNER FREQUENCIES OF THE SAME KIND

The circuits we have studied so far in this programme which have had two corner frequencies have either had these frequencies widely separated (the bandpass circuit analysed in frames 50 to 54) or causing roll-off in opposite senses (the circuit analysed in frames 33 to 39). When a transfer function gives rise to two corner frequencies of the same kind which are closely spaced we can still derive their combined frequency response by plotting the two responses separately and then adding them. It is instructive to see the effect of this addition on the approximate frequency response.

Suppose a circuit has the transfer function:

$$A(j\omega) = \frac{1}{\left(1 + \dfrac{j\omega}{\omega_1}\right)\left(1 + \dfrac{j\omega}{\omega_2}\right)} \quad \text{with} \quad \omega_1 = 2\omega_2$$

Each of the terms in brackets taken separately would produce a low-pass response with corner frequencies at ω_1 and ω_2 respectively. Since ω_1 is only twice ω_2, however, when the combined response is formed the roll-off due to ω_1 will come into effect shortly after that due to ω_2 on the log frequency scale. Can you plot the two separate frequency responses and the combined response? What is the slope of the combined response at high frequencies?

63

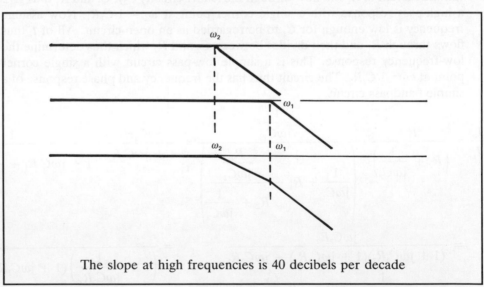

The slope at high frequencies is 40 decibels per decade

The explanation for the above answer is in the next frame.

64

The two separate frequency responses each produce a roll-off at 20 dB per decade for frequencies in excess of their corner frequencies. When the two roll-offs overlap, therefore, it follows that, for each decade increase in frequency, there will be a 20 dB drop in output from each separate graph. The total slope at frequencies above the highest of the two corners is thus 40 dB per decade.

It should be noted that, when ω_1 is close to ω_2, these frequencies can no longer be correctly described as 3 dB points on the accurate graph. Values of $A(j\omega)$ on the accurate graph in the neighbourhood of ω_1 and ω_2 should be calculated from the accurate expression with the appropriate value of ω inserted. For many purposes, however, the information given by the approximate graph is sufficient.

If a low-pass transfer function has three consecutive corner frequencies of the same kind, what is the roll-off on the approximate graph at frequencies high enough for all three to be having an effect? Express your answer both in terms of decibels per decade and decibels per octave.

65

> Three consecutive corner frequencies of the same kind produce a roll-off of 60 dB per decade or 18 dB per octave.

However many corner frequencies are added in, each increases the slope by 20 dB per decade or 6 dB per octave. The final net slope is simply the sum of all the individual slopes. Slopes subtract in the same way. Here is another transfer function:

$$A(j\omega) = \frac{1 + \dfrac{j\omega}{\omega_2}}{\left(1 + \dfrac{j\omega}{\omega_1}\right)\left(1 + \dfrac{j\omega}{\omega_3}\right)}$$

If $\omega_1 < \omega_2 < \omega_3$, can you sketch the approximate frequency response corresponding to this function for frequencies from just above ω_3 to just below ω_1? Say what the slopes of the combined response are in the various well-defined regions of the graph.

66

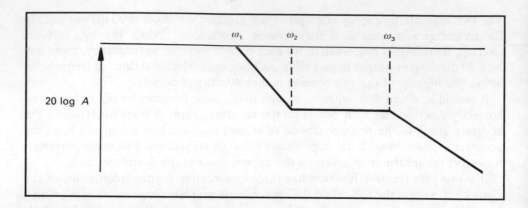

The combined response is, as usual, most easily plotted by first plotting the separate responses. Here they are:

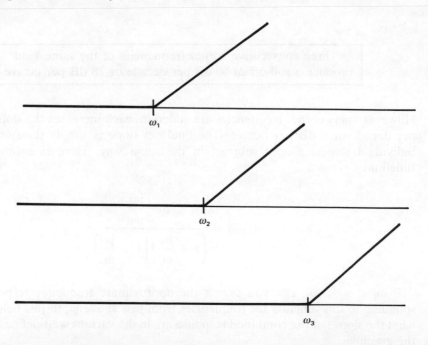

The top and bottom ones are then subtracted from the middle one to give the combined response shown above. The regions over which the different frequencies have their effects can then be deduced. Once again, the corner frequencies are not necessarily 3 dB points on the accurate graph.

LOGARITHMIC GRAPH PAPER

Since logarithmic graph paper is so widely used in plotting frequency and phase response graphs, it is worth spending a few frames examining it and learning how to select the right kind for the right task. Here is a sketch of a piece of logarithmic graph paper.

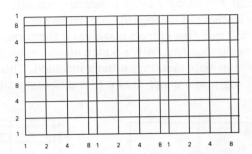

The horizontal axis of the paper is divided into three major sections and the vertical axis into two major sections. These major sections are then subdivided logarithmically. Each major section on the graph paper is called a 'cycle'. The paper is described in terms of the number of cycles there are on each axis. *The vertical axis is always quoted first.* The paper shown above is therefore described as 2 cycle by 3 cycle logarithmic graph paper. How would you describe the paper shown below?

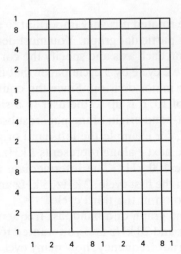

68

3 cycle by 2 cycle

Since the vertical scale is divided into three major sections and the horizontal scale into two, this is 3 cycle by 2 cycle log graph paper. It is important to notice that 2 cycle by 3 cycle and 3 cycle by 2 cycle paper are not interchangeably usable if rotated through 90°. Because of the logarithmic spacing of the minor divisions, only one of the two axes will carry the correct markings if the paper is rotated. Here is a sketch of the paper again together, with a sketch of one major division on each axis enlarged to show intermediate markings usually included. This is, in effect, a piece of 1 cycle by 1 cycle log graph paper drawn to a different scale.

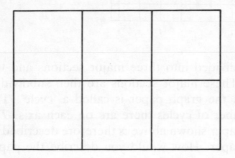
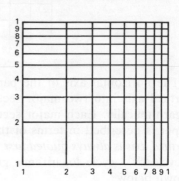

Because paper cannot be rotated it is very important to specify correctly the kind of paper you will need for a particular graph. You must decide what range of values you wish to accommodate on each axis and specify the correct number of cycles for each. You will notice on the 2 cycle by 3 cycle paper that the markings on each axis show the number 1 at each major division. Since the equal major divisions on the paper represent multiples of 10, it is up to the user to assign whatever power of 10 he wishes to the 1 at the left-hand origin of the paper; subsequent 1's then represent increasing powers of 10. If, for example the left-hand origin represents 100 Hz on the frequency scale then the next 1 along represents 1 kHz, the next 10 kHz and the right-hand end of the scale 100 kHz. The intermediate markings then represent 200 Hz, 500 Hz and so on in the first cycle, 2 kHz, 5 kHz and so on in the next cycle, and 20 kHz, 50 kHz and so on in the third cycle.

If you wanted to draw the graph of a bandpass frequency response with known corner frequencies at 50 Hz and 20 kHz and you wanted to allow at least a factor of 5 above and below each corner frequency, how many cycles would you need on the horizontal axis?

69

From 10 Hz to 100 kHz requires 4 cycles

The frequency response quoted is a typical audio amplifier response and paper with a 4 cycle horizontal axis is commonly used for such plots. A full decade margin above or below the corner frequencies would move the plot into the next cycle so, if this was required at both ends of the frequency range, a 6 cycle horizontal axis would be needed.

We will now study how the vertical axis is used. The numbers on this axis correspond to voltage ratios but, once again, the user must specify the power of 10 to be associated with each 1.

Suppose a piece of 2 cycle by 3 cycle graph paper is to be used to plot voltage ratios in dB as $20 \log V_o/V_i$ and the top of the paper is to represent a ratio of unity or zero dB. Can you write the appropriate decibel values against the other two 1's on the vertical axis and show the voltage ratios represented alongside them?

70

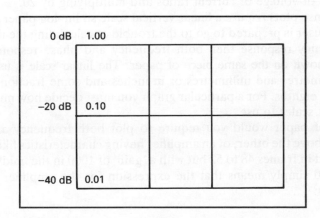

Each decade on the vertical scale represents a voltage ratio of 10:1. This is a difference of 20 dB on a decibel scale. Ratios less than 1 produce negative decibel differences. The advantage of plotting on this kind of paper is that voltage ratios (which are most likely to be the measurements made in the laboratory) can be plotted on the numerical scale on the log graph paper. The paper then 'takes the logs' to give the equivalent number of dB which can be read off from a linear scale placed alongside. Alternatively paper with a linear vertical scale may be used. We will examine this next.

71

SEMI-LOG GRAPH PAPER

Graph paper with one linearly marked axis and one logarithmically marked axis is called semi-log graph paper. It is also more usefully known as lin–log paper if the vertical axis is linear or log–lin paper if the horizontal axis is linear. Here is a sketch of a piece of lin–log paper.

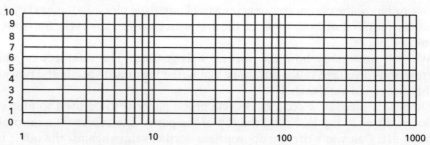

Lin–log paper *may* be used for frequency response plots as suggested in the previous frame. It is then up to the user to calculate the number of decibels corresponding to each reading on the vertical scale. This, we know, involves taking the logarithms of voltage or current ratios and multiplying by 20.

Phase response plots *require* a linear vertical scale so lin–log paper *must* be used for these. If a user is prepared to go to the trouble of calculating the decibel values for the frequency response then both frequency and phase responses can conveniently be shown on the same piece of paper. The linear scale is usually marked in either centimetres and millimetres or in inches and some fraction of an inch – often tenths or eighths. For a particular graph you must decide how much room you want and what scales to use.

What size of paper would you require to plot both frequency and phase responses, one above the other, of an amplifier having characteristics like those of the circuit analysed in frames 48 to 52 but with a 'gain' of 1000 in the 'midband' region. A gain of 1000 simply means that the expression for the amplifier output/input voltage ratio is:

$$\frac{V_o}{V_i} = \frac{1000}{\left(1 + \dfrac{j\omega}{\omega_2}\right)\left(1 - \dfrac{j\omega_1}{\omega}\right)}$$

Assume that you want to plot the log of frequency, f, rather than ω. Think what effect, if any, this will have on the mathematical expression for V_o/V_i. Let $f_1 = 160$ Hz and $f_2 = 8$ kHz and allow enough room to show at least a decade below f_1 and a decade above f_2. Say what scales you would use and what dimension your paper would have to be in the linear direction. Say, too, how many cycles you would need on the logarithmic scale. How would you describe the paper to a vendor if you wished to purchase some?

> Describing a suitable paper as 15 cm by 4 cycle lin–log paper, the scale for gain could be 4 dB per cm and for phase 22.5 degrees per cm.

Many answers are, of course, possible to this question. Let us first consider the effect of plotting frequency, f, rather than ω. Since $\omega = 2\pi f$ but both ω and ω_2 in the first ratio and ω and ω_1 in the second ratio are multiplied by the 2π, the expression for the gain may be written as:

$$\frac{V_o}{V_i} = \frac{1000}{\left(1 + \dfrac{jf}{f_2}\right)\left(1 - \dfrac{jf_1}{f}\right)}$$

The factors of 2π cancel and the mathematical shape of the expression is thus exactly the same as that for the expression involving the ω's so, provided the scales are suitably chosen, the two graphs of gain against log ω and gain against log f will be identical.

To encompass the frequency range allowing a decade above and below the corner frequencies requires frequencies from 16 Hz to 80 kHz to be accommodated. On standard paper this means covering 10 Hz to 100 kHz which is four cycles. Since the slope of frequency responses with single corner frequencies is 20 dB per decade, an allowance for 20 dB of gain vertically will be sufficient to show the significant features of the frequency response. This can conveniently be plotted over a range of 5 cm at a scale of 4 dB per cm.

The combined phase response of a low-pass circuit with a high-pass circuit has a total phase range of $\pm 90°$. Most of this will occur between the lowest and highest points of the frequency scales chosen above so allowance must be made for the full range. A phase range of $\pm 90°$ can conveniently be plotted over a range of 8 cm at a scale of 22.5 degrees per cm. The significant 45 points will then appear on a major division.

Over a range of 15 cm this choice of scales allows some space for annotation.

The next frame carries a summary of all the main ideas in this programme. Study it and then try the revision questions and test which follow it.

73

SUMMARY

1. The frequency and phase responses of a circuit are plotted from the complex expressions for the voltage transfer function V_o/V_i or the current transfer function I_o/I_i of the circuit derived by a j-notation analysis of the circuit. Such transfer functions can be expressed as dimensionless functions of $j\omega$ of the general form $A(j\omega)$. The function $A(j\omega)$ may include a dimensionless ratio A_0 (which is derived from circuit components) together with terms of the form $j\omega/\omega_0$ or $j\omega_0/\omega$ which may appear alone or as terms $(1 \pm j\omega/\omega_0)$ or $(1 \pm j\omega_0/\omega)$. The ω_0's are also derived from circuit components. Only terms of the kind listed here may be used in expressing transfer functions in a form suitable for plotting frequency and phase responses.

2. The frequency response of the circuit is defined as the graph of the amplitude of the complex number $A(j\omega)$ against frequency. The amplitude of $A(j\omega)$ is the ratio of voltage or current amplitudes of the input stimulus and the output response. This graph is usually plotted using a logarithmic scale for frequency and with the amplitude ratio expressed in dB (decibels) – a logarithmic unit used in the measurement of power ratios, voltage ratios or current ratios. The decibel scale may be plotted directly on linear graph paper or as a voltage or current ratio plotted on logarithmic graph paper. An asymptotic (straight-line) approximation to the logarithmic frequency response is called a Bode plot or Bode diagram. The Bode plot of a function which includes a term of the form $(1 \pm j\omega/\omega_0)$ is characterised by a horizontal asymptote and a sloping asymptote which meet at a 'corner frequency' ω_0. The slope of an asymptote corresponding to a single corner frequency is described as '20 db per decade' or '6 dB per octave'. With certain provisos, the corner frequencies are often also known as '3 dB points'.

3. The phase response of the circuit is defined as the graph of the phase angle of the complex number $A(j\omega)$ against frequency. The phase angle of $A(j\omega)$ is the phase difference between the input stimulus and the output response. This graph is usually plotted using a logarithmic scale for frequency and a linear scale for phase. The phase response can be approximated by straight lines joining phase values at frequencies $\omega_0/10$ and $10\omega_0$.

4. If a function is made up of a number of terms multiplied together and a logarithmic frequency response graph is plotted for each of the product terms separately, then the overall logarithmic frequency response of the complete function can be formed by adding together the separate logarithmic frequency responses. A phase response graph can also be plotted for each of the product terms separately and the overall phase response of the complete function formed by adding together the separate phase responses.

5. The frequency and phase responses for all circuits, however many product terms their transfer functions contain, can be made up by the addition or subtraction of graphs selected from the following range of functions:

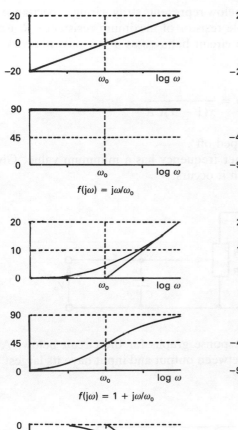

$f(j\omega) = j\omega/\omega_0$

$f(j\omega) = -j\omega_0/\omega$

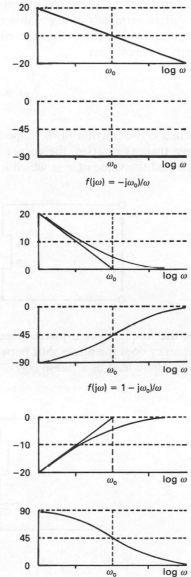

$f(j\omega) = 1 + j\omega/\omega_0$

$f(j\omega) = 1 - j\omega_0/\omega$

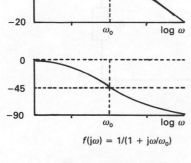

$f(j\omega) = 1/(1 + j\omega/\omega_0)$

The low-pass response

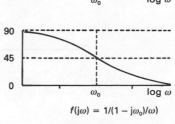

$f(j\omega) = 1/(1 - j\omega_0/\omega)$

The high-pass response

74

1. The capacitance C in the circuit below represents stray wiring capacitance across the output terminals of a variable resistor of maximum resistance R used as a potential divider. Show that the circuit behaves as a low-pass network with a corner frequency at:

$$\omega = \frac{1}{x(1-x)CR}$$

where x is the fraction of R 'tapped off'.

Prove that, as x varies, the corner frequency has a minimum value. Give this value and the value of x at which it occurs.

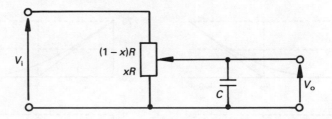

2. Plot the frequency and phase response graphs for the circuit below. At what frequency does the phase shift between output and input have its largest value? Is it a phase lead or a phase lag?

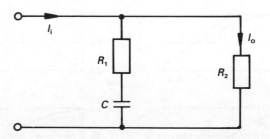

3. The inductor L in the circuit below is used to compensate for the effect of the stray capacitance C in producing high-frequency roll-off in the voltage output of the circuit. Examine its action by analysing the circuit in two parts. First assume that frequencies are low enough for the capacitor to have no effect and analyse the remaining components to determine the corner frequencies introduced by the inductor. Then assume that frequencies are so high that the inductor no longer produces any effect on the output and analyse the remaining effective components (care!) to determine what effect the capacitor has on the frequency response. Superimpose the two frequency responses to obtain the combined response. Sketch the phase response of the complete circuit.

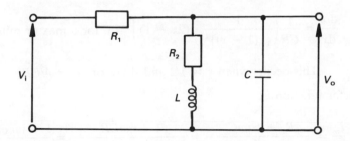

4. Derive the current transfer function I_o/I_i for the circuit below and put it into a form from which the frequency response can be plotted. Say how many corner frequencies there are and write algebraic expressions for them. Sketch the Bode diagrams indicating the corner frequencies and showing the values of I_o/I_i on any horizontal parts of the graphs under the following conditions:

(i) $L_1 >> L_2$ and $R_2 >> R_1$; (ii) $L_1 << L_2$ and $R_2 << R_1$

Find a condition for the output I_o to be independent of frequency. Write an expression for I_o/I_i with this condition and explain what has happened in terms of the frequency response graphs you have drawn.

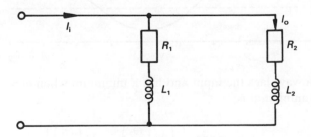

75

1. Regarding the two parts of the variable resistor as two separate resistors, the circuit can be seen to be of the same kind as that analysed in the first 25 frames of the programme. It is thus a low-pass type with a corner frequency defined by the parallel combination of the resistors and the capacitor.

$$R_p = \frac{xR(1-x)R}{xR + (1-x)R} = \frac{x(1-x)R^2}{R} = x(1-x)R \quad \text{so} \quad \omega = \frac{1}{x(1-x)CR}$$

$$\frac{d\omega}{dx} = \frac{1}{CR}\left(\frac{1}{\{x(1-x)\}^2} \cdot (2x-1)\right) = 0 \text{ for a max or min}$$

This occurs when $x = 1/2$ and therefore $\omega = 4/CR$.

2. The transfer function is:

$$\frac{I_o}{I_i} = \frac{R_1 + 1/j\omega C}{R_1 + R_2 + 1/j\omega C} = \frac{1 + j\omega CR}{1 + j\omega C(R_1 + R_2)} = \frac{1 + j\omega/\omega_1}{1 + j\omega/\omega_2}$$

This expression is the same as that analysed in frames 34 to 39 and 45 to 47 with $\omega_1 = 1/CR_1$ and $\omega_2 = 1/C(R_1 + R_2)$. The frequency and phase responses are thus as shown here:

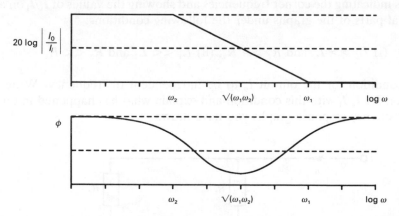

The output always lags the input and has a minimum when $\omega = \sqrt{(\omega_1\omega_2)}$. The value of this minimum is:

$$\phi = \arctan \frac{1}{2}\left\{\sqrt{\left(\frac{\omega_2}{\omega_1}\right)} - \sqrt{\left(\frac{\omega_1}{\omega_2}\right)}\right\}$$

3. When C can be ignored the transfer function is:

$$\frac{V_o}{V_i} = \frac{R_2 + j\omega L}{R_1 + R_2 + j\omega L} = \frac{R_2}{R_1 + R_2} \cdot \frac{(1 + j\omega/\omega_1)}{(1 + j\omega/\omega_2)}$$

where $\omega_1 = R_2/L$ and $\omega_2 = (R_1 + R_2)/L$

When ω is very large, with this response $V_o/V_i = 1$. The impedance of L has, in effect, become infinite and so R_2 and L can be removed for the next piece of analysis. The circuit to analyse at very high frequencies consists simply of R_1 and C. This gives a low-pass response with a corner frequency at $\omega_3 = 1/CR_1$. The combined frequency and phase responses are thus:

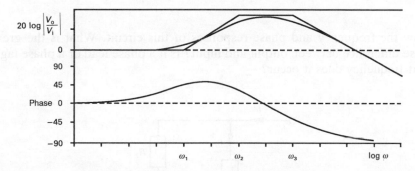

4. The transfer function for this circuit is:

$$\frac{I_o}{I_i} = \frac{R_2 + j\omega L_1}{R_1 + R_2 + j\omega L_1 + j\omega L_2} = \frac{R_1}{R_1 + R_2} \cdot \frac{(1 + j\omega/\omega_1)}{(1 + j\omega/\omega_2)}$$

where $\omega_1 = R_1/L_1$ and $\omega_2 = (R_1 + R_2)/(L_1 + L_2)$

For the conditions given, the two frequency responses are:

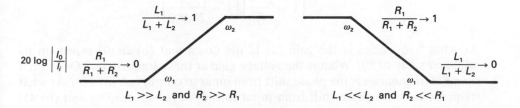

If I_o is frequency-independent, these two responses must be the same horizontal line with $R_1/(R_1 + R_2) = L_1/(L_1 + L_2)$ so $R_1/L_1 = R_2/L_2$ and $\omega_1 = \omega_2$.

TEST ON PROGRAMME 6

1. Draw freehand sketches (do not draw accurate graphs but do show important features) of the frequency and phase responses of the following circuits:

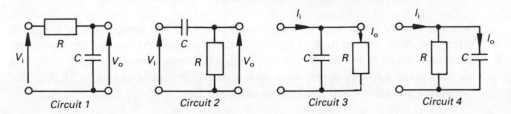

2. Draw the frequency and phase responses of this circuit. What is the greatest phase difference between output and input? Is it a phase lead or a phase lag? At what frequency does it occur?

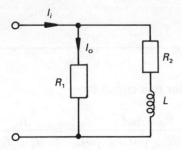

3. A voltage amplifier has a frequency response given by the expression:

$$A = \frac{80}{\left(1 - \dfrac{j100}{f_1}\right)\left(1 + \dfrac{jf_2}{20{,}000}\right)}$$

At what frequencies is the gain (a) 12 dB down and (b) 20 dB down on its midband value of 80? What is the voltage gain at these frequencies? Over what range of frequencies is the phase shift from input to output less than 6°? At what frequencies is the phase shift from input to output (a) 45° leading and (b) 45° lagging? Specify two sheets of graph paper on which you could plot separately (a) the frequency response and (b) the phase response using the same scale for frequency in each case.

FURTHER QUESTIONS ON PROGRAMME 6

1. A voltage amplifier has an input resistance of 2 kΩ. Connecting a signal generator to the amplifier by means of a series capacitor which will 'block' any direct voltage is often called 'a.c. coupling'. What is the smallest preferred value capacitor from the E3 range which can be used to a.c. couple a voltage generator into the circuit if signals of frequency 100 Hz are to pass through with no more than 3 dB of attenuation? At what frequency will there be a 45° phase difference between output and input for the capacitor you select? Will this difference be a phase lead or a phase lag?

2. A voltage amplifier has an output resistance of 100 Ω as seen looking back from the output terminals. If the capacitance across the terminals is 100 pF, at what frequency will there be a 45° phase difference between output and input? Will this difference be a phase lead or a phase lag? What is the largest value of capacitance which can be connected across the output terminals if signals of frequency 10 kHz are to pass through with no more than 3 dB of attenuation?

3. Design an attenuator which provides a 10:1 attenuation for signals whose frequency is in excess of 20 kHz but provides successively less attenuation for lower frequency signals (the 3 dB point is to be designed at 20 kHz). Below what frequency will the attenuation be negligible? That is, the output signal will be equal to the input signal. Give your answer as a 3 dB point. At what frequency will the greatest phase difference between output and input occur? Will it be a phase lead or a phase lag? What will be the value of the phase difference at this frequency?

4. A potential divider circuit has a stray capacitance C_2 in parallel with the resistor R_2 across which the output voltage is measured. Show that this circuit acts as a low-pass circuit. If a capacitor C_1 is place in parallel with the other resistor R_1 show, by considering the frequency response of the circuit as C_1 is varied, that a value can be chosen for C_1 so that the output of the circuit is independent of frequency. What is the value of C_1 and what is the output/input voltage ratio when C_1 has this value? The attenuator is said to be 'frequency compensated' when this is done. Compare this problem with further question 10 in programme 5. You will see that it is the same problem tackled in a different way.

5. Show that the phase response of the circuit in problem 2 of the test exhibits its greatest output/input phase difference at an angle ϕ where:

$$\sin \phi = \frac{R_1}{R_1 + 2R_2}$$

6. Prove the result assumed in frame 46, that the minimum value of the phase response of the circuit analysed in frames 45 and 46 occurs at a frequency $\sqrt{(\omega_1\omega_2)}$ where ω_1 and ω_2 are the two corner frequencies.

7. A certain amplifier circuit has the following voltage transfer function:

$$\frac{V_o}{V_i} = \frac{1000}{(1 + j\omega/120{,}000)(1 - j300/\omega)}$$

Sketch the Bode diagram and calculate the frequencies at which the 3 dB points occur.

8. A filter circuit has the following frequency response:

$$\frac{V_o}{V_i} = \frac{(1 + j\omega/3000)}{(1 + j\omega/1000)(1 + j\omega/2000)}$$

Sketch the Bode diagram and calculate the values of the corner frequencies.

9. Sketch the Bode diagram and phase response for the circuit given in the diagram below left. At what frequency is the phase shift of signals passing through the circuit a maximum and what is the value of this maximum?

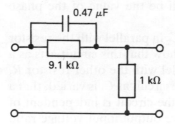
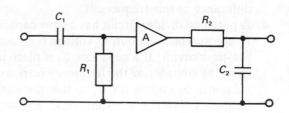

10. In the circuit in the diagram above right the block marked A is an ideal amplifier with a voltage gain of 1000. It has an infinite input impedance, zero output impedance and a frequency response which is 'flat' from zero frequency to infinity. Write an expression for V_o/V_i and put it in a form from which a frequency response can be deduced. Replace any terms involving C's and R's by ω's so that your final expression contains nothing but numbers, j's and ω's.

Programme 7

ANALYSIS OF *LCR* CIRCUITS USING DIFFERENTIAL EQUATIONS TRANSIENT AND STEADY STATE SOLUTIONS

INTRODUCTION

In programmes 4 and 5 we learnt how to analyse LCR circuits which were energised by alternating current and voltage generators. The analysis depended, however, on the assumption that the generators had been connected to the circuits for some time and that any transient phenomena apparent shortly after the initial connection had been made had had time to die away. The analysis was thus a 'steady state' analysis. It is often important, however, to know what happens in a circuit soon after switch-on. Furthermore, generators with outputs which are not sinusoidal are frequently encountered. At the beginning of programme 4 we analysed square waves. Such waveforms are very important and are widely used in 'switching circuit' design.

As well as the methods investigated in earlier programmes then, we also need a method of circuit analysis which allows us to determine both the 'transient response' and the 'steady state response' of circuits. The most basic method involves modelling the circuit with a differential equation or set of differential equations. Such equations can be developed using Kirchhoff's Laws and either mesh or nodal analysis together with the basic relationships relating the instantaneous values of current and voltage in the three kinds of component. In a resistor $v = iR$, in an inductor $v = L di/dt$ and in a capacitor $i = C dv/dt$. Since these relationships involve differential coefficients, the equations formed when the circuits are analysed are differential equations. The complete solutions of these differential equations give us enough information to determine both the transient and the steady state response of any circuit energised by any kind of generator or driving waveform. In fact, as we shall see, the complete solution of the differential equation or equations modelling a system driven by a known set of generators or waveforms *embodies* both the steady state response and the transient response.

In the first few frames of the programme we will look again at the now familiar simple RC and RL circuits and then go on to see how the methods developed can be applied to more complicated circuits.

ANALYSIS OF *LCR* CIRCUITS

THE SIMPLE *RL* CIRCUIT

Here is a simple series connected generator/resistor/inductor circuit. The generator output can be expressed as $v(t)$. This notation implies that the generator produces a voltage output which is a function of time but, as yet, is specified in no more detail than that.

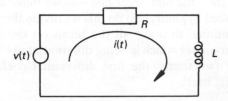

Using the defining relationships between voltage across and current through a resistor and an inductor, can you apply Kirchhoff's Voltage Law to the single loop which comprises this circuit to write a differential equation linking the voltages across the three components? Assume that a current $i(t)$ flows in the circuit in the direction shown by the arrow.

1

2

$$\frac{L\,di(t)}{dt} + i(t)R = v(t)$$

Even though $v(t)$ is undefined, we can assign a current $i(t)$ to the loop as if $v(t)$ were driving it in the direction shown. If this assignment is wrong for any given $v(t)$, the algebra of the resulting equation will result in a negative answer for $i(t)$ thus indicating that it is in the opposite direction to the one we have assumed.

Denoting the voltages across the resistor and the inductor by $v_R(t)$ and $v_L(t)$, Kirchhoff's Voltage Law, which is true at any instant of time, gives:

$$v(t) - v_R(t) - v_L(t) = 0$$

But $v_R(t) = i(t)R$ and $v_L(t) = L\,di(t)/dt$, so rearranging the equation obtained by substituting these values in the loop equation gives the result above.

Can you now re-write this differential equation so that it appears as a standard form? If you are not familiar with differential equations go straight to the next frame to see how this one is usually set out.

359

3

$$\boxed{\frac{\mathrm{d}i(t)}{\mathrm{d}t} + i(t)\frac{R}{L} = \frac{v(t)}{L}}$$

It is conventional, when writing down a differential equation, to make the coefficient of the highest order differential coefficient unity. In this case there is only one differential coefficient – the first order one – so we make *its* coefficient (that is, the quantity it is multiplied by) unity. To do this we divide throughout the equation by L. It is also conventional to make all the terms on the left-hand side of the equation involve the parameter which is being differentiated – in this case $i(t)$. So in this equation we have two terms: the first differential coefficient and the term involving the current $i(t)$ itself.

The term on the right-hand side is the 'driving function'. It is determined by the form of the generator output modified by the algebraic manipulation necessary to reduce the coefficient of the highest order differential coefficient to unity – in this case division by L.

The equation is a '*first-order linear differential equation with constant coefficients*'. It is *first order* because the *highest order* differential coefficient it contains is a *first-order* one. It is linear because both the differential coefficient and the variable $i(t)$ appear only as themselves and not raised to any power other than one. Finally, the coefficients of terms involving the variable and the differential coefficient are constants.

The equation is typical of the kind of equations which are produced when modelling circuits consisting of resistors, inductors and capacitors together with the kind of generators most likely to be met in practice. Such equations will always be linear differential equations with constant coefficients. This is because the relationships between current and voltage in the components making up the circuit are *linear relationships* of the differential coefficients or the variables themselves.

A linear relationship is one in which the related quantities differ by no more than a constant multiplier. Thus $v = iR$ is a linear relationship between voltage and current, $v = L\mathrm{d}i/\mathrm{d}t$ is a linear relationship between voltage and the first differential coefficient of the current. The voltage v and the current i are assumed to be functions of time. Circuits made up with components linked by such relationships are called '*linear circuits*'.

Can you recall the relationship between current through and
voltage across a capacitor and then describe it in the above terms?

4

> $i = C\mathrm{d}v/\mathrm{d}t$ is a linear relationship between the current through a capacitor and the first differential coefficient of the voltage across it

The above relationship confirms the assertion in frame 3 that all circuits made with simple resistors, capacitors and inductors lead to linear differential equations with constant coefficients. (Note, however, that non-linear components *do* exist but will not be covered in this text.)

We now want to solve the equation at the beginning of frame 3. The method we shall use consists of finding the solution in two parts. First we find an expression for the dependent parameter (in this case $i(t)$) which will make the *left-hand side* of the equation zero. We are, in effect, solving a simplified version of the equation with the left-hand side as it is but with the right-hand side set equal to zero. Mathematicians know this part of the solution as the '*complementary function*'. Physicists often refer to it as the '*natural response*'. We shall come to see it as forming part of the '*transient solution*'.

We then look for a solution which is similar in form to the driving function. (If the driving function is sinusoidal then we look for a sinusoidal solution and so on). Mathematicians call this part of the solution the '*particular integral*'. Physicists often refer to it as the '*forced response*'. We shall come to see it as the '*steady state solution*'.

The full solution is then the sum of these two parts adjusted to take account of known values of the variables at a given time. The time is usually $t = 0$ in which case the values are known as '*initial conditions*'.

We will first look for the transient response term by solving the equation:

$$\frac{\mathrm{d}i}{\mathrm{d}t} + \frac{R}{L}\,i = 0$$

From now on, for convenience, we will write $i(t)$ and such terms without the brackets indicating the dependence on time which will nevertheless still be understood as suggested in frame 3. To solve this part of the equation we 'guess' a solution of the form $i = A\mathrm{e}^{mt}$ where, as yet, A and m are unknown constants. It is not really a guess, of course, but knowledge from past experience that a solution of this form will be what is required and that we shall be able to find suitable values for A and m.

Using these ideas, can you find the complementary function, natural response or transient solution of the above equation? In what way is the expression you obtain incomplete?

5

> The transient solution is $i = Ae^{-(R/L)t}$.
> It is incomplete because A is an
> unknown constant

The differential equation whose solution we want is:

$$\frac{di}{dt} + i\,\frac{R}{L} = 0$$

Substituting the trial solution $i = Ae^{mt}$ into the equation we obtain:

$$Ame^{mt} + A\,\frac{R}{L}\,e^{mt} = 0$$

The term Ae^{mt} can be cancelled from both terms leaving:

$$m + \frac{R}{L} = 0 \quad \text{and hence} \quad m = -\frac{R}{L}$$

Thus $i = Ae^{-(R/L)t} = Ae^{-t/(L/R)}$ but, with the information so far provided, A is an unknown constant.

What are the dimensions of the term L/R?

6

> The term L/R has dimensions of time

Since an exponent must be dimensionless as shown in programme 1, the ratio $t/(L/R)$ must be dimensionless, hence the above result. The term L/R is particularly important and is a feature of the solutions of equations of this kind. It is called the 'time constant' of the circuit and is a measure of how long the transient phenomena associated with the complete solution persist. We cannot evaluate A until we know more about the driving function and the initial conditions. We can, however, make another important observation without this knowledge.

What will be the value of the transient solution, whatever the value of A, after a very long time has passed, say as $t \to \infty$?

7

| The value of the transient solution will be zero |

Since the exponent of the exponential term $e^{-v(L/R)}$ is negative, this term 'dies away' as time increases. This is why this contribution to the complete answer is called the 'transient' solution – it is a part of the solution which does not persist. It is worth remarking that, when exponential terms are encountered in practical physical systems, they must have negative exponents. If they had positive exponents this would imply the existence of a term which could increase without limit as time progressed, which is contrary to natural laws such as the principle of conservation of energy. Since A is a constant, the whole term $Ae^{-v(L/R)}$ thus also dies away or 'decays' as t increases. So, 'as t tends to infinity' the expression must eventually decay to zero.

What will be the values of the expression for i in terms of A when $t = 0$, $t = L/R$, $t = 5 \, L/R$ and $t = 10 \, L/R$?

8

When $t =$	0	$i = A$
When $t =$	L/R	$i = 0.368A$
When $t =$	$5 \, L/R$	$i = 0.00674A$
When $t =$	$10 \, L/R$	$i = 0.0000454A$

The value of i when $t = 0$ is called its initial value. After one time constant the value of i has decayed to about a third of its initial value. The other figures show that, even after only five 'time constants', the value of i has decayed to less than one hundredth of its initial value while, after ten 'time constants', it has decayed to less than one ten-thousandth of its initial value. The expression 'as t tends to infinity' in frame 7 above can thus be interpreted in many practical situations as 'greater than five time constants' and in most cases as 'greater than ten time constants'. In many circuits, component values are such that the time constant may be measured in milliseconds or even microseconds. 'Infinity' can, under these circumstances, be quite a short time away!

We will now give the voltage generator a value and obtain a complete solution for the resulting differential equation. We will begin by using a simple direct voltage generator of output V. What does the differential equation become if such a generator is connected into the circuit?

9

> The equation becomes $\dfrac{\mathrm{d}i}{\mathrm{d}t} + i\,\dfrac{R}{L} = \dfrac{V}{L}$

In the equation given at the beginning of frame 3 the function $v(t)$ is simply the constant value V so, substituting $v(t) = V$ in the original equation gives the equation above.

In frame 3 we said that, to find the particular integral or steady state solution, we would look for a solution of the same form as the driving function. What kind of solution do you think should be tried for this equation?

10

> Try a solution of the form $i = B$ where B is constant

Since the driving function, V/L, is constant we try a constant as the particular integral, forced response or steady state solution. We cannot say exactly what this constant will be at this stage so just give it a letter B. We will now try to evaluate B.

If $i = B$ *is* a solution then substituting it into the equation must satisfy this equation. What deduction can you make by doing this?

11

> $B = V/R$

Putting $i = B$ into the equation in frame 9, the first term becomes zero since the differential coefficient of a constant is zero. The remaining terms give the equation:

$$BR/L = V/L \quad \text{whence} \quad B = V/R$$

The full solution is then $i = V/R + A\mathrm{e}^{-t/(L/R)}$

By virtue of the right-hand term, i is seen to be a function of time. The expression above, however, still contains the unknown constant A. What extra piece of information do we need in order to find a value for A?

12

> We need a value for i at a known time, usually $t = 0$

We usually know or can deduce the conditions at $t = 0$. Sometimes, however, we need the concepts of $t = 0+$ and $t = 0-$, times instantaneously before and instantaneously after $t = 0$. These ideas allow us to take account of 'instantaneous changes' at $t = 0$. Such changes are not possible in real situations but are often used in modelling ideal situations. In the present example we will assume that, at time $t = 0-$, the generator has zero output but is switched instantaneously at $t = 0$ to an output V and maintains this output from time $t = 0+$ onwards. The 'initial condition' we require is strictly the value of the current at time $t = 0+$. We can then evaluate the current from time $t = 0+$ onwards.

As a first step towards determining this initial condition, can you give the value of the current in the circuit at time $t = 0-$?

13

> The current in the circuit at time $t = 0-$ is zero

With the assumption that the output of the generator is zero at $t = 0-$, there can be no current flowing through the series combination of the resistor and the inductor so the circuit current is zero at time $t = 0-$.

We must now establish what happens when the generator voltage changes instantaneously to a value V at time $t = 0+$. To do this we must examine the relationship between current and voltage in an inductor. Noting that the generator voltage is across the series combination of the inductor and the resistor, two things are possible when the generator voltage changes instantaneously: the current flow will either remain momentarily at zero or it will jump instantaneously to a fixed value I. If it was the latter then, since $v = L\,di/dt$, a finite change in current in an infinitesimally short time would imply a near infinite voltage across the inductor. Since the energy stored in an inductor is LI, this would also imply the transfer of a finite amount of energy to the inductor in an infinitesimal time, in other words a near infinite power flow. Physical reasoning suggests that neither of these is possible.

So, considering the above analysis, can you deduce the value of the current in the circuit at time $t = 0+$? (Do not confuse this with the value of the transient part of the current when $t = 0$ evaluated in frame 8.)

14

The current in the circuit at time $t = 0+$ is zero

Since infinite voltages and infinite power flows are physically impossible, it follows that the current in the circuit cannot change so must remain at the value it had at time $t = 0-$. That is, it remains at zero. In fact we can extend the result we have just discovered to a more general statement:

The current through an inductor cannot change instantaneously

We shall often make use of this result in calculating the initial conditions in circuits containing inductors.

We have now therefore established that the full expression for the current in the circuit from time $t = 0+$ onwards is:

$$i = V/R + Ae^{-t/(L/R)} \quad \text{and that, at time } t = 0+, i = 0$$

Can you now make use of this information to calculate A?

15

$A = -V/R$

Substituting $i = 0$ when $t = 0$ into the expression for i above gives:

$$0 = V/R + A \quad \text{whence} \quad A = -V/R$$

The full solution for the current is thus:

$$i = \frac{V}{R} - \frac{V}{R} \, e^{-t/(L/R)}$$

This expression for i is seen to satisfy all the conditions required. When $t = 0$ the value of i is 0. The transient part of the solution is the right-hand term. It has an initial value of $-V/R$ which decays to zero because of the negative exponent leaving the steady state solution $i = V/R$.

Notice that the amplitude of the steady state solution depends partly on the circuit components (it involves R) and partly on the driving function. The amplitude of the transient solution also depends partly on the circuit components and partly on the driving function. The time constant of the transient solution, however, depends *only* on the circuit components.

Can you now plot a graph of the current in the circuit? Choose scales which allow you to show all important features of the function represented.

16

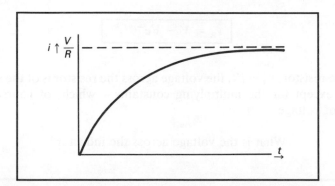

Notice how the current starts at zero, increases rapidly for a short time and then increases more and more slowly as time progresses, ultimately attaining the steady state value V/R. This shape is characteristic of the exponential function. We speak of the current as '*aiming for* the value V/R with a *time constant L/R*'.

The concepts of '*time constant*' and '*aiming value*' are very important in the analysis of electronic circuits which exhibit transient phenomena.

We can now use the value of the current in the circuit to determine the distribution of voltages around the circuit.

17

VOLTAGE DISTRIBUTION AROUND A SIMPLE *RL* CIRCUIT

Here is the simple series connected generator/resistor/inductor circuit again. Knowing the current in the circuit we can now calculate the voltages across the two passive components using the fundamental current/voltage determining relationships: $v = iR$ and $v = L\mathrm{d}i/\mathrm{d}t$.

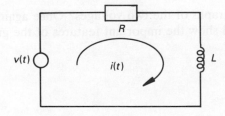

What is the voltage across the resistor?

18

$$v_R = V - Ve^{-t/(L/R)}$$

Since, for the resistor, $v_R = iR$, the voltage across the resistor is of the same form as the current except for the multiplying constants – which, of course, now have dimensions of voltage.

What is the voltage across the inductor?

19

$$v_L = Ve^{-t/(L/R)}$$

Since, for the inductor, $v_L = L\,di/dt$, we need to differentiate the expression for the current to obtain this result.

$$\text{We have } i \;=\; \frac{V}{R} - \frac{V}{R}\,e^{-t/(L/R)}$$

$$\text{so } v_L \;=\; -\,L\frac{V}{R}\left(\frac{-R}{L}\right)e^{-t/(L/R)}$$

$$=\; Ve^{-t/(L/R)}$$

The first term in the expression for i is constant so its differential coefficient is zero. The differential coefficient of the second term results in an exponential term multiplied by constant terms all of which except the V cancel, the two minus signs also cancelling each other's effect.

Can you sketch graphs of the two voltages? Once again, choose scales
that will show the important features of the graphs.

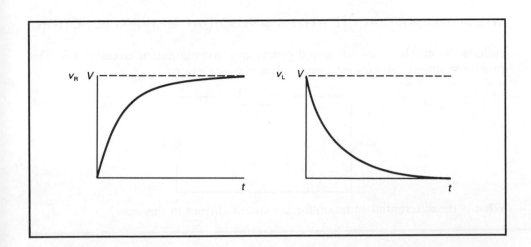

As expected, the shape of the resistor voltage graph is very like that of the current graph. It starts from zero aiming for a maximum of V with a time constant L/R. The inductor voltage graph on the other hand starts from a maximum V aiming for zero with the same time constant L/R.

We can explain these results physically by remembering that current through an inductor cannot change instantaneously. The current in the circuit must therefore start from zero and hence the voltage across the resistor must start from zero. The generator voltage, as soon as it jumps to the value V, must be shared between the resistor and the inductor. Since the resistor voltage is initially zero, all the generator voltage must appear across the inductor so this voltage jumps to V.

As time progresses and an electric field is established around the inductor, the current builds up until the generator voltage is re-distributed between the resistor and the inductor, so that eventually all the generator voltage appears across the resistor and there is zero voltage across the inductor. The current in the circuit is then a direct current of value V/R. Since an inductor is essentially a short-circuit to direct current, this confirms that the voltage across it must be zero.

Notice that, since the time constants of the two graphs are the same, they would 'fit together' if the inductor voltage graph were inverted and placed on top of the resistor voltage graph. This is the same as saying that the sum of the two voltages at any instant of time must be constant and equal to V, the generator voltage.

In the next frame we will analyse the same simple *RL* circuit driven by a sinusoidal generator.

21

THE SIMPLE *RL* CIRCUIT WITH A SINUSOIDAL DRIVING FUNCTION

Here is the simple series connected generator/resistor/inductor circuit again. The generator output can now be expressed as $v(t) = V \sin \omega t$.

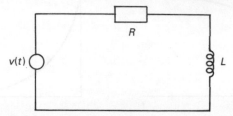

What is the differential equation for the circuit current in this case?

22

$$\frac{\mathrm{d}i}{\mathrm{d}t} + i\,\frac{R}{L} = \frac{V \sin \omega t}{L}$$

Simply substituting the expression $v(t) = V \sin \omega t$ into the equation in frame 3 gives the above result.

What is the transient solution or complementary function?

23

$$i = A\mathrm{e}^{(-R/L)t}$$

Since the left-hand side of the equation has not altered and the transient solution is the solution of the equation with the left-hand side set equal to zero, then the transient solution cannot have altered either. The transient solution will, in fact, be the same, apart from the value of the multiplying constant, for all driving functions. The form of the driving function will, however, help to determine the value of the multiplying constant when the initial conditions are set in to the complete solution.

We now have to find the steady state solution. What form do you think we should try for this part of the solution? Take care with the answer to this question. It is not as straightforward as it might seem.

$$\boxed{\text{Try } i = A \sin \omega t + B \cos \omega t}$$

It is necessary to include both cosine and sine terms in the trial expression for the steady state solution because we cannot guarantee that the expression we want will be a pure *sine* function. It will certainly be *sinusoidal* but may not have the same phase as the driving function. A function formed from the sum of a sine function and a cosine function is the same as a sine function with a phase shift, as we shall see when we arrive at the answer. We can expect a current at a different phase from the generator voltage because we have already found the steady state solution to this problem using phasors and j-notation in earlier programmes. (*Note*: A trial function of the form $i = A' \sin(\omega t + \phi)$ would, in fact, be equally valid and would ultimately lead to the same answer.)

Substituting this expression for i into the differential equation we have:

$$A\omega \cos \omega t - B\omega \sin \omega t + \frac{R}{L} (A \sin \omega t + B \cos \omega t) = \frac{V}{L} \sin \omega t$$

Now, the *solution* to a differential equation which contains differential coefficients with respect to time is a function which is true *for all values of time*. We can thus substitute any value of time we like into this equation and it must be true. Choosing a value which makes the sine functions zero ($t = 0$, for example) makes the cosine functions equal to one. We thus obtain:

$$A\omega + RB/L = 0 \quad \text{and so} \quad A = -RB/\omega L$$

We could have obtained the same result by 'equating the coefficients' of the cosine terms.

What other relationship between A and B can you obtain using these ideas?

$$\boxed{B = RA/\omega L - V/\omega L}$$

Choosing a value of t to make the cosine terms zero and the sine terms one ($t = \pi/\omega$, for example) or, alternatively, equating coefficients of the sine terms we obtain:

$$-B\omega + RA/L = V/L$$

which can be rearranged into the above expression.

What, then, are the values of A and B?

26

$$A = \frac{VR}{R^2 + \omega^2 L^2} \qquad B = \frac{-V\omega L}{R^2 + \omega^2 L^2}$$

We have, from the two previous frames, $A = -RQ/\omega L$ and $B = RP/\omega L - V/\omega L$. Substituting the expression for A into that for B, we obtain:

$$B = \frac{-R^2 B}{\omega^2 L^2} - \frac{V}{\omega L} \quad \text{so} \quad B\left(1 + \frac{R^2}{\omega^2 L^2}\right) = \frac{-V}{\omega L} \quad \text{and} \quad B\left(\frac{\omega^2 L^2 + R^2}{\omega^2 L^2}\right) = \frac{-V}{\omega L}$$

$$\text{Thus} \quad B = \frac{-V\omega L}{R^2 + \omega^2 L^2} \quad \text{and} \quad A = \frac{-RB}{\omega L} = \frac{VR}{R^2 + \omega^2 L^2}$$

What are the dimensions of A and B?

27

$$\boxed{\text{Both have dimensions of current}}$$

The terms ωL and R both have dimensions of resistance so A and B both have dimensions of voltage times resistance divided by resistance squared. That is voltage divided by resistance which is current. This must be so because A and B arise in the expression $i = A \sin \omega t + B \cos \omega t$ and, since sine and cosine are dimensionless, A and B must be currents.

The expression for the steady state solution then becomes:

$$i = \frac{VR \sin \omega t}{R^2 + \omega^2 L^2} - \frac{V\omega L \cos \omega t}{R^2 + \omega^2 L^2}$$

In frames 83 to 85 of programme 4 we found that the relationship between voltage and current in this circuit in the steady state was such that the amplitudes I and V of current and voltage respectively were linked by an expression $V = IZ$ where $Z = \sqrt{(R^2 + \omega^2 L^2)}$ and that the voltage led the current by a phase angle ϕ where $\tan \phi = \omega L/R$.

Can you show that the above result is consistent with these results we obtained earlier? Remember that, if the voltage leads the current by a phase angle ϕ, then the current lags the voltage by the same phase angle. In the present problem we have defined the input to the circuit as a voltage $V \sin \omega t$. It may help you to draw a diagram showing the angle ϕ as defined by its tangent above.

$$\boxed{i = (V/Z) \sin (\omega t - \phi) = I \sin (\omega t - \phi)}$$

Drawing a diagram for the angle ϕ as defined by its tangent, we have:

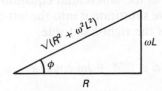

Thus $\quad \sin \phi = \omega L/\sqrt{(R^2 + \omega^2 L^2)} = \omega L/Z \quad$ and

$$\cos \phi = R/\sqrt{(R^2 + \omega^2 L^2)} = R/Z$$

Hence $i = \dfrac{VR \sin \omega t}{R^2 + \omega^2 L^2} - \dfrac{V \omega L \cos \omega t}{R^2 + \omega^2 L^2} = \dfrac{VR}{Z^2} \sin \omega t - \dfrac{V \omega L}{Z^2} \cos \omega t$

$\qquad = \dfrac{V}{Z} \cos \phi \sin \omega t - \dfrac{V}{Z} \sin \phi \cos \omega t = \dfrac{V}{Z} \sin(\omega t - \phi)$

$\qquad = I \sin(\omega t - \phi)$

The current is thus of amplitude V/Z and lags the voltage by the phase angle ϕ. We thus see that the steady state analysis using this more fundamental approach starting with the differential equation for the circuit confirms the use of phasors for a steady state analysis used in programme 4.

Continuing with the analysis to obtain a complete solution for the differential equation we can now combine the above result with the expression from frame 23 to write:

$$i = Ae^{-(R/L)t} + I \sin(\omega t - \phi)$$

If no current flows in the circuit before the generator is switched on, that is at time $t = 0$, what is the value of the constant A?

$$\boxed{A - I \sin \phi = \dfrac{V \omega L}{\sqrt{(R^2 + \omega^2 L^2)}}}$$

To obtain A we set $i = 0$ when $t = 0$. The above result follows because the exponential function is unity when $t = 0$ and $\sin (-\phi) = -\sin \phi$.

Now write down the complete solution to the differential equation and show, by substituting it back into the equation, that it does indeed satisfy it.

30

The complete solution is $i = I \sin \phi \, e^{-(R/L)t} + I \sin (\omega t - \phi)$

To show that this is a solution to the differential equation
$di/dt + (R/L)i = (V/L) \sin \omega t$ we substitute it into the left-hand side and show that
the result of doing this matches the right-hand side:

$$\frac{di}{dt} = -\frac{RI}{L} \sin \phi \, e^{-(R/L)t} + I\omega \cos (\omega t - \phi)$$

$$\frac{R}{L} i = \frac{R}{L} I \sin \phi \, e^{-(R/L)t} + \frac{R}{L} I \sin(\omega t - \phi)$$

If we add these two equations together, the left-hand side of the resulting
equation is the same as the left-hand side of the differential equation. The right-
hand side must therefore be equal to the right-hand side of the differential equation. The first two terms on the right-hand side cancel so we need to show that:

$$\omega I \cos(\omega t - \phi) + \frac{RI}{L} \sin(\omega t - \phi) = \frac{V}{L} \sin \omega t$$

Writing $I = V/Z$ and expanding the trigonometric functions, the left-hand side of
the above expression becomes:

$$\frac{\omega V}{Z} \cos \omega t \cos \phi + \frac{\omega V}{Z} \sin \omega t \sin \phi + \frac{RV}{LZ} \sin \omega t \cos \phi - \frac{RV}{LZ} \cos \omega t \sin \phi$$

Substituting $\sin \phi = \omega L/Z$ and $\cos \phi = R/Z$ into this expression we have:

$$\frac{\omega VR}{Z^2} \cos \omega t + \frac{\omega^2 VL}{Z^2} \sin \omega t + \frac{R^2 V}{LZ^2} \sin \omega t - \frac{RV\omega L}{LZ^2} \cos \omega t$$

The cosine terms now cancel leaving:

$$V \left(\frac{\omega^2 L}{Z^2} + \frac{R^2}{LZ^2} \right) \sin \omega t = V \left(\frac{\omega^2 L^2 + R^2}{LZ^2} \right) \sin \omega t = \frac{V}{L} \sin \omega t$$

Because $\omega^2 L^2 + R^2 = Z^2$

It is always useful to check that the solution of a differential equation truly satisfies
the equation. It must do, of course, if all algebraic manipulations have been
performed correctly, but making the check can help you to pick up any algebraic
errors you may have made.

A TABLE OF PARTICULAR INTEGRALS (FORCED RESPONSES OR STEADY STATE SOLUTIONS)

The method of solving linear differential equations with constant coefficients which we have developed in the previous few frames is applicable to all such first-order equations and, indeed, to higher order equations as well as we shall see later. The trial function used for the transient solution is always of the form Ae^{mt} where m is found to be the time constant of the circuit. However, since the method involves using a *suitable* trial function for the steady state solution, it is useful to have a reference table of such functions. The table given here lists several commonly encountered forcing functions likely to be met in practical circuit design.

Forcing function	*Trial function for particular integral*
A (a constant)	B (a constant)
At	$B_1 t + B_2$
At^n	$B_n t^n + B_{n-1} t^{n-1} + \ldots + B_1 t + B_0$ (The same trial function would be used if the forcing function was a polynomial of order n)
Ae^{at}	Be^{at}
$A \sin \omega t$ or $A \cos \omega t$	$B_1 \sin \omega t + B_2 \cos \omega t$ or $B_3 \sin (\omega t + \phi)$
$Ae^{at} \sin \omega t$	$\exp at \, (B_1 \sin \omega t + B_2 \cos \omega t)$
or	or
$Ae^{at} \cos \omega t$	$B_3 \exp at \sin (\omega t + \phi)$

If the forcing function is a linear combination of two or more of the above forcing functions, then the trial function is a linear combination of appropriate functions selected from the above table.

In programme 4 we looked at waveforms. We can often build up waveforms from suitably modified versions of the above functions. A ramp function, for example, is a function of the form $v = Vt/T$ defined over an interval from $t = 0$ to $t = T$. A saw-tooth waveform is simply a repeated ramp.

Here is another example. A circuit is described by the differential equation $dv/dt + v/CR = Vt/CRT$. What is the time constant of the circuit and what is the form of the trial function for the steady state solution? If the voltage v is zero when $t = 0$, what is the complete solution of the equation?

32

> The circuit time constant is CR
> The steady state trial function is $v = B_1 t + B_2$
> The complete solution is $v = \dfrac{VCR}{T}(\mathrm{e}^{-t/CR} - 1) + \dfrac{Vt}{T}$

The circuit time constant is, by inspection, the reciprocal of the coefficient of the term in v.

The forcing function is a linear function of time. That is, a first-order polynomial. The trial function is therefore also a first-order polynomial with all coefficients shown and to be evaluated. Substituting the trial function into the equation gives:

$$B_1 + B_1 t/CR + B_2/CR = Vt/CRT$$

Equating coefficients of t and the constant terms gives:

$$B_1 = V/T \quad \text{and} \quad B_1 + B_2/CR = 0 \quad \text{so} \quad B_2 = -CRB_1 = -VCR/T$$

The complete solution is thus:

$$v = A\mathrm{e}^{-t/CR} + \frac{V}{T}(t - CR)$$

When $t = 0$, $v = 0$ so $A = VCR/T$. Hence:

$$v = \frac{VCR}{T}(\mathrm{e}^{-t/CR} - 1) + \frac{Vt}{T}$$

Now, if instead of the above forcing function, the forcing function had been $(Vt/CRT) + (V/CR)\,\mathrm{e}^{-st}\sin \omega t$, what would the trial function for the steady state solution be? (The full solution will not be evaluated.)

33

> $$v = B_1 t + B_2 + \mathrm{e}^{-st}\{B_3 \sin(\omega t + \phi)\}$$

The forcing function is a linear combination of functions so the trial function is a linear combination of the appropriate functions selected from the table. If the B's in this new function were to be evaluated, B_1 and B_2 would be likely to be different from the values in frame 32. B_3 and ϕ are two new constants which would also have to be evaluated to complete the problem.

34

THE SIMPLE *RC* CIRCUIT

Here is a simple series connected generator/resistor/capacitor circuit. The generator output can be expressed as $v(t)$. It produces a voltage output which is a function of time but, as for the *RL* circuit considered in frame 1, is at present specified in no more detail than that.

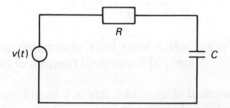

Using the defining relationships between voltage across and current through a resistor and a capacitor, can you apply Kirchhoff's Voltage Law to the single loop which comprises this circuit to write a differential equation linking the voltages across the three components? Assign a current to the loop as shown and use it to help you derive the equation. When you have an equation, set it out in a standard form.

35

$$\frac{dv_C}{dt} + \frac{v_C}{CR} = \frac{v(t)}{CR}$$

The sense of the current i is arbitrary but it is conventional to choose a clockwise current. If this assignment is wrong for any given $v(t)$, the resulting algebra will produce a negative answer for i thus indicating that it is in the opposite direction to the one we have assumed.

Denoting the voltages across the resistor and the capacitor by v_R and v_C, Kirchhoff's Voltage Law gives us $v(t) - v_R - v_C = 0$. But $v_R = iR$ and $i = Cdv/dt$. Substituting this last expression for i into the expression for the voltage across the resistor gives a differential equation in v, the capacitor voltage. Rearranging and dividing by C to make the coefficient of the differential coefficient unity gives the standard form shown above.

What can you say about the left-hand side of this equation compared with the left-hand side of the equation in frame 3?

36

> Apart from the fact that one has a current as the variable and the other has a voltage, both equations are essentially of the same form.

Both equations are first-order differential equations of the general form:

$$\frac{dx}{dt} + \frac{x}{\tau} = f(t)$$

The term τ is a constant which must have dimensions of time. It is the time constant of the circuit. The term $f(t)$ is a general function of time whose dimensions must be $[x]/T$.

Looking for '*mathematical shapes*' like this is a useful skill to cultivate. If the analyses of two different problems result in the production of two equations which have the same mathematical shape, then the solutions of those equations will also have the same mathematical shapes.

Now, can you deduce the time constant τ in the equation $\dfrac{dv_c}{dt} + \dfrac{v_c}{CR} = \dfrac{v(t)}{CR}$

and express the transient solution in terms of this time constant?

37

$$\tau = CR \qquad v = Ae^{-t/\tau}$$

The form of the transient solution can be seen by direct comparison with the form of the solution to the equation for the *RL* circuit given in frame 4. The time constant for the *RL* circuit was L/R. The time constant for the *RC* circuit is CR. It is worth memorising the facts that the quotient of an inductor and a resistor is a time constant and that the product of a capacitor and a resistor is also a time constant. Expressions involving terms such as these are met with very frequently in circuit analysis and design.

In frame 13 we obtained an expression $i = (V/R) - (V/R)\,e^{-t(L/R)}$ as the solution to the differential equation $\dfrac{di}{dt} + \dfrac{i}{L/R} = \dfrac{V}{L}$ for the *RL* circuit when driven by an input voltage switching from 0 to V at $t = 0$.

Now, if the *RC* circuit is subject to a similar switched voltage, can you write down an expression for the complete solution to the differential equation for v just by comparison with the above result? You may find simple dimensional reasoning helpful in determining the 'shape' of your answer.

$$v_c = V - Ve^{-t/\tau} \quad \text{where} \quad \tau = CR$$

If we place the two equations and the two solutions side by side, the similarities between them become easier to see:

$$\frac{di}{dt} + \frac{i}{L/R} = \frac{V}{L} \qquad \frac{dv_c}{dt} + \frac{v_c}{CR} = \frac{V}{CR}$$

$$\text{so } i = \frac{V}{R} - \frac{V}{R}e^{-t/(L/R)} \text{ and } v_c = V - Ve^{-t/CR}$$

The left-hand equation is an equation in i and all terms in the answer necessarily have dimensions of I/T because the first term is di/dt. Since the right-hand equation is an equation in v, all terms in the solution to this equation must necessarily have dimensions of V/T. In the solutions all terms have 'dimensions' of I and V respectively.

The first term in the solution to the left-hand equation is the steady state term. It is the value of current when all transients have died away and is given by the expression V/R. The first term in the solution of the right-hand equation must therefore be the steady state value of the voltage across the capacitor. Inspection of the circuit diagram shows that this must be V. If no current is flowing which will be the case when all transients have died away, there can be no current through R and therefore no voltage across it. The voltage across C must therefore equal the generator voltage V.

The second term in the solution of the current equation just cancels the first term to give $i = 0$ when $t = 0$. The second term in the solution to the voltage equation must therefore just cancel the first term to give $v = 0$ when $t = 0$. The 'exponential decay' of the two terms is determined by the two time constants, the exponents $t/(L/R)$ and t/CR both being dimensionless.

We could, of course, solve the problem by carrying out a full analysis. To do this we first find the transient part of the complete solution by trying a solution of the form $v_c = Ae^{mt}$ with the right-hand side of the equation set equal to zero. Following the form of analysis in frame 4 and substituting this expression for v_c into the differential equation yields the result that $m = (-1/CR) = (-1/\tau)$. To evaluate the steady state part of the solution we try an expression $v_c = B$ (a constant) because the right-hand side of the equation is constant. Substituting this expression into the full equation yields the result that $B = V$. The complete solution is thus $v_c = V + Ae^{-t/\tau}$ where A is to be found from the initial conditions. If $v_c = 0$ when $t = 0$ we find that $A = -V$.

The full solution is thus $v_c = V - Ve^{-t/\tau}$ as before.

39

SUMMARY

1. Kirchhoff's Laws can be used to set up differential equations describing the behaviour of circuits containing generators, resistors, capacitors and inductors. Kirchhoff's Laws apply at any given instant of time, and the defining relationships for current and voltage in the circuit components can be used to give the values of current through and voltage and voltage across the components at any instant. The defining relationships are:

$$\text{Resistor: } v = iR \qquad \text{Capacitor: } i = C\mathrm{d}v/\mathrm{d}t \qquad \text{Inductor: } v = L\mathrm{d}i/\mathrm{d}t$$

2. An equation of the form $\mathrm{d}x/\mathrm{d}t + x/\tau = f(t)$ is called a first-order linear differential equation with constant coefficients. It is first order because the highest order differential coefficient it contains is a first-order coefficient. When the equation is derived from an electric circuit, x may be either a current or a voltage. The constant term is called the 'time constant' of the circuit. It is determined solely by the circuit components. The function $f(t)$ is called the driving function of the circuit.

3. The solution of such an equation consists of two parts: a transient part, natural response or complementary function and a steady state part, forced response or particular integral.

4. The transient part is always of the form $x = Ae^{-t/\tau}$ where the value of A is affected by the form of the driving function and possibly by the values of the components making up the circuit. The exact value of A is determined by a known value of x at a given time, usually $t = 0$. In this case the known value of x is called an 'initial condition'.

5. The steady state part is always of the same form as the driving function – if the driving function is constant it is constant, if the driving function is sinusoidal it is sinusoidal, and so on. As is the case for the transient part, the steady state part will also contain multiplying factors determined partly by the form of the driving function and partly by the circuit components.

6. Many circuits (and, indeed, many other time-dependent physical systems) exhibit the characteristic 'mathematical shape' of the first-order linear differential equation with constant coefficients. Once one has been solved for a given driving function, the solution to all others having the same kind of driving function can be deduced by comparison with the known solution. Dimensional reasoning can help in formulating such solutions.

1. Find the current through and voltage across both components in the left-hand circuit below. The voltage across the capacitor is initially zero. The current generator is switched from zero to a constant value I at $t = 0$. Set up a differential equation for the circuit and solve it by substituting suitable trial functions for the transient solution and steady state solution into the equation. Derive other results from the solution of the equation.

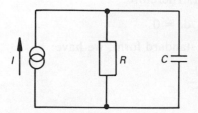 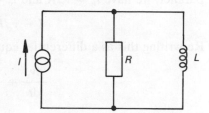

2. Find the current through and voltage across both components in the right-hand circuit above. The current through the inductor is initially zero. The generator is as in question 1. Set up a differential equation for the circuit and solve it by recognising the essential 'mathematical shape' of the equation and hence its solution. Determine the steady state solution by physical reasoning and use dimensional reasoning to deduce important terms in the answer. Derive other results from the solution of the differential equation.

3. The left-hand circuit below is in a steady state before the switch is closed. The switch is closed at time $t = 0$ at which time the left-hand generator starts giving an output $I \sin \omega t$. Obtain expressions for the voltage across and current through the capacitor.

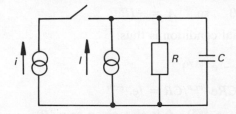 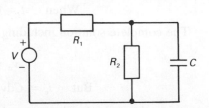

4. If $R_1 = R_2 = R$, find the voltage across the capacitor in the right-hand circuit above if the generator is switched from zero to V at time $t = 0$ and the capacitor is initially uncharged. Solve the problem (a) by using node voltage analysis and deriving a suitable differential equation and (b) by applying Thevenin's theorem before deriving a suitable differential equation. What are the currents in the three components? Can you answer this question from solution (b)?

41

1. Applying Kirchhoff's Current Law to the node at the top of the diagram, we have:

$$I - i_R - i_c = 0$$

If we call the voltage across the capacitor v_c then, since this is also the voltage across the generator and across the resistor because the three components are in parallel, we have $i_R = v_c/R$ and $i_c = Cdv_c/dt$. Therefore:

$$I - v_c/R - Cdv_c/dt = 0$$

Re-writing this as a differential equation in standard form, we have:

$$\frac{dv_c}{dt} + \frac{v_c}{CR} = \frac{I}{C}$$

Setting the left-hand side of the equation equal to zero, a suitable trial function for the transient solution is $v_c = Ae^{mt}$. Substituting this expression into the equation gives:

$$Ame^{mt} + (A/CR)e^{mt} = 0$$

$$\text{Hence} \quad m = -1/CR$$

Since the right-hand side of the equation is a constant, a suitable trial function for the steady state solution is $v_c = B$ where B is a constant. Substituting this value into the equation gives:

$$B = IR$$

The complete solution is thus $\quad v_c = Ae^{-t/CR} + IR$

When $\quad t = 0, v_c = 0 \quad$ so $\quad A = -IR$

The complete solution including the initial condition is thus:

$$v_c = IR\,(1 - e^{-t/CR})$$

But $\quad i_c = Cdv_c/dt = ICRe^{-t/CR}/CR = Ie^{-t/CR}$

and $\quad i_R = I - i_c \quad$ so $\quad i = I\,(1 - e^{-t/CR}) \quad$ (*i* is also given as v_c/R)

The full answer is thus:

$$\begin{aligned} v_c &= IR\,(1 - e^{-t/CR}) \\ i_c &= Ie^{-t/CR} \\ i_R &= I\,(1 - e^{-t/CR}) \end{aligned}$$

2. Applying Kirchhoff's Current Law to the node at the top of the diagram, we have:

$$I + i_R + i_L = 0$$

If we call the voltage across the inductor v_L and the current through the inductor i_L then $v_L = L di_L/dt$. But, because the three components are in parallel, this is also the voltage across the resistor. The current through the resistor is thus $v_L/R = (L/R)di_L/dt$. Substituting these values in the above current equation, we have:

$$I + (L/R)di_L/dt + i_L = 0$$

Re-writing this as a differential equation in standard form, we have:

$$\frac{di_L}{dt} + \frac{i_L}{L/R} = \frac{I}{L/R}$$

This is a first-order linear differential equation with constant coefficients. The dependent variable is a current i_L and it is differentiated with respect to time t. The quantity L/R is thus the time constant of the circuit. The transient solution must therefore be of the form $i_L = Ae^{-t/(L/R)}$.

The steady state solution is the value of the current in the inductor when all transients have died away. When this is so, all the generator current must be flowing in the inductor and none in the resistor. The steady state value of the inductor current is thus I.

By comparison, for example, with the equation in frame 13, the full solution must be:

$$i_L = I\left(1 - e^{-t/(L/R)}\right)$$

When $t \to \infty$ and all transient terms have died away, $i = I$ so the steady state condition is satisfied. When $t = 0$, $i_L = I[1 - 1] = 0$ so the initial condition is satisfied.

$$\text{But} \quad v_L = L di_L/dt = ILe^{-t/(L/R)}/(L/R) = IRe^{-t/(L/R)}$$

$$\text{and} \quad i_R = I - i_L = Ie^{-t/(L/R)} \quad (i_R \text{ is also given by forming } v_L/R)$$

The full answer is thus:

$$i_L = I\left(1 - e^{-t/(L/R)}\right)$$

$$v_L = IRe^{-t/(L/R)}$$

$$i_R = Ie^{-t/(L/R)}$$

3. Applying Kirchhoff's Current Law to the node at the top of the diagram after the switch has been closed, we have:

$$I \sin \omega t + I - i_R - i_C = 0$$

If we call the voltage across the capacitor v_C then, since this is also the voltage across the generator and across the resistor because the three components are in parallel, we have $i_R = v_C/R$ and $i_C = C dv_C/dt$. Therefore:

$$I \sin \omega t + I - v_C/R - C dv_C/dt = 0$$

Re-writing this as a differential equation in standard form, we have:

$$\frac{dv_C}{dt} + \frac{v_C}{CR} = \frac{I}{C} + \frac{I \sin \omega t}{C}$$

By comparison with question 1, the transient solution is of the form:

$$v_C = A e^{-t/CR}$$

Since the right-hand side of the equation is a constant plus a sine function, a suitable trial function for the steady state solution is $v_C = B + P \sin \omega t + Q \cos \omega t$ where B, P and Q are constants. Substituting this expression into the equation gives:

$$P\omega \cos \omega t - Q\omega \sin \omega t + \frac{B}{CR} + \frac{I}{CR}(P \sin \omega t + Q \cos \omega t) = \frac{I}{C} + \frac{I \sin \omega t}{C}$$

Equating coefficients to evaluate the constants, the constant terms give:

$$B/CR = I/C \quad \text{so} \quad B = IR$$

The coefficients of the cosine and sine terms give respectively:

$$P\omega + Q/CR = 0 \quad \text{and} \quad -Q\omega + P/CR = I/C$$

Solving these equations for P and Q gives

$$P = \frac{IR}{1 + \omega^2 C^2 R^2} \quad \text{and } Q = \frac{-I\omega CR^2}{1 + \omega^2 C^2 R^2}$$

The complete solution is:

$$v_C = A e^{-t/CR} + IR + \frac{IR}{1 + \omega^2 C^2 R^2} (\sin \omega t - \omega CR \cos \omega t)$$

But, because the constant current generator has reached a steady state before the sinusoidal generator is connected through the switch, the initial voltage across the capacitor is IR. Putting in this initial condition gives $A = -I\omega CR^2/(1+\omega^2 C^2 R^2)$.

The complete solution including the initial condition is:

$$v = \frac{-I\omega CR^2}{1 + \omega^2 C^2 R^2} e^{-t/CR} + IR + \frac{IR}{1 + \omega^2 C^2 R^2} (\sin \omega t - \omega CR \cos \omega t)$$

4. (a) We will call the capacitor voltage v_C and assume that current from the generator enters the node at the top of the diagram and that currents through the resistor and capacitor leave the node. Now, performing a node voltage analysis for the node at the top of the diagram, using the node at the bottom as the reference node, we have, for $t > 0$:

$$(V - v_C)/R_1 - v_C/R_2 - Cdv_C/dt = 0$$

Rearranging this equation we have, when $R_1 = R_2 = R$:

$$\frac{dv_C}{dt} + \frac{v_C}{C}\left(\frac{1}{R} + \frac{1}{R}\right) = \frac{V}{CR}$$

A further slight rearrangement gives:

$$\frac{dv_c}{dt} + \frac{v_c}{CR/2} = \frac{V}{CR}$$

This equation can now be seen to be of exactly the same mathematical shape as the equation solved in frames 35 to 38. The time constant is $CR/2$. The steady state value of the voltage across the capacitor when all transient currents have died away is $V/2$. This voltage is determined by the potential divider action of the two resistors on the voltage generator. The solution to the equation is then, by comparison with the result in frame 38:

$$v_C = V/2 - (V/2)e^{-t/\tau} \quad \text{where} \quad \tau = CR/2$$

Differentiating and multiplying by C gives the capacitor current as:

$$i_C = (V/R)e^{-t/\tau}$$

If the currents in R_1 and R_2 are respectively i_1 and i_2 then:

$$i_2 = v_C/R = (V/2R)(1 - e^{-t/\tau}) \quad \text{and} \quad i_1 = (V - v_C)/R = (V/2R)(1 + e^{-t/\tau})$$

(b) Applying Thevenin's theorem to the left of the capacitor gives a circuit consisting of a generator $V/2$ in series with a resistor $R/2$ and the capacitor. This circuit is now identical in form to the circuit shown in frame 35 except for the values of the voltage generator and the resistor.

The solution to the problem must thus be the same but with the appropriate substitutions made. The equation and its solution are thus the same as those found above. Since, however, the loop on the left of the original diagram no longer exists in this equivalent circuit 'as seen from the capacitor', the currents in the two resistors cannot be calculated directly for this circuit. Knowing the capacitor voltage and returning the rest of the circuit to its original form would, of course, allow them to be calculated as above.

42

SECOND-ORDER DIFFERENTIAL EQUATIONS

If a circuit consists of more than one loop and contains energy storage elements in more than one loop, then analysing it using a differential equation approach will lead to a set of simultaneous differential equations which may be of higher order than one. Even a single loop which contains more than one kind of energy storage element will inevitably lead to a second-order equation. In fact, any circuit which contains both capacitors and inductors will lead to an equation of order two or greater. We will analyse a single loop circuit first. Here is a circuit consisting of a series connection of a generator, a resistor, a capacitor and an inductor.

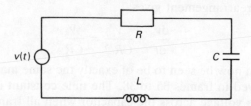

Can you obtain a second-order differential equation for the voltage across the capacitor? Postulate a current i and then apply Kirchhoff's Voltage Law to the circuit. Use the current/voltage relationship in a capacitor to help you derive the differential equation from the resulting equation.

43

$$\frac{d^2 v_C}{dt^2} + \frac{R dv_C}{L dt} + \frac{v_C}{LC} = \frac{v(t)}{LC}$$

Using Kirchhoff's Voltage Law, we have:

$$v(t) = iR + v_C + L di/dt \quad \text{but} \quad i = C dv_C/dt$$

$$\text{so} \quad v(t) = CR dv_C/dt + v_C + LC d^2 v_C/dt^2$$

Dividing throughout by LC and rearranging this equation into standard form gives the result above.

We again use $v = A e^{mt}$ as a trial solution for the transient part of the answer. What equation results from substituting this expression for v_C into the homogeneous equation (that is, the left-hand side set equal to zero)?

$$m^2 + \frac{R}{L}m + \frac{1}{LC} = 0$$

Substituting $v = Ae^{mt}$ into the differential equation gives:

$$m^2 Ae^{mt} + m\,\frac{R}{L}\,Ae^{mt} + \frac{1}{LC}\,Ae^{mt} = 0$$

Cancelling by Ae^{mt} gives the result above. This is, of course, a quadratic in m so will have two roots which may be real or complex. If the roots are m_1 and m_2, the transient part of the solution will be of the form:

$$v_C = Ae^{m_1 t} + Be^{m_2 t}$$

That is, there are two unknown constants to be determined in evaluating fully the transient part of the complete solution. The value of these constants will depend on the forcing function just as was the case for the first order equation. We will evaluate them for a particular case later. First we will examine the form of the solutions to the 'indicial equation' or 'characteristic equation' at the beginning of this frame.

Can you write an expression for the roots of the equation?

$$m = \frac{-R}{2L} \pm \sqrt{\left\{ \left(\frac{R}{2L} \right)^2 - \frac{1}{LC} \right\}}$$

Since the equation is a quadratic of the form $am^2 + bm + c = 0$ it can be solved by the standard formula for the solution of quadratics:

$$m = \frac{-b \pm \sqrt{(b^2 - 4ac)}}{2a}$$

Since $a = 1$, $b = R/L$ and $c = 1/LC$, we obtain the result above.

In the expression for m at the beginning of this frame it has become conventional to make the substitution $\alpha = R/2L$ and $\omega_0^2 = 1/LC$. Re-write the equation and the expression for its roots using these substitutions. What are the dimensions of α and ω_0?

46

> The equation becomes $m^2 + 2\alpha m + \omega_0^2 = 0$
>
> Its roots are $m = -\alpha \pm \sqrt{(\alpha^2 - \omega_0^2)}$
>
> α and ω_0 both have dimensions of $1/T$. That is, frequency.

The form of the equation above and its roots are obtained simply by making the appropriate substitutions. As you will see, they are much less unwieldy to manipulate in this form. Since m appears in the expression Ae^{mt}, it must have dimensions of $1/T$. In the expression for m, α has the same dimensions as m since it is equal to $m \pm$ another quantity. ω_0 has the same dimensions as α since it occurs squared under a square root sign with α^2.

There are three types of transient solution depending on the relative sizes of α and ω_0. Recalling that the roots can be either real or complex, what can you say about them if $R^2 > 4L/C$? Consider their relative size and their sign as well as whether they are real or complex.

47

> If $R^2 > 4L/C$ the roots are real, unequal and negative.

If $R^2 > 4L/C$ then dividing both sides of the inequality by $4L^2$ gives $R^2/4L^2 > 1/LC$ or $\alpha^2 > \omega_0^2$ and so $\alpha > \omega_0$ (only positive values of α and ω have any meaning since R, L and C are all positive). The roots are thus:

$$m_1 = -\alpha + \sqrt{(\alpha^2 - \omega_0^2)} \quad \text{and} \quad m = -\alpha - \sqrt{(\alpha^2 - \omega_0^2)}$$

Since $\alpha > \omega_0$ the quantity under the square root sign is positive but less than α. Adding it to minus α therefore still leaves a negative quantity so m_1 is negative with $-\alpha < m_1 < 0$. Subtracting the quantity under the square root sign from minus α gives the other negative root, m_2, with $m_2 < -\alpha$. The transient solution is thus:

$$v_C = Ae^{m_1 t} + Be^{m_2 t}$$

where m_1 and m_2 are both real and negative with m_2 more negative than m_1.

The steady state solution is found, as for the first-order equations already solved, by trying a solution of the same form as the forcing function. We will take $v(t)$ to be switched from zero to a constant value V at $t = 0$. So, for $t > 0$ the forcing function is constant and we try $v_C = D$, a constant.

What value do we get for D by substituting it in the equation?

48

$$\boxed{D = V}$$

The equation is $\dfrac{d^2 v_C}{dt^2} + \dfrac{R}{L}\dfrac{dv_C}{dt} + \dfrac{v_C}{LC} = \dfrac{V}{LC}$

On substituting $v_C = D$ into this equation, both differential coefficients become zero. Only the term in v_C is left giving $D/LC = V/LC$ and so $D = V$.

It is worth arguing this steady state solution from physical reasoning too. Recalling that the circuit consists of a constant voltage source in series with a resistor, a capacitor and an inductor then, in the steady state, there can be no direct current flowing in the circuit *because there is a capacitor in a series connected path*. There can therefore be no voltage across the resistor. There is no voltage across the inductor either because we *are* dealing with the steady state so the zero current is a steady value and not the momentary value of a changing current. All the constant generator voltage must therefore be across the capacitor.

It is always worth carrying out a physical check of this kind to confirm results derived from purely mathematical reasoning. The more often you can do this, the more confident will you become in using the mathematics. If we now impose a set of initial conditions we can obtain the complete solution with all constants evaluated.

How many initial conditions do we need?

49

$$\boxed{\text{Two initial conditions are needed}}$$

The equation is second order so there are two unknown constants. Two simultaneous equations in these constants are therefore required to evaluate them, so two initial conditions are needed. We will take the circuit to be '*initially inert*'. This means there is no stored energy in it, so *no voltage across the capacitor* and *no current through the inductor*. These initial conditions are often met in practice. They would occur naturally, for example, when the circuit was first connected up but nothing had been switched on.

What equations in A and B do we get by substituting these conditions into the complete solution with A and B unknown? Recall that, since all components are in series, the inductor current also flows through the capacitor.

50

$$v_C = 0 \text{ when } t = 0 \text{ gives } 0 = V + A + B$$
$$i_L = 0 \text{ when } t = 0 \text{ gives } 0 = m_1 A + m_2 B$$

The complete solution is:

$$v_C = V + Ae^{m_1 t} + Be^{m_2 t}$$

where A and B are to be determined. Putting $t = 0$ in this equation gives:

$$0 = V + A + B$$

We now observe that $i_L = i_C$ and $i_C = C dv_C/dt$ so $i_L = 0$ implies $i_C = 0$ and therefore $dv_C/dt = 0$. With the solution for v_C above:

$$dv_C/dt = Am_1 e^{m_1 t} + Bm_2 e^{m_2 t}$$

Substituting $dv_C/dt = 0$ when $t = 0$ into this equation gives:

$$0 = Am_1 + Bm_2$$

Can you now find A and B in terms of α, ω_0 and V?

51

$$A = \frac{-\{\alpha + \sqrt{(\alpha^2 - \omega_0^2)}\}V}{2\sqrt{(\alpha^2 - \omega_0^2)}} \qquad B = \frac{+\{\alpha - \sqrt{(\alpha^2 - \omega_0^2)}\}V}{2\sqrt{(\alpha^2 - \omega_0^2)}}$$

The second equation in frame 50 gives $A = -m_2 B/m_1$. Substituting this expression into the first equation in frame 50 gives:

$$B\left(\frac{m_2}{m_1} - 1\right) = V \qquad \text{so} \qquad B = \frac{Vm_1}{m_2 - m_1}$$

$$\text{Thus} \qquad A = \frac{-Vm_2}{m_2 - m_1}$$

$$\text{But} \qquad m_1 = -\alpha + \sqrt{(\alpha^2 - \omega_0^2)} \qquad \text{and} \qquad m_2 = -\alpha - \sqrt{(\alpha^2 - \omega_0^2)}$$

$$\text{Thus} \qquad m_2 - m_1 = -2\sqrt{(\alpha^2 - \omega_0^2)}$$

$$\text{So} \qquad A = \frac{-\{\alpha + \sqrt{(\alpha^2 - \alpha_0^2)}\}V}{2\sqrt{(\alpha^2 - \omega_0^2)}} \qquad \text{and} \qquad B = \frac{+\{\alpha - \sqrt{(\alpha^2 - \alpha_0^2)}\}V}{2\sqrt{(\alpha^2 - \omega_0^2)}}$$

Can you now write down the complete solution for v_C with all constant coefficients evaluated?

52

$$v_C = V\left\{1 - \left(\frac{\alpha + \sqrt{(\alpha^2 - \omega_0^2)}}{2\sqrt{(\alpha^2 - \omega_0^2)}}\right)e^{\{-\alpha + \sqrt{(\alpha^2 - \omega_0^2)}\}t} + \left(\frac{\alpha - \sqrt{(\alpha^2 - \omega_0^2)}}{2\sqrt{(\alpha^2 - \omega_0^2)}}\right)e^{\{-\alpha - \sqrt{(\alpha^2 - \omega_0^2)}\}t}\right\}$$

This expression for v_C is simply(!) the one near the top of frame 50 with the values of A, B, m_1 and m_2 expressed in terms of V, α and ω_0. We will put in some numerical values now to examine the shape of the 'response' of the circuit to the voltage change caused by the generator being switched on.

Using values of $R = 1$ kΩ, $L = 1$ mH and $C = 4.5$ nF with $V = 10$ V, can you write down the numerical expression for v_C in the form:

$$v_C = V - V_1 e^{-t/\tau_1} + V_2 e^{-t/\tau_2} \quad \text{where } t \text{ is measured in microseconds?}$$

53

$$\boxed{v_C = 10 - 20e^{-t/3} + 10e^{-t/1.5}\ V}$$

$$\alpha = R/2L = 10^3/(2 \times 10^{-3}) = 0.5 \times 10^6 \quad \text{So } \alpha^2 = 0.25 \times 10^{12}$$

$$\omega_0^2 = 1/LC = 1/(10^{-3} \times 4.5 \times 10^{-9}) = 0.222 \times 10^{12}$$

$$\text{So} \quad \alpha^2 - \omega_0^2 = (0.25 - 0.222) \times 10^{12}$$

$$\text{and} \quad \sqrt{(\alpha^2 - \omega_0^2)} = \sqrt{(0.0278 \times 10^{12})} = 0.167 \times 10^6$$

To get the answer asked for above we note that $\tau_1 = -1/m_1$ and $\tau_2 = -1/m_2$.

But $m_1 = -\alpha + \sqrt{(\alpha^2 - \omega_0^2)} = -0.5 \times 10^6 + 0.167 \times 10^6$

$$= -0.333 \times 10^6 \quad \text{so } \tau_1 = 3.0 \times 10^{-6} = 3 \text{ μs}$$

and $m_2 = -\alpha - \sqrt{(\alpha^2 - \omega_0^2)} = -0.5 \times 10^6 - 0.167 \times 10^6$

$$= -0.667 \times 10^6 \quad \text{so } \tau_2 = 1.5 \times 10^{-6} = 1.5 \text{ μs}$$

$$\text{Also} \quad V_1 = \frac{10(0.5 + 0.167) \times 10^6}{2(0.167) \times 10^6} = \frac{10(0.667) \times 10^6}{2(0.167) \times 10^6} = 20 \text{ V}$$

$$\text{and} \quad V_2 = \frac{10(0.5 - 0.167) \times 10^6}{2(0.167) \times 10^6} = \frac{10(0.333) \times 10^6}{2(0.167) \times 10^6} = 10 \text{ V}$$

Notice that v_C is made up of a constant term which has arisen from the forcing function and two transient exponential terms of opposite sign and with different time constants. It will be instructive for you to plot the expression for v_C. Plot each term separately first and then sum them to give the complete solution. Use a scale of 2 mm/V vertically and 0.5 cm/μs horizontally. Plot points every microsecond from 0 to 9 μs and every 2 μs from 10 to 24 μs.

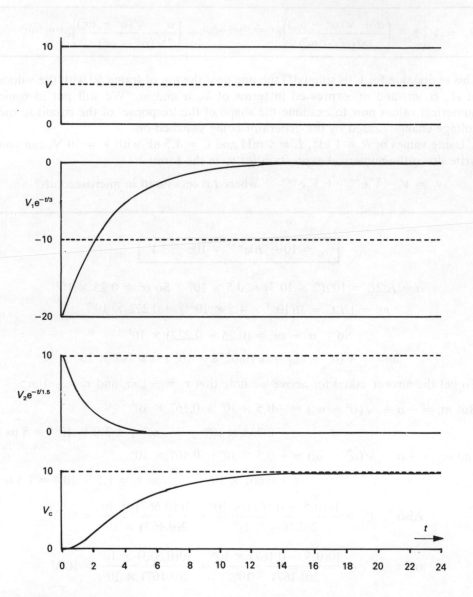

The value of v_C starts from zero and increases very slowly at first. In fact, as we shall see shortly, the rate of increase at $t = 0$ is zero. After about 6 μs the transient due to V has almost died away and the remainder of the curve describing v_C follows that for V. This, in turn, has nearly died away after about 12 μs.

What is the current flowing in the circuit for $t > 0$? Obtain an expression for it and plot a graph for it using the same horizontal scale as before. Be careful to quote the units.

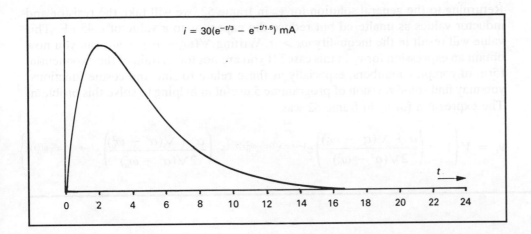

$$i = 30(e^{-t/3} - e^{-t/1.5}) \text{ mA}$$

Knowing the voltage across the capacitor, the current through it is given by $i_C = C dv_C/dt$. Differentiating the expression for v_C term-by-term and multiplying by C gives the result above. The current is thus the difference of two exponentials of equal amplitude but of different time constants. It starts from zero, rises to a maximum and falls to zero again. To determine the units of current we must examine the amplitude term. This term, of numerical value 30, arises as the product of the capacitance C measured in nF and the quotient of the voltage V in volts and the time constant τ in μs. Its units are thus $(10^{-9} \times 1)/10^{-6} = 10^{-3}$. It is of the form CV/τ but τ can have dimensions of CR so $[CV]/[\tau] = [CV]/[CR] = [V/R] = [I]$. The amplitude term can thus be seen as a current measured in milliamps.

Notice that, because the current is given by the expression $i_C = C dv_C/dt$, the current graph, apart from the scaling factor C, represents the slope of the graph for v_C. Thus $i_C = 0$ when $t = 0$ confirms our earlier observation that the slope of the voltage graph is zero when $t = 0$.

For reasons which will become clear shortly the response of the circuit when $\alpha > \omega_0$ is called the 'over-damped' response. In the next frame we will examine a circuit with component values which give the relationship $\alpha < \omega_0$.

56

Returning to the general solution for v_C in frame 52, we will take the resistor and inductor values as unaltered but reduce the capacitor to a value of 0.45 nF. This value will result in the inequality $\omega_0 > \alpha$. Writing $\sqrt{(\omega_0^2 - \alpha^2)} = \omega_d$, can you now obtain an expression for v_C in this case? If you are not too certain of the exponential form of complex numbers, especially as these relate to sine and cosine functions, you may find some revision of programme 5 useful in helping to solve this problem. The expression for v_C in frame 52 was:

$$v_C = V\left\{ 1 - \left(\frac{\alpha + \sqrt{(\alpha^2 - \omega_0^2)}}{2\sqrt{(\alpha^2 - \omega_0^2)}} \right) e^{\{-\alpha + \sqrt{(\alpha^2 - \omega_0^2)}\}t} + \left(\frac{\alpha - \sqrt{(\alpha^2 - \omega_0^2)}}{2\sqrt{(\alpha^2 - \omega_0^2)}} \right) e^{\{-\alpha - \sqrt{(\alpha^2 - \omega_0^2)}\}t} \right\}$$

57

$$\boxed{v = 10 - 3.56e^{-t/2}[\sin(1.4t)] - 10e^{-t/2}[\cos(1.4t)]}$$

As before, we have $\quad \alpha = R/2L = 10^3/(2 \times 10^{-3}) = 0.5 \times 10^6$

so $\alpha^2 = 0.25 \times 10^{12}$

In this case $\quad \omega_0 = 1/LC = 1/(10^{-3} \times 0.45 \times 10^{-9}) = 2.22 \times 10^{12}$

So $\quad \alpha^2 < \omega_0^2 \quad$ and $\quad \alpha^2 - \omega_0^2 = -\omega_d^2 = -(0.25 - 2.222) \times 10^{12}$

Thus $\quad \sqrt{(\alpha^2 - \omega_0^2)} = \sqrt{(-1.97 \times 10^{12})} = \pm j1.4 \times 10^6 = \pm j\omega_d$

Substituting these values in the expression for v_C gives:

$$v_C = 10\left\{ 1 - \left(\frac{0.5 + j1.4}{j2.8} \right) e^{(-0.5 + j1.4)t} + \left(\frac{0.5 - j1.4}{j2.8} \right) e^{(-0.5 - j1.4)t} \right\}$$

The factors of 10^6 in the two quotient terms cancel and t is now measured in μs.

Collecting up real and imaginary terms, this expression can be rearranged into the following form:

$$v_C = 10\left[1 - \frac{0.5}{1.4}\left\{ \frac{e^{(-0.5 + j1.4)} - e^{(-0.5 - j1.4)t}}{j2} \right\} \right.$$

$$\left. - \frac{j1.4}{1.4}\left\{ \frac{e^{(-0.5 + j1.4)t} + e^{(-0.5 - j1.4)}}{j2} \right\} \right]$$

With further rearrangement, using the rules of indices, we obtain:

$$v_C = 10 \left\{ 1 - 0.357e^{-0.5t} \frac{e^{(j1.4)t} - e^{(-j1.4)t}}{j2} \right.$$

$$\left. - e^{-0.5t} \frac{e^{(j1.4)t} + e^{(-j1.4)t}}{2} \right\}$$

The complex exponential terms can now be recognised as complex expansions of the sine and cosine functions so the final result, taking the factor 10 inside the brackets, is:

$$v_C = 10 - 3.57e^{-0.5t} \sin(1.4t) - 10e^{-0.5t} \cos(1.4t)$$

Notice that the exponential decay time constant is the same for both the sine function and the cosine function and that the frequency of the sine function is the same as that of the cosine function. These facts are a consequence of the way the exponential function in the general algebraic solution can be broken up when $\alpha < \omega_0$ and are characteristic of the solution to the second-order equation under these conditions. As we have seen before, the sinusoidal functions could also be expressed in the form $\sin(\omega t \pm \phi)$.

Can you now plot a graph of this expression for v_C? Plot v_C from 0 V to 20 V, and t from 0 μs to 12 μs.

58

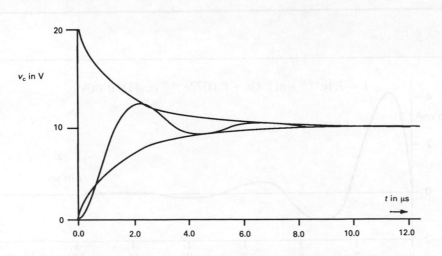

Comparing this graph with the one in frame 54, the over-damped response, can you suggest how the response might be described in this case?

59

When $\omega_0 < \alpha$ the response of the circuit is called 'under-damped'.

An abrupt voltage change such as the circuit in the previous two examples experienced can be thought of as the application of a '*step function*' to the circuit. The voltage graph over all time shows an abrupt 'step' at $t = 0$. The 'response' of the circuit is thus called its '*step response*'. Evaluating the step response of a circuit or, indeed, any system which can be described by a second-order linear differential equation with constant coefficients, is a widely used test method. Different responses characterise different kinds of circuit behaviour. The response we found for this circuit with $\alpha > \omega_0$ we called the 'over-damped' response. The voltage across the capacitor was seen to approach its final value slowly. When $\alpha < \omega_0$ the response exhibits an '*overshoot*' and there is subsequent oscillation or '*ringing*' on the waveform before the steady state value is reached. This phenomenon leads to the description of the response in this case as '*under-damped*'. The term α is called the '*damping coefficient*'. It is the reciprocal of the time constant of the exponentially decaying factor in the expression for v_C. It can be shown analytically (but will not be done here) that the '*envelope*' of the waveform (the broken lines in the diagram in frame 58) has an exponential decay with a time constant equal to the reciprocal of the damping coefficient.

What is the current in the circuit with the new expression for v_C?
Derive an expression for it and plot its graph.

60

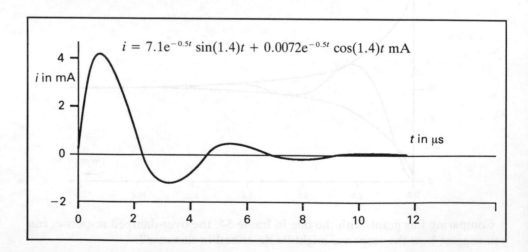

$$i = 7.1e^{-0.5t}\sin(1.4)t + 0.0072e^{-0.5t}\cos(1.4)t \text{ mA}$$

$$\text{Again} \quad i_C = Cdv_C/dt$$

$$\text{So} \quad i_C = 0.45 \times 10^{-9} \frac{d}{dt} \{10 - 3.57e^{-0.5t}\sin(1.4t) - 10e^{-0.5t}\cos(1.4t)\}$$

$$= 0.45 \times 10^{-9} \{-(3.57)(1.4 \times 10^6)e^{-0.5t}\cos(1.4t)$$
$$+ (3.57)(0.5 \times 10^6)e^{-0.5t}\sin(1.4t)$$
$$+ (10)(1.4 \times 10^6)e^{-0.5t}\sin(1.4t)$$
$$+ (10)(0.5 \times 10^6)e^{-0.5t}\cos(1.4t)\}$$

(Note: the factors 10^6 are introduced because t is in μs.)

Collecting up terms, this becomes:

$$i = 7.1e^{-0.5t}\sin(1.4)t + 0.0072e^{-0.5t}\cos(1.4)t \text{ mA}$$

A special case of the condition $\alpha < \omega_0$ is when $\alpha = 0$ but $\omega_0 \neq 0$. What implication does this special case have for the component values of the circuit? Draw the appropriate circuit diagram.

61

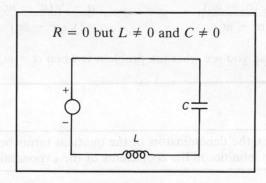

$R = 0$ but $L \neq 0$ and $C \neq 0$

If $\alpha = 0$ then $R/2L = 0$. Either $R = 0$ or $L = \infty$. But $\omega_0 = 1/LC$ and, if $L = \infty$ then $\omega_0 = 0$. So $R = 0$ is the only valid solution. Furthermore, if $L = 0$ or $C = 0$, we would have $\omega_0 = \infty$ which is impractical. The only practical solution, then, is $R = 0$ with L and $C \neq 0$. The resistor can thus be removed from the circuit diagram. With these conditions what does the general solution become? Here it is again:

$$v_C = V\left\{1 - \frac{\alpha + \sqrt{(\alpha^2 - \omega_0^2)}}{2\sqrt{(\alpha^2 - \omega_0^2)}}e^{\{-\alpha + \sqrt{(\alpha - \omega_0^2)}\}t} + \frac{\alpha - \sqrt{(\alpha^2 - \omega_0^2)}}{2\sqrt{(\alpha^2 - \omega_0^2)}}e^{\{-\alpha - \sqrt{(\alpha^2 - \omega_0^2)}\}t}\right\}$$

62

$$v_C = V(1 - \cos \omega_0 t)$$

Since α is zero the factors multiplying the exponential terms reduce to $\{\sqrt{(-\omega_0^2)}\}/\{2\sqrt{(-\omega_0^2)}\} = 1/2$ and $\{-\sqrt{(-\omega_0^2)}\}/\{2\sqrt{(-\omega_0^2)}\} = -1/2$. The exponents of the exponential terms reduce to $\{\sqrt{(-\omega_0^2)}\}t = \pm j\omega_0 t$. The whole expression thus becomes:

$$v_C = V\left\{1 - \left(\frac{e^{j\omega_0 t} + e^{-j\omega_0 t}}{2}\right)\right\} = V(1 - \cos \omega_0 t)$$

Since there is no resistance in the circuit to dissipate energy, once energy is put into the circuit from the generator there is a continual interchange of energy between the capacitor and the inductor. The circuit therefore exhibits an 'undamped' or 'oscillatory' response. It is sinusoidal in nature and varies from zero to a maximum value of V. The frequency of oscillation, ω_0, is called the 'natural' frequency of the circuit.

The final case to consider arises when $\alpha = \omega_0$. This condition produces a problem in the general solution and it is necessary to return to it again to see what it is and how to overcome it. Here is the general solution again:

$$v_C = V\left\{1 - \frac{\alpha + \sqrt{(\alpha^2 - \omega_0^2)}}{2\sqrt{(\alpha^2 - \omega_0^2)}}e^{\{-\alpha + \sqrt{(\alpha^2 - \omega_0^2)}\}t} + \frac{\alpha - \sqrt{(\alpha^2 - \omega_0^2)}}{2\sqrt{(\alpha^2 - \omega_0^2)}}e^{\{-\alpha - \sqrt{(\alpha^2 - \omega_0^2)}\}t}\right\}$$

Can you see what the problem is when $\alpha = \omega_0$?

63

When $\alpha = \omega_0$ the denominators of the quotient terms become zero, leading to infinities in the coefficients of the exponential terms.

We solve this problem by using a mathematical device which often helps to overcome difficulties of this kind. Rather than setting $\alpha = \omega_0$, we allow the quantity $\sqrt{(\alpha^2 - \omega_0^2)}$ to become very small. That is, we let it approach very close to zero without actually reaching it and then manipulate the expression which causes the problem before *finally* allowing the very small quantity to become zero. We will assume that $\alpha > \omega_0$ but by so small an amount that we can write $\sqrt{(\alpha^2 - \omega_0^2)} = \varepsilon$ where ε is a very small quantity.

What does the expression for v_C become with this substitution?

$$v_C = V\left\{1 - \frac{\alpha + \varepsilon}{2\varepsilon} e^{(-\alpha + \varepsilon)t} + \frac{\alpha - \varepsilon}{2\varepsilon} e^{(-\alpha - \varepsilon)t}\right\}$$

If we now collect up terms in α and ε we obtain:

$$v_C = V\left\{1 - \frac{\alpha}{2\varepsilon}\left(e^{(-\alpha + \varepsilon)t} - e^{(-\alpha - \varepsilon)t}\right) - \frac{1}{2}\left(e^{(-\alpha + \varepsilon)t} + e^{(-\alpha - \varepsilon)t}\right)\right\}$$

Now, again using the rules of indices, we can take out a factor $e^{-\alpha t}$ from each of the exponential terms to obtain:

$$v_C = V\left\{1 - e^{-\alpha t}\left(\alpha\frac{e^{\varepsilon t} - e^{-\varepsilon t}}{2\varepsilon} + \frac{e^{\varepsilon t} + e^{-\varepsilon t}}{2}\right)\right\}$$

We now use the series expansion for the exponential functions whose arguments are εt and $-\varepsilon t$ but ignoring terms of order two and greater. The justification for this is that, because εt is a small quantity, terms of order higher than two are so small as to be insignificant. Can you do this? For each exponential in εt, substitute an expansion including only terms of order less than two. Then simplify the resulting expression as far as you can to obtain a final expression for v_C.

$$v_C = V[1 - e^{-\alpha t}(\alpha t + 1)]$$

The series expansion of e^x is $1 + x + \frac{x^2}{2!}$ and so on. Letting $x = \varepsilon t$ and $x = -\varepsilon t$ as appropriate above and ignoring terms in x^2 and higher powers gives:

$$v_C = V\left\{1 - e^{-\alpha t}\left(\alpha\frac{1 + \varepsilon t - (1 - \varepsilon t)}{2\varepsilon} + \frac{1 + \varepsilon t + 1 - \varepsilon t}{2}\right)\right\}$$

This reduces to $v_C = V\left(1 - e^{-\alpha t}\frac{2\alpha t + 2}{2}\right) = V\left\{1 - e^{-\alpha t}(\alpha t + 1)\right\}$

Now, keeping $R = 1\text{ k}\Omega$ and $L = 1\text{ mH}$, can you find a value for C which will produce the above result? When you have done this, draw the new graph for v_C using the same horizontal scale as for the other two graphs.

66

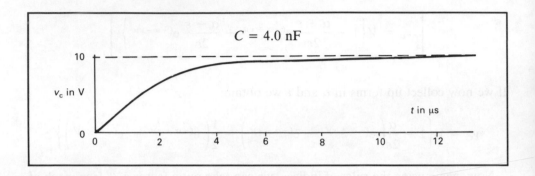

We have $\alpha = R/2L$ with $R = 1$ kΩ and $L = 1$ mH so $\alpha = 0.5 \times 10^6$

But $\alpha^2 = \omega_0^2$ and $\omega_0^2 = 1/LC$ so $0.25 \times 10^{12} = 1/(10^{-3} \times C)$

Therefore $C = 10^3/(0.25 \times 10^{12}) = 4 \times 10^{-9} = 4$ nF

The graph is similar to the one for the under-damped case which is not, perhaps, surprising since the capacitor value has not changed very much. The capacitor voltage can, however, be seen to approach its final value a little more quickly. In this case the response is said to be '*critically damped*'.

What is the current in this case? Derive an expression for current from the one for v_C in frame 65 and check that it has the dimensions of current.

67

$$i = \alpha^2\, CVte^{-\alpha t}$$

We have $v_C = V\{1 - e^{-\alpha t}(\alpha t + 1)\}$ and $i_C = Cdv_C/dt$

so $i_C = CV\{-e^{-\alpha t} \times \alpha - (\alpha t + 1)(-\alpha e^{-\alpha t})\}$

$= CV\{-\alpha e^{-\alpha t} + \alpha^2 te^{-\alpha t} + \alpha e^{-\alpha t}\} = \alpha^2 CVte^{-\alpha t}$

The dimensions of the term on the right are those of the expression $\alpha^2 CVt$. α is $R/2L$ so has dimensions of $1/T$. $\alpha^2 CVt$ thus has dimensions of CV/T. But t can be thought of as 'having dimensions of CR' because CR has dimensions of T. CV/T thus has dimensions of $CV/CR = V/R$ which has dimensions of current.

Can you now draw a graph for i_C and find its maximum value?

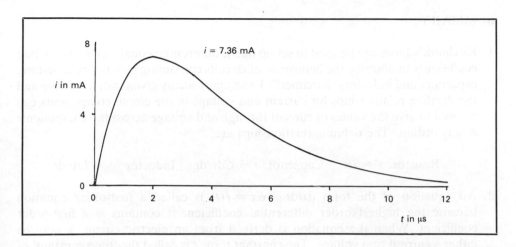

For a maximum or minimum we differentiate the expression for i and equate the result to zero. Thus:

$$\frac{di}{dt} = CV\{t(-\alpha e^{-\alpha t}) + e^{-\alpha t}\} = CV(e^{-\alpha t})(1 - \alpha t) = 0$$

There is thus a maximum or minimum when $1 - \alpha t = 0$; that is, when $t = 1/\alpha$.

We could check whether this quantity was a maximum or minimum by differentiating again and considering the sign of the second differential coefficient. In this case, however, it is sufficient to note that the expression for i_C is zero at $t = 0$ and at $t = \infty$ and is positive for all positive values of t. The zero-gradient term we have found must therefore be a maximum.

Substituting $t = 1/\alpha$ into the equation for i shows that the value of the maximum current is:

$$i_C = CVe^{-1} = \frac{RCV}{2L} e^{-1} = \frac{10^3 \times 4 \times 10^{-9} \times 10 \times e^{-1}}{2 \times 10^{-3}} = 7.36 \text{ mA}$$

The maximum occurs when $t = 1/\alpha = 2L/R = 2 \times 10^{-6} = 2 \text{ μs}$.

69

SUMMARY

1. Kirchhoff's Laws can be used to set up linear differential equations with constant coefficients to describe the behaviour of circuits containing generators, resistors, capacitors and inductors. Kirchhoff's Laws apply at any given instant of time and the defining relationships for current and voltage in the circuit components can be used to give the values of current through and voltage across the components at any instant. The defining relationships are:

$$\text{Resistor: } v = iR \quad \text{Capacitor: } i = C\,dv/dt \quad \text{Inductor: } v = L\,di/dt$$

2. An equation of the form $dx/dt + x/\tau = f(t)$ is called a first-order equation because the highest order differential coefficient it contains is a first-order coefficient. When the equation is derived from an electric circuit, x may be either a current or a voltage. The constant term τ is called the 'time constant' of the circuit. It is determined solely by the circuit components. The function $f(t)$ is called the driving function or forcing function of the circuit.

3. An equation of the form $d^2x/dt^2 + p\,dx/dt + qx = f(t)$ where p and q are constants is called a second-order equation because the highest order differential coefficient it contains is a second-order coefficient. When the equation is derived from an electric circuit, x may be either a current or a voltage. The constants p and q are determined by the component values of the circuit. The function $f(t)$ is called the driving function or forcing function of the circuit.

4. The solution of a differential equation consists of two parts: a transient part which is also known as the natural response or complementary function and a steady state part which is also known as the forced response or particular integral.

5. For a first-order equation, the transient part is always of the form $x = Ae^{-t/\tau}$ where the value of A is affected by the form of the driving function and possibly by the values of the components making up the circuit. The exact value of A is determined by a known value of x at a given time, usually $t = 0$. In this case the known value of x is called an 'initial condition'.

6. For a second-order equation, the transient part is obtained by assuming a solution of the form $x = Ae^{mt}$ to the homogeneous part of the equation where A is an arbitrary constant. This leads to a 'characteristic equation' for the circuit of the form $m^2 + pm + q = 0$. The form of the transient solution depends on the roots of this characteristic equation. There are three cases to consider. They are listed on the next page.

6(a) If the roots are real but unequal (in practical problems they must also both be negative) they can be written as m_1 and m_2 and the solution is of the form:

$$x = A_1 e^{m_1 t} + A_2 e^{m_2 t}$$

The circuit is said to be 'over-damped'.

6(b) If the roots are real and equal (they must again be negative in practical problems) they can both be written as m and the solution is of the form:

$$x = A_1 t e^{m_1 t} + A_0$$

The circuit is said to be 'critically damped'.

6(c) If the roots are complex then they will be conjugate and may be written as $\alpha + j\omega_0$ and $\alpha - j\omega_0$ (α must be negative in practical problems). The solution, which can be derived via the complex form of sine and cosine functions, is of the form:

$$v = e^{\alpha t}(A_1 \sin \omega_0 t + A_2 \cos \omega_0 t)$$

The circuit is said to be 'under-damped'. In the particular case when $\alpha = 0$, the circuit is said to be 'undamped' and the response is then oscillatory.

7. The steady state part of the solution of a linear differential equation is always of the same form as the driving function – if the driving function is constant it is constant, if the driving function is sinusoidal it is sinusoidal, and so on. As is the case for the transient part, the steady state part will also contain multiplying factors determined partly by the form of the driving function and partly by the circuit components.

8. The complete solution is obtained by combining the transient and steady state solutions and using initial conditions to evaluate any unknown constants. One initial condition is needed for a first-order equation, two for a second-order equation.

9. Many circuits (and, indeed, many other time-dependent physical systems) exhibit the characteristic 'mathematical shapes' of first- or second-order linear differential equations with constant coefficients. Once one has been solved for a given driving function, and, in the case of the second-order equation, a given set of roots of the characteristic equation, then the solution to all others having the same kind of driving function and the same kind of roots can be deduced by comparison with the known solution. Dimensional reasoning can often help in formulating such solutions.

---

1. When the inductance of its leads and 'stray' circuit capacitance must be taken into account, a resistor can be modelled by the circuit diagram shown below. (Stray capacitance is any capacitance associated with a circuit or component by virtue of its construction. It is not designed in but must be estimated or measured and taken account of in a detailed analysis to see if it can cause any problems.)

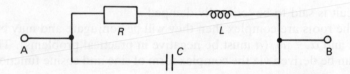

If a constant current generator I is connected to the 'resistor' between its terminals A and B, derive an equation for the voltage across the generator terminals if the generator is switched from zero to full output at time $t = 0$. To derive the equation note that the required voltage is the same as that across the capacitor and, working in terms of the current I and the capacitor current i_C, apply Kirchhoff's Voltage Law to the loop made by the three components. If the resistor is 1 kΩ and its lead inductance is 1 µH, what will be the voltages across a 10 mA generator for stray capacitances of 1 pF, 4 pF and 10 pF? How would you describe the circuit response in these three cases?

2. A constant current generator is connected to a resistor, an inductor and a capacitor all connected in parallel as shown in the circuit below.

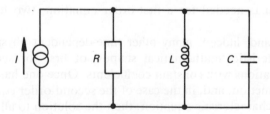

If the generator is switched on at $t = 0$ to give an output I, derive a differential equation for the inductor current. If the resistor is 1 kΩ and the capacitor is 0.5 nF, what currents would flow from a 10 mA generator through inductors of value 0.2 mH, 2 mH and 20 mH? How would you describe the circuit response in these three cases?

ANSWERS TO REVISION QUESTIONS ON PROGRAMME 7

1. Here is the circuit diagram of the resistor together with its associated reactive 'stray' components connected to the current generator:

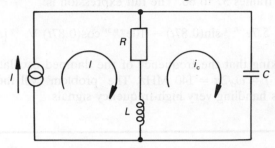

Loop currents can be postulated as shown and Kirchhoff's Voltage Law applied to the right hand loop thus:

$$v_R + v_L + v_C = 0$$

$$(i_C - I)R + L\,\frac{d}{dt}(i_C - I) + v_C = 0$$

But $i_C = C\dfrac{dv_C}{dt}$ so, if I is constant

$$CR\frac{dv_C}{dt} - IR + LC\frac{d^2v_C}{dt^2} + v_C = 0$$

Rearranging this equation into standard form, we obtain:

$$\frac{d^2v_C}{dt^2} + \frac{R}{L}\frac{dv_C}{dt} + \frac{v_C}{LC} = \frac{IR}{LC}$$

We can see by comparison that this equation is of exactly the same form as the one in frame 43. Terms on the left-hand side are identical. The term on the right-hand side is a constant which is dimensionally equivalent to the term on the right-hand side of the earlier equation.

The solution will therefore depend on the relative magnitudes of the damping factor $\alpha = R/2L$ and the natural frequency $\omega_0 = 1/LC$.

With $R = 1$ kΩ and $L = 1$ μH, $\alpha = 0.5 \times 10^9$ so $\alpha^2 = 0.25 \times 10^{18}$

The value of ω_0 depends on C and is different for the three cases. We will take each, in turn, in the next three frames.

72

When $C = 1$ pF, $\omega_0^2 = 1/LC = 1/(10^{-6} \times 10^{-12}) = 10^{18}$

Thus $\omega_0^2 > \alpha^2$ and $\sqrt{(\alpha^2 - \omega_0^2)} = \sqrt{(-0.75 \times 10^{18})} = \pm j8.7 \times 10^8$

With this value of capacitance the circuit is 'under-damped'. The solution is thus of the form given in frames 57 to 60. The full expression is:

$$v = 10 - 5.7e^{-0.5t} \sin(0.87t) - 10e^{-0.5t} \cos(0.87t) \text{ V} \quad [t \text{ is in ns}]$$

It is worth remarking that the frequency of the damped oscillation is very high: $\omega_d = 8.7 \times 10^8$ so $f = \omega_d/2\pi = 140$ MHz. The 'problem' will therefore be apparent only in circuits handling very high-frequency signals.

73

When $C = 4$ pF, $\omega_0^2 = 1/LC = 1/(10^{-6} \times 4 \times 10^{-12}) = 0.25 \times 10^{18}$

Thus $\alpha = \omega_0 = 0.5 \times 10^9$ and the circuit is 'critically damped'. The solution is thus of the form given in frames 65 to 68. The full expression is:

$$v = V[1 - e^{-0.5t}(0.5t + 1)] \text{ V} \quad [t \text{ is in ns}]$$

The time constant of the exponential term is the reciprocal of α and, in this case, is 2×10^{-9} or 2 ns. Such a value will only cause problems in very high speed switching circuits but is comparable, for example, with the switching speeds of modern transistors.

74

When $C = 10$ pF, $\omega_0^2 = 1/LC = 1/(10^{-6} \times 10 \times 10^{-12}) = 0.1 \times 10^{18}$

Thus $\omega_0^2 < \alpha^2$ and $\sqrt{(\alpha^2 - \omega_0^2)} = \sqrt{(0.15 \times 10^{18})} = \pm 3.9 \times 10^8$

With this value of capacitance the circuit is 'over-damped'. The solution is thus of the form given in frames 53 to 55. The full expression is:

$$v = 10 - 11.4e^{-0.11t} + 1.4e^{-0.89t} \text{ V} \quad [t \text{ is in ns}]$$

The exponential time constants in this expression are still in the nanosecond region so, again, the effects will be noticed only with high speed switching circuits.

2. The circuit diagram below shows the connections described in this question.

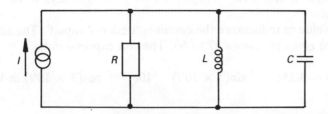

Applying Kirchhoff's current law to the circuit gives:

$$I = i_R + i_L + i_C$$

$$= \frac{v_R}{R} + i_L + C\frac{dv_C}{dt}$$

But $v_R = v_C = v_L = L di_L/dt$ so the above equation becomes:

$$I = \frac{L}{R}\frac{di_L}{dt} + i_L + LC\frac{d^2i_L}{dt^2}$$

Re-writing the equation in standard form, we have:

$$\frac{d^2i_L}{dt^2} + \frac{1}{CR}\frac{di_L}{dt} + \frac{i_L}{LC} = \frac{I}{LC}$$

The equation can now again be seen to be of the same form as the one in frame 43. The dependent variable in this case is current rather than voltage. The first-order differential coefficient is multiplied by a term which has dimensions of $1/T$ but the time constant is now CR rather than L/R. Since the term $1/LC$ has dimensions of 'frequency squared', both the last term on the left-hand side and that on the right-hand side of the equation have the same dimensions as those of the other terms in the equation.

The solution again depends on the damping factor α (which is now given by $\alpha = 1/2CR$) and the natural frequency $\omega_0 = 1/LC$.

With $R = 1$ kΩ and $C = 0.5$ nF, $\alpha = 10^6$ and $\alpha^2 = 10^{12}$

The value of ω_0 depends on L and is different for the three cases. We will take each, in turn, in the next three frames.

76

When $L = 0.2$ mH, $\omega_0^2 = 1/LC = 1/(0.2 \times 10^{-3} \times 0.5 \times 10^{-9}) = 10^{13}$

Thus $\omega_0 > \alpha$ and $\sqrt{(\alpha^2 - \omega_0^2)} = \sqrt{(-9 \times 10^{12})} = \pm j3 \times 10^6$

With this value of inductance the circuit is 'under-damped'. The solution is thus of the form given in frames 57 to 60. The full expression is:

$$i_C = 10 - 3.33e^{-t/10^6} \sin(3 \times 10^6 t) - 10e^{-t/10^6} \cos(3 \times 10^6 t) \text{ mA} \quad [t \text{ is in s}]$$

77

When $L = 2$ mH, $\omega_0^2 = 1/LC = 1/(2 \times 10^{-3} \times 0.5 \times 10^{-9}) = 10^{12}$

Thus $\omega_0 = \alpha = 10^6$ and the circuit is 'critically damped'. The solution is thus of the form given in frames 65 to 68. The full expression is:

$$i = 10[1 - e^{-t/10^6}(t/10^6 + 1)] \text{ mA} \quad [t \text{ is in s}]$$

78

When $L = 20$ mH, $\omega_0^2 = 1/LC = 1/(20 \times 10^{-3} \times 0.5 \times 10^{-9}) = 10^{11}$

Thus $\omega_0 < \alpha$ and $\sqrt{(\alpha^2 - \omega_0^2)} = \sqrt{(0.9 \times 10^{12})} = 0.95 - 10^6$

With this value of capacitance the circuit is 'over-damped'. The solution is thus of the form given in frames 53 to 55. The full expression is:

$$i = 10 - 10.25e^{(-0.05 \times 10^6)t} + 0.25e^{(-1.95 \times 10^6)t} \text{ mA}$$
$$[t \text{ is in s}]$$

TEST ON PROGRAMME 7

1. The voltage output of the generator in the left-hand circuit below is initially zero but gives an output which can be represented as $v = V \sin \omega t$ from time $t = 0$ onwards. Obtain an expression for the voltage across the capacitor for $t > 0$. Assuming that an exponential decay is complete for all practical purposes after five time constants have elapsed, how many cycles of the forcing signal will have occurred before the steady state is reached? What is the steady solution expressed as a phase-shifted sinewave?

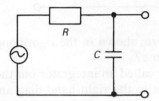 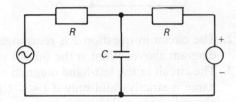

2. The circuit in problem 1 is modified by the addition of a direct generator and resistor as shown in the right-hand diagram above. The outputs of both are initially zero. The sine-wave generator is switched on as above at $t = 0$. The direct generator is switched to its full output at the same instant. Obtain an expression for the voltage across the capacitor for $t > 0$ by writing and solving a nodal equation for the *RCR* node.

3. When the inductance of its leads and 'leakage resistance' must be taken into account, a capacitor can be modelled by the circuit shown below. (Leakage resistance is the resistance which exists between the plates of a capacitor because of its construction. It is often a megohm or more.)

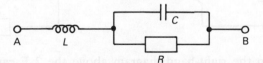

A voltage generator is connected between terminals A and B and has an output which is an abrupt step from zero to a value V at time $t = 0$. Obtain a differential equation for the voltage across C and say under what conditions this voltage would be: (a) under-damped; (b) critically damped and (c) over-damped. Writing $1/CR = 2\alpha$ and $\sqrt{(1/LC)} = \omega_0$, find an expression for the voltage across the capacitor when $\omega_d = \sqrt{(\omega_0^2 - \alpha^2)} > 0$, assuming that there is no stored energy in the system before the input step occurs.

80

1. In the left-hand circuit below the voltage generator gives an output $v(t) = Vt/T$ for $t > 0$ (it is zero for $t < 0$). What is the output voltage V_o?

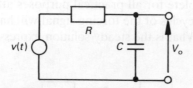

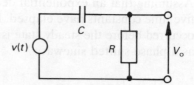

2. The circuit in question 1 is rearranged into the form shown in the right-hand diagram above. What is the output voltage this time?

3. The circuit in the left-hand diagram above is often called an integrator but the name is strictly valid only if $t << CR$. The circuit in the right-hand diagram above is often called a differentiator but, in this case, the name is strictly valid only if $t >> CR$. Justify these assertions for the input voltages in questions 1 and 2 and also if the voltage generator provides a voltage step as its output.

4. Find i_R and i_L in the left-hand circuit below if the current generator gives an output $i(t) = It/T$ for $t > 0$ (zero for $t < 0$). Compare the results with those in questions 1 and 2 and say under what conditions this circuit could be regarded as (a) an integrator and (b) a differentiator.

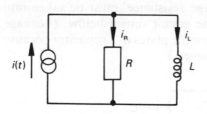

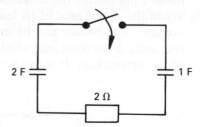

5. In the circuit in the right-hand diagram above the 2 F capacitor is initially charged to a voltage of 6 V. Find the current in the circuit and hence the voltage across the 1 F capacitor after the switch is closed. What are the values of the initial and final energies stored in the system? Why are these not the same and what happens to the difference?

6. Find the current in the inductor in the circuit below if the switch is changed over at time $t = 0$.

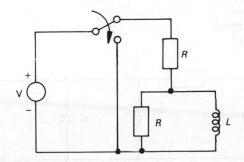

7. Find the voltage across the 10 kΩ resistor in the circuit below if the alternating voltage generator gives an output which can be represented as $v(t) = V \sin \omega t$ and both generators are switched on at time $t = 0$.

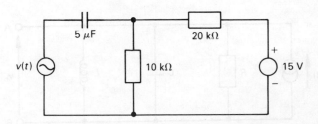

8. The switch in the circuit below has been closed for some time so that steady state conditions prevail in the circuit. What are these steady state conditions and what is the output voltage between the terminals AB after the switch is opened?

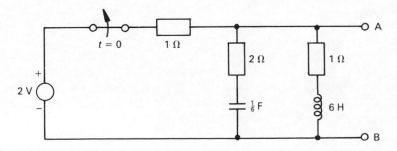

9. Under what conditions in the circuit below will the transient output $v_o(t)$ to an input stimulus $v_i(t)$ be:

(a) under-damped
(b) critically damped
(c) over-damped?

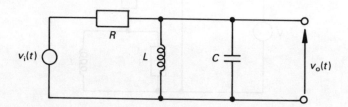

10. If the current generator in the circuit below gives an output which is a step of height I (that is, it switches from zero to a value I at time $t = 0$), what is the voltage between the output terminals AB?

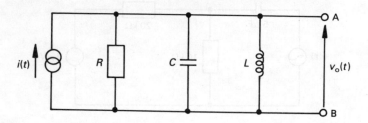

ANSWERS TO FURTHER
QUESTIONS

INTRODUCTION

This section contains answers to all the further questions set at the end of each programme. In some of the more difficult problems you will also find a brief description of a possible method of tackling the problem. The method given is, in most cases, by no means the only possible method since, if you have followed this text closely, you will by now be aware that there are usually many ways of solving engineering problems. The skilled problem-solver is the one who learns how to use quick, accurate and easily checkable methods.

Many of the further questions include design problems and, in these cases, the *answer* given is by no means the only possible one. Most design problems involve the designer in taking one or more arbitrary decisions and, if the decisions you have made are different from those made in obtaining the solution given here, then your solution will probably be different. In such cases you should check your working carefully to see that the solution you have obtained is consistent with the assumptions you have made.

ANSWERS TO FURTHER QUESTIONS ON PROGRAMME 1

1. $[E] = [MLT^{-2}Q^{-1}]$ $[H] = [L^{-1}T^{-1}Q]$

2. $e = mc^2$ 'Dimensions' of energy $[ML^2T^{-2}]$
    $v^2 = u^2 + 2as$ 'Dimensions' of velocity squared $[L^2T^{-2}]$
    $R = \rho l/A$ 'Dimensions' of resistance $[ML^2T^{-1}Q^{-2}]$

3. (i) h is wrong

$$\frac{[p]}{[\rho]} = \frac{[ML^{-1}T^{-2}]}{[ML^{-3}]} = [L^2T^{-2}]$$

h needs an extra term $[LT^{-2}]$ (acceleration)

The correct form is $\dfrac{p}{\rho} = \dfrac{p_0}{\rho} + \dfrac{v^2}{2} + gh$

(ii) at_2 is wrong; all other terms have dimensions of length

$$[at_2] = [LT^{-2}][T] = [LT^{-1}]$$

An extra time term is needed, at_2 should probably be at_2^2
(iii) $R_1R_2/(R_1 + R_2)$ is wrong; all other terms have 'dimensions' of voltage
A factor I is required. The term must be of the form $IR_1R_2/(R_1 + R_2)$

4. $\omega^2 C^2 R^2$ should be of the form $\omega^2 C^2 R^3$

5. (i) $\dfrac{F}{ma}$ $\dfrac{Ft}{mv}$ $\dfrac{v}{at}$ $\dfrac{s}{vt}$ $\dfrac{s}{at}$ (ii) $\dfrac{M}{m}$ $\dfrac{Mg}{F}$ $\dfrac{mg}{F}$

(iii) $\dfrac{V}{IR}$ $\dfrac{P}{VI}$ $\dfrac{P}{I^2R}$ $\dfrac{PR}{V^2}$ (iv) $\dfrac{\omega}{\omega_0}$ ωCR $\dfrac{\omega L}{R}$ $\omega^2 LC$ $\dfrac{CR^2}{L}$

6. $A = \dfrac{n}{n-1}(e^{-x/n} - e^{-x})$ when $n \neq 1$; $A = xe^{-x}$ when $n = 1$

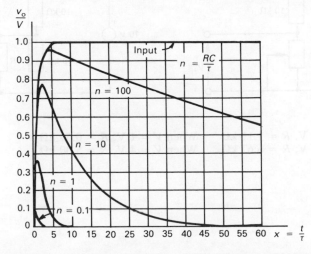

ANSWERS TO FURTHER QUESTIONS ON PROGRAMME 2

1.

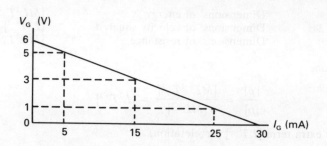

The point 5 V, 5 mA is obtained for a load of 1 kΩ
The point 3 V, 15 mA is obtained for a load of 200 Ω
The point 1 V, 25 mA is obtained for a load of 40 Ω

The generator looks most like a voltage generator at the point 5 V, 5 mA
The generator looks most like a current generator at the point 1 V, 25 mA

2. $R_1 = 15$ kΩ, $R_2 = 5$ kΩ, $R_3 = 10$ kΩ
3. $R_1 = 5$ kΩ, $R_2 = 1.25$ kΩ, $R_3 = 500$ Ω
4. (a) V_0 max = 4.33 V   (b) V_0 max = 4.13 V
     V_0 min = 3.85 V V_0 min = 4.03 V
5. (a) I_o max = 16.72 mA   (b) I_o max = 15.84 mA
     I_o min = 14.57 mA   (b) I_o min = 15.41 mA
6.

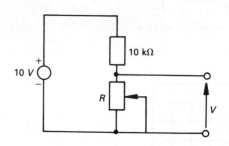

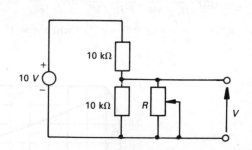

When $V = 1$ V, $R = 1.11$ kΩ   When $V = 1$ V, $R = 0.59$ kΩ
When $V = 4$ V, $R = 6.67$ kΩ   When $V = 4$ V, $R = 5.00$ kΩ

7. All the circuit configurations are meaningful. (a) and (b) are essentially the same circuit. (c) and (d) are also essentially the same.
In (a) and (b)
The voltage across the load is IR_L, the current through the load is I, the voltage across the current generator is $IR_L - V$, the current through the voltage generator is I.
In (c) and (d)
The voltage across the load is V, the current through the load is V/R_L, the voltage across the current generator is V, the current through the voltage generator is $I - V/R_L$.

8. If each attenuator consists of two resistors R_1 and R_2 in series where R_2 is the instrument resistance, then the values of R for 2:1, 5:1 and 10:1 attenuators are respectively 10 kΩ, 40 kΩ and 90 kΩ.

9. If each attenuator consists of two resistors R_1 and R_2 in series where R_2 is in parallel with the instrument resistance, then the values of R_1 and R_2 for 2:1, 5:1 and 10:1 attenuators are respectively

$R_1 = 500$ kΩ, $R_2 = 1$ MΩ; $R_1 = 800$ kΩ, $R_2 = 250$ kΩ; and $R_1 = 900$ kΩ, $R_2 = 111$ kΩ
10. $R_1 = 25$ kΩ, $R_2 = 15$ kΩ, $R_3 = 10$ kΩ

ANSWERS TO FURTHER QUESTIONS ON PROGRAMME 3

1. $R_1 = \dfrac{R_a R_c}{R_a + R_b + R_c}$ $R_2 = \dfrac{R_a R_b}{R_a + R_b + R_c}$ $R_3 = \dfrac{R_b R_c}{R_a + R_b + R_c}$

$R_a = \dfrac{R_1 R_2 + R_2 R_3 + R_1 R_3}{R_3}$ $R_b = \dfrac{R_1 R_2 + R_2 R_3 + R_1 R_3}{R_1}$ $R_c = \dfrac{R_1 R_2 + R_2 R_3 + R_1 R_3}{R_2}$

2. $R = \dfrac{5}{6}\,\Omega$

3. $R_1 = 12$ kΩ, $R_2 = 6$ kΩ, $I = 75$ µA   when $R_L = 36$ kΩ

4. $R_1 = 7.74$ kΩ, $R_2 = 2.7$ kΩ; NPV: $R_1 = 7.5$ kΩ, $R_2 = 2.7$ kΩ

5. 4.72 mA from 10 V clockwise, 4.28 mA from 9 V anticlockwise
   31 mV across 2.0 kΩ, +ve to left

6. 238 mW in 220 Ω so select from 250 mW range
   484 mW in 200 Ω so select from 500 mW range

7. (a) $3.5\,R$ (b) $R_1 + \dfrac{R_2(R_3 R_4 + R_3 R_5 + R_4 R_5)}{R_2 R_4 + R_3 R_5 + R_3 R_4 + R_3 R_5 + R_4 R_5}$ (c) 4 kΩ

8. Thevenin circuit is 12.5 V in series with 5 kΩ, +ve terminal nearest to A .

9. Norton circuit is 2 mA in parallel with 5 kΩ, current flow from top to bottom.

10. Internal resistance of galvanometer $= 150\ \Omega$. Scale error when variable resistor is $100.5\ \Omega \approx 0.5\%$.

ANSWERS TO FURTHER QUESTIONS ON PROGRAMME 4

1. Peak value $= I_p$ Peak-to-peak value $= I_p$
  Mean value $= 2I_p/\pi$ r.m.s. value $= I_p/\sqrt{2}$
  Period $= T$ Frequency $= 1/T$

2. Peak value $= V_p$ Peak-to-peak value $= V_p$
  Mean value $= V_p/2$ r.m.s. value $= V_p/\sqrt{2}$
  Period $= 2T$ Frequency $= 1/2T$

3. $i = (V \sqrt{3}/R) \sin(\omega t + \pi/6)$

4. Let $i = 5 \sin(400\pi t)$ mA
  (a) For the resistor: $v = 50 \sin(400\pi t)$ V   r.m.s. voltage $= 50/\sqrt{2}$ V
              $p = 250(1 - \cos 800\pi t)$ mW

  (b) For the capacitor: $v = -(5/2\pi) \cos(400\pi t)$ V   r.m.s. voltage $= 5/2\pi\sqrt{2}$ V
              $p = -(25/2\pi) \sin(800\pi t)$ mW

  (c) For the inductor: $v = 10\pi \cos(400\pi t)$ V   r.m.s. voltage $= 50\pi/\sqrt{2}$ μV
              $p = 25\pi \sin (800\pi t)$ nW

Waveforms:

	Resistor	Capacitor	Inductor

Current

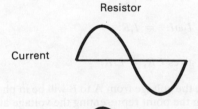 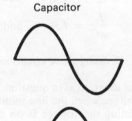 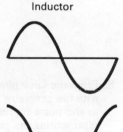

Voltage

Power

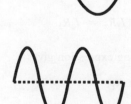 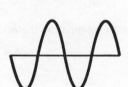 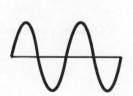

5. The r.m.s. value of a sinusoidal quantity is simply the amplitude multiplied by a scaling factor. A phasor diagram using r.m.s. values will thus be the same geometrical shape as one drawn using amplitudes but to a different scale.
The generator voltage is (a) 13 V r.m.s. or (b) $13\sqrt{2}$ V in amplitude.
The generator frequency is $48/\pi$ Hz = 15.28 Hz.

6. If the generator output is written as $v_G = 20 \sin(100\pi t)$ then
$i_R = 1 \sin(100\pi t)$ mA $\quad i_C = 1.26 \cos(100\pi t)$ mA $\quad i_G = 1.61 \sin(100\pi t + \phi)$
where $\phi = \arctan 0.9$ rads = 51.56°

7. The phasor direction diagrams and the resulting phasor diagrams (superimposed on the same generator phasor) are:

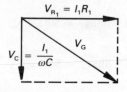
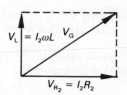
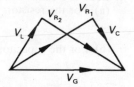

For zero voltage difference between A and B we must have:

$$V_C = V_{R_2} \quad \text{and} \quad V_L = V_{R_1}$$

$$\frac{I_1}{\omega C} = I_2 R_2 \quad \text{and} \quad I_2 \omega L = I_1 R_1$$

Dividing these equations gives $CR_1 = L/R_2$

8. From the same phasor diagram as in question 7, the voltage from A to B will be in phase with the generator voltage when the line joining the point representing the voltage at A to the point representing the voltage B on the phasor diagram is parallel to the line representing the generator voltage. In this case we have:

$$V_C = V_L \quad \text{and} \quad V_{R_1} = V_{R_2}$$

$$\frac{I_1}{\omega C} = I_2 \omega L \quad \text{and} \quad I_1 R_1 = I_2 R_2$$

Dividing equations and manipulating the resulting expression gives

$$\omega = \sqrt{(R_2/LCR_1)}$$

9.

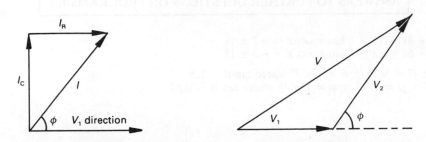

The left-hand phasor diagram above is drawn by first choosing an arbitrary direction for the voltage across the parallel RC combination, say V_1. The phasor direction of I, the current through this combination, can then be determined. The values of I and its components I_R and I_C can thus be deduced in terms of V_1, the voltage across the combination.

The right-hand phasor diagram uses the assumed direction for V_1 together with the derived direction for V_2 (the voltage across the separate resistor which must be in the same direction as the current through this resistor) to derive a direction for V, the generator voltage. But the generator voltage is known so the scale of the diagram is determined.

Trigonometrical analysis of the diagram then yields the result that the required phase angle ϕ is given as:

$$\phi = \arctan \frac{\omega CR}{2 + \omega^2 C^2 R^2}$$

10.

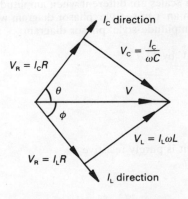

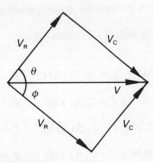

The left-hand phasor diagram above shows the relative sizes and directions of the phasors representing voltages in the circuit in a general case. The right-hand diagram shows how this diagram looks when $R = \sqrt{(L/C)}$. This condition implies that $\theta + \phi = 90°$ and further trigonometrical analysis of the diagram results in the deduction that the current through the circuit must be in phase with the voltage across it. Hence the circuit 'appears' purely resistive.

ANSWERS TO FURTHER QUESTIONS ON PROGRAMME 5

1. $x^2 + 4x + 13 = 0$ has roots $x = -2 \pm j3$
   $x^2 - 6x + 13 = 0$ has roots $x = -3 \pm j2$

2. $2 \pm j3 = \sqrt{13}\underline{/\pm}\ \theta = 13e^{\pm j\theta}$ where $\tan \theta = 1.5$
   $-3 \pm j2 = \sqrt{13}\underline{/\pm}\ \phi = 13e^{\pm j\phi}$ where $\tan \phi = 0.67$

3.

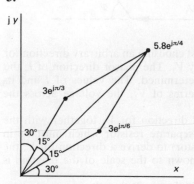
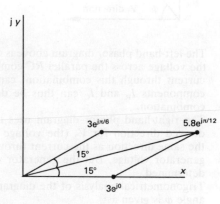

The right-hand diagram is, in effect, rotated clockwise by an angle $\pi/6$. This is achieved by multiplying each complex phasor by $1e^{-j\pi/6}$.

4. This is, in effect, the same problem as that raised in further question 4 in programme 4 but, in this case, 'mapped onto the complex plane'. All diagrams representing the same circuit are the same geometrical shape. Only their scales are different when amplitudes or r.m.s. values are used. All linear dimensions in an 'r.m.s.-style' phasor diagram will be $1/\sqrt{2}$ times the corresponding lengths in an 'amplitude-style' phasor diagram.

5. $Z_{\text{tot}} = 6.36\underline{/13.7°}$ ohms so $I_{\text{rms}} = 15.8$ A lagging V by $13.7°$

6.

    (a) When $f = (1/2\pi)$ kHz $\mathbf{Z} = (30 - j60)\ \Omega$

    (b) When $f = (2/\pi)$ kHz $\mathbf{Z} = (90 + j15)\ \Omega$

    (c) When $f = (1/\pi)$ kHz $\mathbf{Z}$ is real so the circuit is purely resistive

    (d) When $f = (1/\pi)$ kHz $\mathbf{Z} = 60\ \Omega$

7. I_L has amplitude 55.9 mA lagging V_{gen} by $26.57°$

8. The output of the circuit is zero for any sinusoidal input when $\omega = 1/CR$.
The output is equal to the input at very high and at very low frequency.

9. When $\omega = 1/CR$ in the circuit in problem 8, $\quad Z = \dfrac{R}{2}(1 - j)$
V_i lags I_i by 45°

10. The attenuator is 'compensated' when $C_1 = C_2R_2/R_1$.
A suitable circuit configuration to give the required attenuation factors while preserving an input impedance of 1 MΩ is shown below:

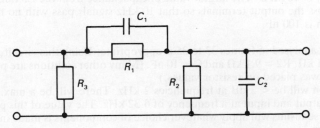

For 2:1 attenuation $\quad R_3 = 2$ MΩ, $R_1 = 1$ MΩ and $C_1 = 22$ pF
For 5:1 attenuation $\quad R_3 = 1.25$ MΩ, $R_1 = 4$ MΩ and $C_1 = 5.5$ pF
For 10:1 attenuation $R_3 = 1.1$ MΩ, $R_1 = 9$ MΩ and $C_1 = 2.5$ pF

ANSWERS TO FURTHER QUESTIONS ON PROGRAMME 6

1. The smallest preferred value capacitor from the E3 range to pass signals of frequency 100 Hz with no more than 3 dB attenuation is 1 μF. With this capacitor there will be a phase lead of 45° at a frequency of 80 Hz.

2. If the capacitance across the output terminals is 100 pF there will be a phase lag of 45° at a frequency of 16 MHz. The largest value of capacitance from the E3 range which can be added across the output terminals so that 10 kHz signals pass with no more than 3 dB attenuation is 100 nF.

3. The circuit analysed in frames 33 to 35 is appropriate. Using this circuit, suitable values are: R1 = 1 kΩ, R2 = 9.1 kΩ and C = 10 nF. (Many other solutions are possible since no restriction was placed on resistor values.)
   Attenuation will be < 3 dB at frequencies 2 kHz. There will be a maximum phase lag between output and input at a frequency of 6.32 kHz. The value of this phase lag will be 54.8°. (These results will apply whatever choice of components is made in the first part of the question.)

4. When the attenuator is frequency compensated:

$$C_1 = \frac{C_2 R_2}{R_1} \quad \text{and} \quad \frac{V_o}{V_i} = \frac{R_2}{R_1 + R_2}$$

5.
6. } The answer to these questions are proofs of expressions given in the texts.

7. The Bode diagram is:

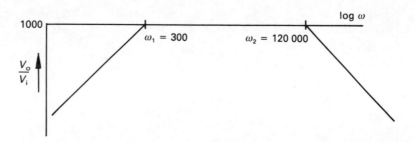

The 3 dB points are at frequencies of f = 47.75 Hz and f = 19.1 kHz.

8. The Bode diagram is:

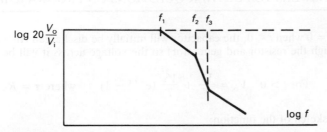

The corner frequencies are at $f_1 = 159.2$ Hz, $f_2 = 318.3$ Hz and $f_3 = 477.5$ Hz.

9. The Bode diagram and phase response are:

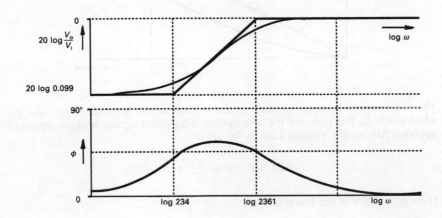

The maximum phase shift occurs at a frequency of 118 Hz and has a value of 54.8°.

10.

$$\frac{V_o}{V_i} = \frac{1}{(1 + j\omega/\omega_2)(1 - j\omega_1/\omega)}$$

where $\omega_1 = 1/C_1R_1$ and $\omega = 1/C_2R_2$. The response is of the same form as that given above in question 7.

ANSWERS TO FURTHER QUESTIONS ON PROGRAMME 7

1. Since $v(t) = 0$ when $t < 0$, the capacitor will initially be discharged (there is a discharge path through the resistor and generator) so the voltage across it will be zero at $t = 0$.

$$\text{For } t > 0 \quad V_o = \frac{Vt}{T} + \frac{V\tau}{T} (e^{-t/\tau} - 1) \quad \text{where } \tau = RC$$

Here is a sketch of the function:

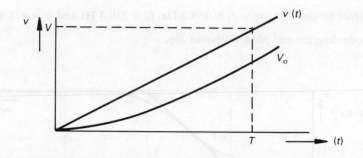

2. The same conditions apply initially so the voltage across the resistor will also be zero when $t = 0$. In this case, via the appropriate differential equation or, more simply, by applying Kirchhoff's Voltage Law to the circuit:

$$\text{For } t > 0 \quad V = \frac{V\tau}{T} (1 - e^{-t/\tau})$$

Here is a sketch of the function:

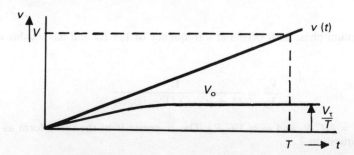

3. To see how the circuit in question 1 acts as an integrator we expand the exponential function as a series and ignore terms with powers of t greater than 2 because $t \ll \tau$ and it appears in the series in the expression t/τ. We find that:

$$V = \frac{Vt^2}{T\tau}$$

That is, the output is a square law or parabolic function. It is the integral of the input function which is linear.

If the input is a step function of the form $v(t) = V$ (a constant) for $t > 0$ then the output is:

$$v(t) = V(1 - e^{-t/\tau}) \quad \text{where } \tau = RC$$

When $t \ll \tau$ we can again expand the exponential function and ignore terms in t of order 2 or more to obtain:

$$v(t) = Vt/\tau$$

That is, the output is a linear function and a linear function is the integral of a constant. When the circuit in question 2 has an input $v(t) = Vt/T$ and $t \gg \tau$ the exponential term has completely decayed so the output is $v(t) = V\tau/T$. That is, the output is constant and the differential of a linear function *is* a constant.

If the input is a step function of the form $v(t) = V$ for $t > 0$ then the output is:

$$v(t) = Ve^{-t/\tau}$$

When $t \gg \tau$ this exponential function will have decayed completely away so the output is $v(t) = 0$. But the differential of a constant *is* zero so, again, the circuit is as a differentiator when $t \gg \tau$.

Note: If the output is plotted as a graph on a timescale which is long compared with τ, then it appears as a 'spike'. Such circuits are widely used in many applications as 'trigger' circuits. It is a popular misconception that it is the presence of the spike which makes this circuit into a differentiator. This is not so because, when the spike is present, the time conditions for differentiation are not met. True differentiation occurs only after the spike has fully decayed.

4. Since $i(t)$, the generator output, is zero for $t < 0$ the currents in the resistor and the inductor are both also zero for $t < 0$. For $t > 0$ we find that:

$$i(t) = \frac{It}{T} + \frac{I\tau}{T}\,(e^{-t/\tau} - 1) \quad \text{and} \quad i(t) = \frac{I\tau}{T}\,(1 - e^{-t/\tau}) \text{ where } \tau = L/R$$

These expressions are the same mathematical shapes as the expressions for the voltages across the capacitor and resistor in questions 1 and 2. The current through the inductor can thus be taken as the integral of the input current when $t \ll \tau$ and the current through the resistor can be taken as the differential of the input current when $t \gg \tau$.

5. The current in the circuit is $3e^{-3t/4}$ A
   The voltage across the 1 F capacitor is $4(e^{-3t/4} - 1)$ V
   The initial stored energy is 36 J   The final stored energy is 24 J
   The difference is the energy dissipated as heat in the resistor while the current is flowing.

6. The current in the inductor is $\dfrac{V}{R}\,e^{-Rt/2L}$

7. This problem can be tackled by treating each generator separately with the other short-circuited and using the superposition theorem. The voltage across the 10 kΩ resistor is:

$$v = 5(1 - e^{-t/\tau}) + \frac{V}{1 + \omega\tau}\,(\omega\tau e^{-t/\tau} + \sin \omega t - \omega\tau \cos \omega t) \quad \text{where } \tau = 33 \text{ ms}$$

8. Initially $v_0 = 1$ V so the capacitor voltage is 1 V and the inductor current is 1 A.
   After the switch is opened $v_{AB} = e^{-t/4} \cos \sqrt{15}t/4 - (67/3\sqrt{15})e^{-t/4} \sin \sqrt{15}t/4$

9. The circuit is under-damped when $L/R < 4CR$
   The circuit is critically damped when $L/R = 4CR$
   The circuit is over-damped when $L/R > 4CR$

10. The output voltage is $v(t) = e^{-\alpha t}(I/\omega_0 C) \sin \omega_0 t$

$$\text{where } \alpha = 1/2CR \text{ and } \omega_0 = \sqrt{\{(1/LC) - (1/2CR)^2\}}$$

SOLUTIONS TO TEST
QUESTIONS

INTRODUCTION

In this section you will find worked solutions to all the problems set as tests at the end of each programme. You are strongly advised not to consult the solutions to a test on a given programme until you have attempted the whole test on that programme.

When you have completed a test, check your answers against those given here and award yourself a 'mark' out of 100, giving all questions in the test equal weightings – three questions carry 33 marks each, four questions carry 25 and five questions carry 20. Test scores in excess of 60% show that you have attained reasonable mastery of the material in a programme. Scores in excess of 80% represent a very good performance.

SOLUTIONS TO TEST ON PROGRAMME 1

1. $[\text{Stress}] = \dfrac{[\text{Force}]}{[\text{Area}]} = \dfrac{[MLT^{-2}]}{[L^2]} = [ML^{-1}T^{-2}]$

$[\text{Strain}] = \dfrac{[\text{Extension}]}{[\text{Length}]} = \dfrac{[L]}{[L]} = [L^0]$

That is, strain has zero dimensions.

$[\text{Young's modulus}] = \dfrac{[\text{Stress}]}{[\text{Strain}]} = \dfrac{[ML^{-1}T^{-2}]}{[L^0]} = [ML^{-1}T^{-2}]$

Young's modulus has the same dimensions as stress.

2. Efficiency is a dimensionless ratio so the numerator and denominator of the expression suggested should have the same dimensions.

$$VI \text{ has 'dimensions' of power}$$
$$Fr \text{ has 'dimensions' of work}$$

Since we are looking for a power ratio, the denominator must be divided by something having the dimension of time. (Power is rate of doing work.) The appropriate quantity is number of revolutions per second, N. Number is dimensionless and the 'per second' part gives the necessary extra time term. The final formula may require a dimensionless scaling term, k, so could be:

$$\text{Efficiency} = \frac{kVI}{NFr}$$

3. Joules are a measure of energy so have 'dimensions' of power times time. All terms in the denominator of the suggested expression should thus have 'dimensions' of power.

$$(V - V_1)I_1 \text{ has 'dimensions' of power.}$$

$$I_1R_1 \text{ has 'dimensions' of voltage so cannot be correct.}$$

$$V^2/R_2 \text{ has 'dimensions' of power.}$$

Two terms have the correct dimensions so could be correct. The term I_1R_1 is wrong and should probably be $I_1^2R_1$.

SOLUTIONS TO TEST ON PROGRAMME 2

1. (a) $V = IR$ so $V = 20 \times 10^{-3} \times 520 = 1.04$ V
$P = I^2R$ so $P = 20 \times 20 \times 10^{-6} \times 520 = 20.8 \times 10^{-3} = 20.8$ mW

(b) $I = V/R$ so $I = 9.3/(200 \times 10^3) = 46.5 \times 10^{-6} = 46.5$ μA
$P = V^2/R$ so $P = 9.3 \times 9.3/(200 \times 10^3) = 432.45 \times 10^{-6} = 432.45$ μW

(c) $R = V/I$ so $R = 5/(2 \times 10^{-3}) = 2.5 \times 10^3 = 2.5$ kΩ
Nearest preferred value is 2.4 kΩ
Actual value is $(0.1/2.4) \times 100\% = 4.2\%$ greater than nominal value.
$P = VI$ so $P = 5 \times 2 \times 10^{-3} = 10 \times 10^{-3} = 10$ mW

2. Design value $= V/I = 9.0/(20 \times 10^{-3}) = 0.45 \times 10^3 = 450$ Ω
The nearest values in the 5% range are 430 Ω and 470 Ω
Either could be selected
If the 430 Ω resistor is selected:

largest value is 451.5 so current is 9/451.5 = 19.93 mA
smallest value is 408.5 so current is 9/408.5 = 22.03 mA

If the 470 Ω resistor is selected:

largest value is 493.5 so current is 9/493.5 = 18.24 mA
smallest value is 446.5 so current is 9/446.5 = 20.16 mA

3.

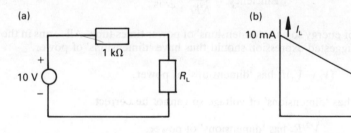

$I_L = 10 - V_L$ where I_L is measured in mA

A 10 mA current generator in parallel with a 1 kΩ resistor would produce the same effect.

4. $R = 5 \text{ V}/5 \text{ mA} = 1 \text{ k}\Omega$

$1 \Omega << 1 \text{ k}\Omega$ and $2 \Omega << 1 \text{ k}\Omega$

The generator resistance is much greater than the load resistance so the generator looks most like a current generator. The load current should be much the same for both loads but the load voltage may be different.

$$\text{Check: } I_L = \frac{R_G}{R_G + R_L} \times I_G \text{ by the current splitter rule}$$

With 1, $I_L = (1000/1001) \times 5 = 4.995 \text{ mA}$ so $V_L = 4.995 \text{ mV}$
With 2, $I_L = (1000/1002) \times 5 = 4.99 \text{ mA}$ so $V_L = 9.98 \text{ mV}$

$$1 \text{ M}\Omega >> 1 \text{ k}\Omega \quad \text{and} \quad 2 \text{ M}\Omega >> 1 \text{ k}\Omega$$

The generator resistance is much less than the load resistance so the generator looks most like a voltage generator. The load voltage should be much the same for both loads but the load current may be different.

$$\text{Check: } V_L = \frac{R_L}{R_L + R_G} \times V_G \text{ by the potential divider rule}$$

With 1 MΩ, $V_L = (1{,}000{,}000/1{,}001{,}000) \times 5 = 4.995 \text{ V}$ so $I_L = 4.995 \text{ }\mu\text{A}$
With 2 MΩ, $V_L = (1{,}000{,}000/1{,}002{,}000) \times 5 = 4.99 \text{ V}$ so $I_L = 2.495 \text{ }\mu\text{A}$

5.

$$P = \frac{V_G^2 R_L^2}{(R_L + R_G)^2 \times R_L} = \frac{V_G^2 R_L}{(R_L + R_G)^2}$$

$$\frac{dP}{dR_L} = V_G^2 \times \frac{\{(R_L + R_G)^2 \times 1 - 2R_L (R_L + R_G)\}}{(R_L + R_G)^4} = 0 \text{ for a maximum or minimum}$$

Cancelling by $(R_L + R_G)$ which cannot be zero, we have

$$R_L + R_G - 2R_L = 0$$

$$\text{so } R_L = R_G$$

Differentiating a second time or drawing a graph would confirm that this value is a maximum. Hence maximum power is dissipated in the load resistor when the load resistor equals the source resistor. The load is said to 'match' the source.

1. Input resistance $= \dfrac{(2.2 + 4.7) \times 6.8}{2.2 + 4.7 + 6.8} + 1.5 = 4.92 \text{ k}\Omega$

Current drawn $= \dfrac{10 \text{ V}}{4.92 \text{ k}\Omega} = 2.03 \text{ mA}$

Voltage developed $= (2 \text{ mA}) \times (4.92 \text{ k}\Omega) = 9.84 \text{ V}$

2.

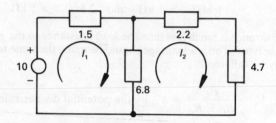

All working is done in volts and kilohms so the answers will be given directly in milliamps. Summing voltages clockwise round the left- and right-hand meshes gives:

$$10 - 1.5I_1 - 6.8(I_1 - I_2) = 0 \qquad 6.8(I_2 - I_1) + 2.2I_2 + 4.7I_2 = 0$$

Collecting terms and rearranging gives:

$$8.3I_1 - 6.8I_2 = 10 \qquad - 6.8I_1 + 13.7I_2 = 0$$

In matrix form this is:

$$\begin{bmatrix} 8.3 & -6.8 \\ -6.8 & 13.7 \end{bmatrix} \begin{bmatrix} I_1 \\ I_2 \end{bmatrix} = \begin{bmatrix} 10 \\ 0 \end{bmatrix}$$

Reducing the matrix to upper triangular form by Gaussian elimination:

$$\begin{bmatrix} 8.3 & -6.8 \\ 0 & 8.13 \end{bmatrix} \begin{bmatrix} I_1 \\ I_2 \end{bmatrix} = \begin{bmatrix} 10 \\ 8.19 \end{bmatrix}$$

Hence $I_2 = \dfrac{8.19}{8.13} = 1.01 \text{ mA}$

Substituting back gives: $8.3I_1 - 6.8 \times 1.01 = 10$

So $I_1 = \dfrac{10 + (6.8 \times 1.01)}{8.3} = 2.03 \text{ mA}$

Currents through and voltages across the resistors are:

R	I		V
1.5	2.03	l. to r.	3.05
6.8	1.02	down	6.94
2.2	1.01	l. to r.	2.22
4.7	1.01	down	4.75

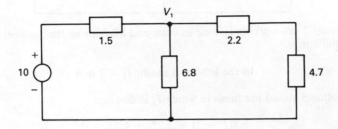

Using nodal analysis:

$$\frac{V_1 - 10}{1.5} + \frac{V_1}{6.8} + \frac{V_1}{2.2 + 4.7} = 0$$

$$V_1 \left(\frac{1}{1.5} + \frac{1}{6.8} + \frac{1}{6.9} \right) = \frac{10}{1.5}$$

$$V_1 (0.96) = \frac{10}{1.5}$$

$$\text{So } V_1 = \frac{10}{1.5 \times 0.96} = 6.94 \text{ V}$$

This result is the voltage across the 6.8 kΩ resistor confirming the result above. All other currents and voltages thus follow.

3.

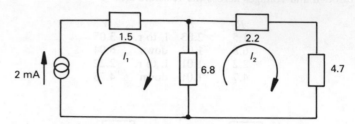

As for question 2, all working is done in volts and kilohms so the answers will be given directly in milliamps.

In the left-hand mesh: $I_1 = 2$ mA

Summing voltages round the mesh in which I_2 is flowing:

$$6.8(I_2 - 2) + 2.2I_2 + 4.7I_2 = 0$$

$$13.7I_2 = 2 \times 6.8 \quad \text{so} \quad I_2 = \frac{13.6}{13.7} = 0.99 \text{ mA}$$

Currents through and voltages across the resistors are:

R	I		V
1.5	2.00	l. to r.	3.00
6.8	1.01	down	6.87
2.2	0.99	l. to r.	2.18
4.7	0.99	down	4.67

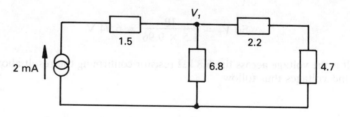

Using nodal analysis

$$-2 + \frac{V_1}{6.8} + \frac{V_1}{6.9} = 0$$

$$V_1 \left(\frac{1}{6.8} + \frac{1}{6.9} \right) = 2 \quad \text{so} \quad V_1 = \frac{2.00}{0.29} = 6.84 \text{ V}$$

This is the voltage across the 6.8 kΩ resistor which is the same as calculated above using mesh analysis to within calculation rounding errors so all other currents and voltages follow.

4.

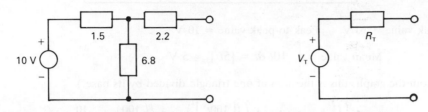

The circuit on the left reduces to the circuit on the right where:

$$V_T = \frac{6.8 \times 10}{6.8 + 1.5} = 8.19 \text{ V} \qquad R = 2.2 + \frac{6.8 \times 1.5}{6.8 + 1.5} = 3.43 \text{ k}\Omega$$

$$\text{So } V_{4.7} = \frac{4.7}{4.7 + R_T} \times V_T = \frac{4.7}{4.7 + 3.43} \times 8.19 \text{ V} = 4.74 \text{ V}$$

Hence $I_{4.7} = 1.01$ mA These are the same values as in question 2.

(a) $I_{2.4} = \dfrac{8.19}{3.43 + 2.4} = 1.4$ mA (b) $I_{9.1} = \dfrac{8.19}{3.43 + 9.1} = 0.65$ mA

5.

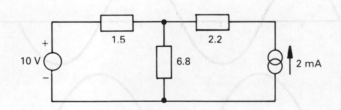

Using superposition (a) with the 10 V generator alone while the 2 mA generator is open-circuited gives:

$$I_1 = \frac{10}{1.5 + 6.8} = 1.2 \text{ mA}$$

(b) with the 2 mA generator alone while the 10 V generator is short circuited gives:

$$I_2 = \frac{2 \times 1.5}{1.5 + 6.8} = 0.36 \text{ mA}$$

$$I_{6.8} = I_1 + I_2 = 1.56 \text{ mA}$$

1. Peak value = 10 V   Peak-to-peak value = 10 V

$$\text{Mean value} = \int_0^1 10t \, dt = [5t^2]_0^1 = 5 \text{ V}$$

(From the graph, this is the area of one triangle divided by its base.)

$$\text{r.m.s. value} = \sqrt{\left(\int_0^1 (10t)^2 \, dt\right)} = \sqrt{\left(\left[\frac{100t^3}{3}\right]_0^1\right)} = \sqrt{\left(\frac{100}{3}\right)} = \frac{10}{\sqrt{3}} \text{ V} = 5.77 \text{ V}$$

Frequency = 1 Hz   Period = 1 s

2. (a) $V_{\text{rms}} = \dfrac{I}{\sqrt{2}\,\omega C} = \dfrac{10 \times 10^{-3}}{\sqrt{2} \times 10^3 \times 10^{-6}} = \dfrac{10}{\sqrt{2}} = 5\sqrt{2} = 7.07 \text{ V}$

$$P_{\max} = \frac{\omega C V^2}{2} = \frac{10^3 \times 10^{-6} \times 10^2}{2} = 50 \times 10^{-3} = 50 \text{ mW}$$

The peak power is 50 mW

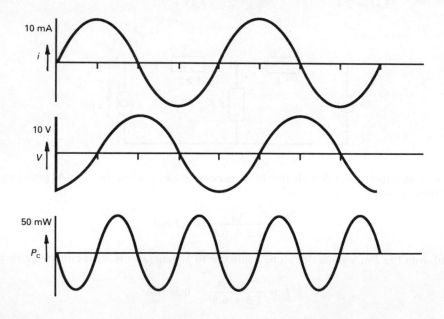

(b) $V_{rms} = \dfrac{I\omega L}{\sqrt{2}} = \dfrac{10 \times 10^{-3} \times 10^3 \times 10 \times 10^{-3}}{\sqrt{2}} = \dfrac{100 \times 10^{-3}}{\sqrt{2}}$

$= 50\sqrt{2} \times 10^{-3} = 50\sqrt{2} \text{ mV} = 70.7 \text{ mV}$

$P_{max} = \dfrac{\omega L I^2}{2} = \dfrac{10^3 \times 10 \times 10^{-3} \times 100 \times 10^{-6}}{2}$

$= 0.5 \times 10^{-3} \text{ W} = 0.5 \text{ mW}$

The peak power is 0.5 mW

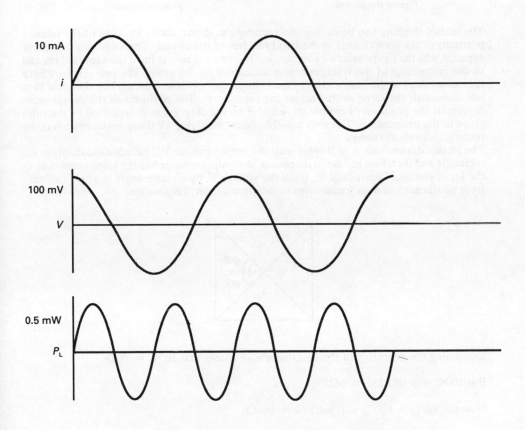

3.

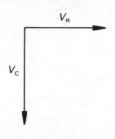

Phasor directions

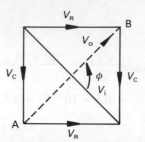

Phasor diagram

The phasor diagram can be drawn as a rectangle as shown above because of the relative positions of the components in the two branches of the circuit. The following argument explains why the figure *must* be a rectangle. The two capacitors have the same values and so the magnitudes of the voltages across them must be the same. The two resistors have the same values so the magnitudes of the voltages across them must also be the same (but not necessarily the same as that across the capacitors). The positions of the components determine the positions of the points A and B on the diagram as determined by the rules given in the programme. The only possible figure satisfying all these requirements is the rectangle drawn as shown.

The phasor drawn from A to B represents the output voltage V_o. Because the diagram is a rectangle and therefore has equal diagonals, the output voltage has the same amplitude as the input voltage. The voltage V_o leads the voltage V_i by a phase angle ϕ which can vary from nearly zero at high frequencies to nearly π at low frequencies.

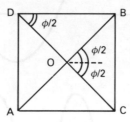

Examining the geometry of the diagram above shows that $\mathrm{B\hat{O}C} = 2\mathrm{B\hat{D}C}$.

But $\mathrm{B\hat{O}C} = \phi$ so $\mathrm{B\hat{D}C} = \phi/2$

Now $\tan(\phi/2) = V_\mathrm{c}/V_\mathrm{R} = (I/\omega C)/IR = 1/\omega CR$

By trigonometry $\tan \phi = \dfrac{2 \tan \phi/2}{1 - \tan^2 \phi/2} = \dfrac{2/\omega CR}{1 - 1/\omega^2 C^2 R^2} = \dfrac{2\omega CR}{\omega^2 C^2 R^2 - 1}$

4.

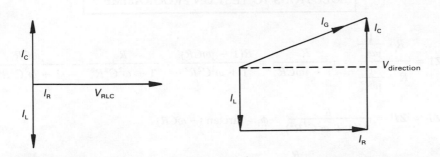

The phasor sum of the three currents I_L, I_C and I_R must be equal to the generator phasor current I_G as shown on the phasor diagram.

Now, I_G is in phase with V_G when I_G lies in the V_G direction, that is, when I_G and I_R are parallel.

It can be seen from the diagram that this will be true when:

$$I_L = I_C$$

$$\text{So} \quad V_G/\omega L = V_G \omega C$$

$$\text{and therefore} \quad \omega = 1/\sqrt{(LC)}$$

This is the condition of resonance.

$$\text{Now } Z = \frac{V_G}{I_G} = \frac{V_G}{\sqrt{\{(I_C - I_L)^2 + I_R^2\}}} = \frac{V_G}{\sqrt{\{(V_G\omega C - V_G/\omega L)^2 + V_G^2/R^2\}}}$$

$$\text{So} \quad Z = \frac{1}{\sqrt{\{(\omega C - 1/\omega L)^2 + 1/R^2\}}}$$

When $\omega = 1/\sqrt{(LC)}$ at resonance then

$$Z = R$$

SOLUTIONS TO TEST ON PROGRAMME 5

1.

$$Z1 = \frac{R \cdot \dfrac{1}{j\omega C}}{R + \dfrac{1}{j\omega C}} = \frac{R}{1 + j\omega CR} = \frac{R(1 - j\omega CR)}{1 + \omega^2 C^2 R^2} = \frac{R}{1 + \omega^2 C^2 R^2} - \frac{j\omega CR}{1 + \omega^2 C^2 R^2}$$

$$Z1 = |Z1| = \frac{R}{\sqrt{(1 + \omega^2 C^2 R^2)}} \quad \phi_1 = \arctan(-\omega CR)$$

$$Z1 = \frac{R}{\sqrt{(1 + \omega^2 C^2 R^2)}} \cdot e^{j\phi_1}$$

If $Z1 = X + jY = R' e^{j\phi_1}$

then X, Y and R' have 'dimensions' of resistance. ϕ is dimensionless.

$$Z2 = \frac{R \cdot j\omega L}{R + j\omega L} = \frac{j\omega LR(R - j\omega L)}{R^2 + \omega^2 L^2} = \frac{\omega^2 L^2 R + j\omega LR^2}{R^2 + \omega^2 L^2} = \frac{\omega^2 L^2 R}{R^2 + \omega^2 L^2} + \frac{j\omega LR^2}{R^2 + \omega^2 L^2}$$

$$Z2 = |Z2| = \frac{\omega LR}{\sqrt{(R^2 + \omega^2 L^2)}} \quad \phi = \arctan \frac{\omega LR^2}{\omega^2 L^2 R} = \arctan \frac{R}{\omega L}$$

$$Z2 = \frac{\omega LR}{\sqrt{(R^2 + \omega^2 L^2)}} \cdot e^{j\phi_2}$$

If $Z2 = X + jY = R' e^{j\phi_2}$

then X, Y and R' have 'dimensions' of resistance. ϕ is dimensionless.

2.

$$Z = \frac{R\left(R + \dfrac{1}{j\omega C}\right)}{R + R + \dfrac{1}{j\omega C}} = \frac{R(1 + j\omega CR)}{1 + 2j\omega CR}$$

$$Z = |Z| = \frac{R\sqrt{(1 + \omega^2 C^2 R^2)}}{\sqrt{(1 + 4\omega^2 C^2 R^2)}}$$

$$\phi = \arg Z = \arg\left(\frac{R(1 + j\omega CR)(1 - 2j\omega CR)}{1 + 4\omega^2 C^2 R^2}\right)$$

$$= \arg\left(\frac{R(1 + 2\omega^2 C^2 R^2 - j\omega CR)}{1 + 4\omega^2 C^2 R^2}\right)$$

$$= \arctan \frac{-\omega CR}{1 + 2\omega^2 C^2 R^2}$$

3.

$$\frac{V_o}{V_i} = \frac{\dfrac{R \cdot \dfrac{1}{j\omega C}}{R + \dfrac{1}{j\omega C}}}{\dfrac{R \cdot \dfrac{1}{j\omega C}}{R + \dfrac{1}{j\omega C}} + j\omega L} = \frac{\dfrac{R}{1 + j\omega CR}}{\dfrac{R}{1 + j\omega CR} + j\omega L} = \frac{R}{R + j\omega L - \omega^2 LCR}$$

$$= \frac{R}{R(1 - \omega^2 LC) + j\omega L}$$

When $\omega^2 = \dfrac{1}{LC}$ $\qquad \dfrac{V_o}{V_i} = \dfrac{R}{j\omega L} = \dfrac{-jR}{\omega L}$

This ratio is wholly imaginary so there is a phase shift of 90° between V_o and V_i. Since the j-term is negative, V_o lags V_i.

4. If there is to be no current through a resistor connected between A and B then it is necessary that:

$$V_A = V_B$$

$$V_A = \frac{RV_i}{R + j\omega L} \qquad V_B = \frac{\dfrac{V_i}{j\omega C}}{\dfrac{1}{j\omega C} + R} = \frac{V_i}{1 + j\omega CR}$$

So it must follow that:

$$\frac{R}{R + j\omega L} = \frac{1}{1 + j\omega CR}$$

Thus $R(1 + j\omega CR) = R + j\omega L$

so $R + j\omega CR = R + j\omega L$

and hence $CR = L$ or $CR = \dfrac{L}{R}$

In general the Thevenin voltage V_T is $V_A - V_B$

$$V_T = \left(\frac{R}{R + j\omega L} - \frac{1}{1 + j\omega CR} \right) V_i$$

$$= \left(\frac{R(1 + j\omega CR) - R - j\omega L}{(R + j\omega L)(1 + j\omega CR)} \right) V_i$$

$$= \left(\frac{j\omega CR^2 - j\omega L}{R - \omega^2 LCR + j\omega L + j\omega CR^2} \right) V_i$$

The Thevenin impedance Z_T is (R in parallel with L) in series with (R in parallel with C):

$$Z_T = \frac{j\omega LR}{R + j\omega L} + \frac{R/j\omega C}{R + 1/j\omega C} = \frac{j\omega LR}{R + j\omega L} + \frac{R}{1 + j\omega CR}$$

$$= \frac{j\omega LR(1 + j\omega CR) + R(R + j\omega L)}{(R + j\omega L)(1 + j\omega CR)}$$

$$= \frac{R^2 - \omega^2 LCR^2 + 2\,j\omega LR}{R - \omega^2 LCR + j\omega L + j\omega CR^2}$$

When this Thevenin equivalent generator is connected to a single resistor R, the current I_R is $V_T/(Z_T + R)$:

$$I_R = \frac{(j\omega CR^2 - j\omega L)\, V_i}{R - \omega^2 LCR + j\omega L + j\omega CR^2} \Bigg/ R + \frac{R^2 - \omega^2 LCR^2 + 2\,j\omega LR}{R - \omega^2 LCR + j\omega L + j\omega CR^2}$$

$$= \frac{(j\omega CR^2 - j\omega L)V_i}{2R^2 - 2\omega^2 LCR^2 + 3j\omega LR + j\omega CR^3}$$

I_R is in phase with V_i when this expression is real and positive. That is, when $2R^2 - 2\omega^2 LCR^2 = 0$ or $\omega^2 = 1/LC$

Then $I_R = \left(\dfrac{CR^2 - L}{3LR + CR^3}\right) V_i$

Hence, if $CR^2 > L$ then I_R is in phase with V_i
if $CR^2 < L$ then I_R is 180° out-of-phase with V_i
If $CR^2 = L$ then $I_R = 0$ as before.

5. Applying Norton's theorem to the left of the broken line, the left-hand circuit is transformed into the right-hand circuit below:

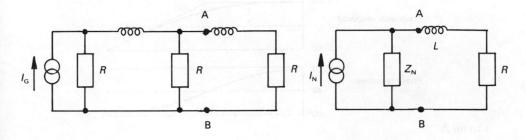

Where $I_N = \dfrac{RI_G}{R + j\omega L}$ $\qquad Z_N = \dfrac{R(R + j\omega L)}{2R + j\omega L}$

We disconnect the components to the right of A and B and replace them with a short-circuit to find I_N and look back into AB to find Z_N.
Analysing the right-hand circuit, the current in R is:

$$I_R = \frac{Z_N I_N}{Z_N + R + j\omega L} = \frac{\dfrac{R(R + j\omega L)}{(2R + j\omega L)} \cdot \dfrac{RI_G}{(R + j\omega L)}}{\dfrac{R(R + j\omega L)}{2R + j\omega L} + R + j\omega L}$$

$$= \frac{R^2 I_G}{R(R + j\omega L) + (R + j\omega L)(2R + j\omega L)} = \frac{R^2 I_G}{R^2 + j\omega LR + 2R^2 + 3j\omega LR - \omega^2 L^2}$$

$$= \frac{R^2 I_G}{3R^2 - \omega^2 L^2 + 4j\omega LR}$$

I_R is wholly imaginary and therefore 90° out of phase with I_G when $\omega^2 = 3R^2/L^2$ or $\omega = \sqrt{3}R/L$.

Then $I_R = \dfrac{R^2 I_G}{4j\omega LR} = \dfrac{R^2 I_G}{j4\sqrt{3}\dfrac{R}{L} \cdot R} = \dfrac{I_G}{j4\sqrt{3}} = -\dfrac{jI_G}{4\sqrt{3}}$

So $i_R = -\dfrac{I}{4\sqrt{3}} \sin(wt - 90°)$

or $i_R = -\dfrac{I}{4\sqrt{3}} \cos \omega t$

SOLUTIONS TO TEST ON PROGRAMME 6

1. *Circuit 1*

$$\frac{V_o}{V_i} = \frac{\dfrac{1}{j\omega C}}{\dfrac{1}{j\omega C} + R} = \frac{1}{1 + j\omega CR} = \frac{1}{1 + \dfrac{j\omega}{\omega_0}} \text{ where } \omega_0 = \frac{1}{CR}$$

Frequency response

0 dB

−20 dB

Phase response

0°

−45°

−90°

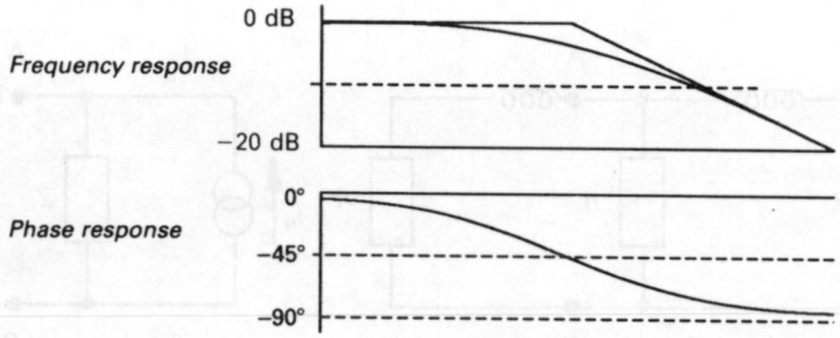

Circuit 2

$$\frac{V_o}{V_i} = \frac{R}{R + \dfrac{1}{j\omega C}} = \frac{1}{1 + \dfrac{j}{\omega CR}} = \frac{1}{1 - \dfrac{j\omega_0}{\omega}} \text{ where } \omega_0 = \frac{1}{CR}$$

Frequency response

0 dB

−20 dB

log ω →

Phase response

90°

45°

0°

−1   0   1

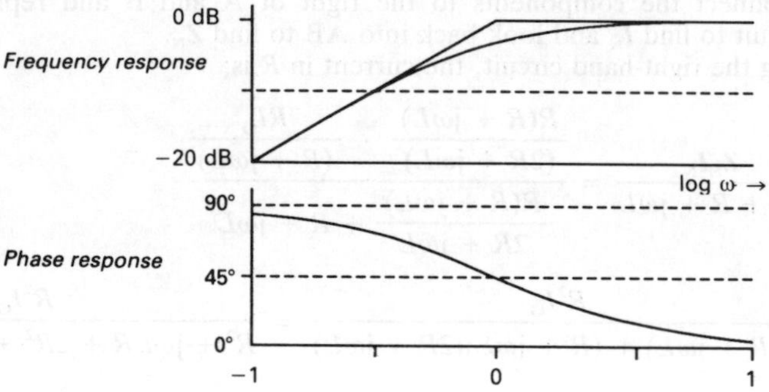

Circuit 3

$$\frac{I_o}{I_i} = \frac{\dfrac{1}{j\omega C}}{\dfrac{1}{j\omega C} + R} = \frac{1}{1 + j\omega CR} = \frac{1}{1 + \dfrac{j\omega}{\omega_0}} \text{ where } \omega_0 = \frac{1}{CR}$$

Same diagrams as for circuit 1.

Circuit 4

$$\frac{I_o}{I_i} = \frac{R}{R + \dfrac{1}{j\omega C}} = \frac{1}{1 + \dfrac{j}{\omega CR}} = \frac{1}{1 - \dfrac{j\omega_0}{\omega}} \text{ where } \omega_0 = \frac{1}{CR}$$

Same diagrams as for circuit 2.

2. $\dfrac{I_o}{I_i} = \dfrac{R_2 + j\omega L}{R_1 + R_2 + j\omega L}$

$$= \dfrac{R_2 \left(1 + \dfrac{j\omega L}{R}\right)}{(R_1 + R_2)\left(1 + \dfrac{j\omega L}{R_1 + R_2}\right)}$$

$$= \dfrac{R_2}{R_1 + R_2}\left(\dfrac{1 + j\omega/\omega_1}{1 + j\omega/\omega_2}\right)$$

Where $\omega_1 = \dfrac{R_2}{L}$ and $\omega_2 = \dfrac{R_1 + R_2}{L}$ so $\omega_2 > \omega_1$

When $\omega \gg \omega_2$ (and therefore also $\gg \omega_1$) we can ignore the 1's compared with the j-terms so that:

$$\dfrac{I_o}{I_i} \to \dfrac{R_2}{R_1 + R_2} \cdot \dfrac{\omega/\omega_1}{\omega/\omega_2} = \dfrac{R_2}{R_1 + R_2} \cdot \dfrac{\omega_2}{\omega_1} = 1$$

When $\omega \ll \omega_1$ (and therefore also $\ll \omega_2$) we can ignore the j-terms compared with the 1's so that:

$$\dfrac{I_o}{I_i} \to \dfrac{R_2}{R_1 + R_2}$$

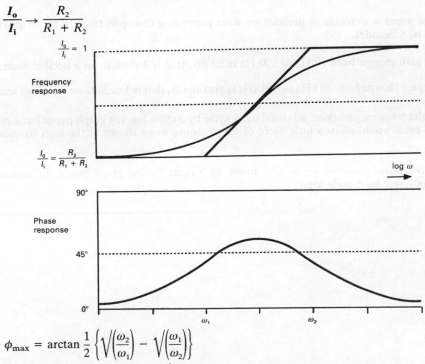

$\phi_{max} = \arctan \dfrac{1}{2}\left\{\sqrt{\left(\dfrac{\omega_2}{\omega_1}\right)} - \sqrt{\left(\dfrac{\omega_1}{\omega_2}\right)}\right\}$

This value occurs when $\omega - \sqrt{(\omega_1 \omega_2)}$
(Compare this example with Revision example 3 in frame 57.)

3. The 3 dB frequencies of the frequency response are:

$$f_1 = 100 \text{ Hz} \quad \text{and} \quad f_2 = 20 \text{ kHz}$$

The sloping parts of the frequency response 'roll off' at 6 dB per octave or 20 dB per decade from the 3 dB points.

Hence the gain changes are:

12 db down at 25 Hz (2 octaves down from 100 Hz, that is, 100 ÷ 4)
12 db down at 80 kHz (2 octaves up from 20 kHz, that is, 100 × 4)
20 db down at 10 Hz (1 decade down from 100 Hz that is 100 ÷ 10)
20 db down at 200 kHz (1 decade up from 20 kHz, that is 100 × 10)

The phase shift is less than 6° from a decade above the lower 3 dB point to a decade below the upper 3 dB point, that is from 1 kHz to 2 kHz.

The phase shift is 45° at the 3 dB points:

45° leading at 100 Hz
45° lagging at 20 kHz

To plot the graphs we need paper which will encompass a frequency range from 10 Hz to 200 kHz.

Since paper is available in decades we want paper that can span from 10 Hz to 1 MHz, that is, 5 decades.

The gain change from 10 Hz to 100 Hz is 20 dB, that is 1 decade on a decibel scale.

The gain change from 20 kHz to 200 kHz is also 20 dB, that is 1 decade on a decibel scale.

For the frequency respone we could use 1 cycle by 5 cycle log–log graph paper but 2 cycle by 5 cycle would allow a little more of the response to be shown at the high-frequency end.

For the phase response we require linear by 5 cycle lin–log graph paper, for example 10 cm linear by 5 cycle log.

Although not required in the question typical graphs of the frequency and phase responses are shown below:

Frequency response

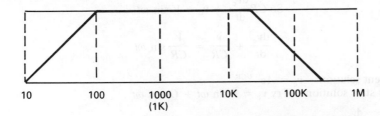

10   100   1000   10K   100K   1M
              (1K)

or

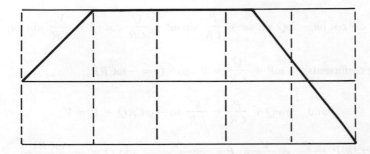

Phase response

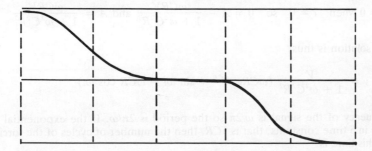

1. $V \sin \omega t = iR + v_c$ but $i = C \, dv_c/dt$

$$\text{So } CR\frac{dv_c}{dt} + v_c = V \sin \omega t$$

$$\frac{dv_c}{dt} + \frac{v}{CR} = \frac{V}{CR} \sin \omega t$$

Transient solution: $v_c = Ae^{-t/CR}$

Steady state solution: Try $v_c = P \sin \omega t + Q \cos \omega t$

So: $\frac{dv_c}{dt} = \omega P \cos \omega t - \omega Q \sin \omega t$

Substituting these expressions into the equation:

$$\omega P \cos \omega t - \omega Q \sin \omega t + \frac{P}{CR} \sin \omega t + \frac{Q}{CR} \cos \omega t = \frac{V}{CR} \sin \omega t$$

Equating coefficients: $\omega P + \frac{Q}{CR} = 0$ so $Q = -\omega CRP$

and $-\omega Q + \frac{P}{CR} = \frac{V}{CR}$ so $-\omega CRQ + P = V$

Hence $\omega^2 C^2 R^2 P + \frac{P}{CR} = \frac{V}{CR}$ so $P = \frac{V}{1 + \omega^2 C^2 R^2}$ and $Q = \frac{-\omega CRV}{1 + \omega^2 C^2 R^2}$

The solution is thus $v_c = Ae^{-t/CR} + \frac{V}{1 + \omega^2 C^2 R^2} (\sin \omega t - \omega CR \cos \omega t)$

But $v_c = 0$ when $t = 0$ so $0 = A - \frac{\omega CRV}{1 + \omega^2 C^2 R^2}$ and $A = \frac{\omega CRV}{1 + \omega^2 C^2 R^2}$

The full solution is thus:

$$v = \frac{V}{1 + \omega^2 C^2 R^2} (\omega CRe^{-t/CR} + \sin \omega t - \omega CR \cos \omega t)$$

The frequency of the signal is $\omega/2\pi$ so the period is $2\pi/\omega$. If the exponential decay is complete in 5 time constants, that is $5CR$, then the number of cycles of the forcing wave form in this time is:

$$\frac{5CR}{2\pi/\omega} = \frac{2.5}{\pi} \omega CR$$

The steady state solution is: $v_c = \dfrac{V}{1 + \omega^2 C^2 R^2} (\sin \omega t - \omega CR \cos \omega t)$

$$= V' \sin(\omega t + \phi)$$

$$= V' (\sin \omega t \cos \phi + \cos \omega t \sin \phi)$$

So $V' \cos \phi = \dfrac{V}{1 + \omega^2 C^2 R^2}$ and $V' \sin \phi = \dfrac{-V}{1 + \omega^2 C^2 R^2}$

Thus $\phi = \arctan - \omega CR$

Also $V'^2(\cos^2 \phi + \sin^2 \phi) = \dfrac{V^2 + V^2 \omega^2 C^2 R^2}{(1 + \omega^2 C^2 R^2)^2}$ so $V'^2 = \dfrac{V^2}{1 + \omega^2 C^2 R^2}$

Hence $V' = \dfrac{V}{\sqrt{(1 + \omega^2 C^2 R^2)}}$

So the steady state solution is $v_c = \dfrac{V}{\sqrt{(1 + \omega^2 C^2 R^2)}} \sin(\omega t - \phi)$

So v_c lags v_i by an angle ϕ where $\tan \phi = \omega CR$.
Note: This result could be obtained by the use of j-notation.

2.

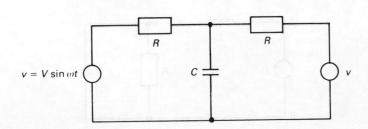

For $t > 0$ the nodal equation is:

$$\frac{v_c - V \sin \omega t}{R} + C \frac{dv_c}{dt} + \frac{v_c - V}{R} = 0$$

Rearranging, $\dfrac{dv_c}{dt} + \dfrac{2v_c}{CR} = \dfrac{V}{CR} (1 + \sin \omega t)$

Transient solution: $v_c = Ae^{-2t/CR}$
Steady state solution: Try $v_c = P + Q \sin \omega t + S \cos \omega t$

So: $\dfrac{dv_c}{dt} = \omega Q \cos \omega t - \omega S \sin \omega t$

Substituting these expressions into the equation:

$$\omega Q \cos \omega t - \omega S \sin \omega t + \frac{2}{CR}(P + Q \sin \omega t + S \cos \omega t) = \frac{V}{CR}(1 + \sin \omega t)$$

Hence $P = \frac{V}{2}$ $\omega Q + \frac{2S}{CR} = 0$ $-\omega S + \frac{2Q}{CR} = \frac{V}{CR}$

Solving gives: $Q = \frac{2V}{4 + \omega^2 C^2 R^2}$ $S = \frac{-\omega CRV}{4 + \omega^2 C^2 R^2}$

So $v_c = Ae^{-2t/CR} + \frac{V}{2} + \frac{V}{4 + \omega^2 C^2 R^2}(2 \sin \omega t - \omega CR \cos \omega t)$

Using $v_c = 0$ when $t = 0$ gives $A = -\frac{V}{2} + \frac{\omega CRV}{4 + \omega^2 C^2 R^2}$

The full solution is thus:

$$v_c = V\left\{ \frac{(1 - e^{-2t/CR})}{2} + \frac{1}{4 + \omega^2 C^2 R^2}(\omega CR\, e^{-2t/CR} + 2 \sin \omega t - \omega CR \cos \omega t) \right\}$$

3. The circuit with voltage generator may be drawn as shown below:

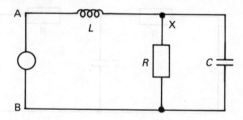

At node X $i_L + i_c + i_R = 0$

So $i_L + C\dfrac{dv_C}{dt} + \dfrac{v_C}{R} = 0$ . . . . (1)

But $L\dfrac{di_L}{dt} = v_L = v_C - V$

Differentiating equation (1) gives:

$$\frac{di_L}{dt} + C\frac{d^2 v_C}{dt^2} + \frac{1}{R}\frac{dv_C}{dt} = 0$$

Substituting for di_L/dt the last equation becomes:

$$\frac{v_c - V}{L} + C \frac{d^2 v_c}{dt^2} + \frac{1}{R} \frac{dv_c}{dt} = 0$$

Rearranging this equation into standard form gives:

$$\frac{d^2 v_c}{dt^2} + \frac{1}{CR} \frac{dv_c}{dt} + \frac{v_c}{LC} = \frac{V}{LC}$$

Or, using the recommended substitutions:

$$\frac{d^2 v_c}{dt^2} + 2\alpha \frac{dv_c}{dt} + \omega_0^2 v_c = \omega_0^2 V$$

The characteristic equation (for a solution $v_c = Ae^{mt}$) is:

$$m^2 + 2\alpha m + \omega_0^2 = 0$$

The roots are real if $\alpha^2 > \omega_0^2$ (Over-damped)

The roots are equal if $\alpha = \omega_0$ (Critically damped)

The roots are complex if $\alpha^2 < \omega_0^2$ (Under-damped)

When $\omega_0^2 - \alpha^2 > 0$ the solution is

$$v_c = V + e^{-\alpha t}(A \sin \omega_0 t + B \cos \omega_0 t)$$

But $v_c = 0$ when $t = 0$ and $i_L = 0$ when $t = 0$

$$v_c = 0 \rightarrow 0 = V + B \text{ so } B = -V$$

$i_L = 0$ and $v_c = 0 \rightarrow i_c = 0$ and $i_c = Cdv_c/dt$ so $dv_c/dt = 0$

Now, $\dfrac{dv_c}{dt} = e^{-\alpha t} \omega_0 A \cos \omega_0 t - e^{-\alpha t} A \sin \omega_0 t$

$$- e^{-\alpha t} \omega_0 B \sin \omega_0 t - e^{-\alpha t} B \cos \omega_0 t$$

When $t = 0$ this gives:

$$0 = \omega_0 A - \alpha B \quad \text{so} \quad A = \frac{\alpha B}{\omega_0} = \frac{-\alpha V}{\omega_0}$$

The full solution is thus $v_c = V\left(1 - \dfrac{\alpha}{\omega_0} \sin \omega_0 t - \cos \omega_0 t\right)$

Substituting for dt/dr the last equation becomes:

$$\frac{v}{L} + C\frac{d^2v}{dt^2} + \frac{1}{R}\frac{dv}{dt} = 0$$

Rearranging this equation into standard form gives:

$$\frac{d^2v}{dt^2} + \frac{1}{CR}\frac{dv}{dt} + \frac{v}{LC} = \frac{V}{LC}$$

Or, using the intended substitutions:

$$\frac{d^2v}{dt^2} + 2\sigma\frac{dv}{dt} + \omega_0^2 v = \omega_0^2 V$$

The characteristic equation (for a solution $v = Ne^{rt}$) is:

$$r^2 + 2\sigma r + \omega_0^2 = 0$$

The roots are $r = -\sigma \pm \sqrt{(\sigma^2 - \omega_0^2)}$

The roots are equal if $\sigma = \omega_0$ (critically damped).

The roots are complex if $\sigma < \omega_0$ (under-damped).

When $\sigma < \omega_0$ the solution is

$$v = V + e^{-\sigma t}(A\sin\omega_d t + B\cos\omega_d t)$$

Initially, $v = 0$ when $t = 0$ and $v_c = 0$ when $t = 0$

$v = 0 + 0 = V + B$ so $B = -V$

$i_c = 0$ and $v_c = 0 \Rightarrow t = 0$ and $i_c = Cdv/dt$ so $dv/dt = 0$

Now,

$$\frac{dv}{dt} = -\sigma e^{-\sigma t}(A\cos\omega_d t - B\sin\omega_d t) + e^{-\sigma t}\omega_d(A\sin\omega_d t + B\cos\omega_d t)$$

When $t = 0$ this gives:

$$0 = -\sigma A - \omega_d B \quad \text{so} \quad A = \frac{-\sigma V}{\omega_d}$$

The full solution is thus $v = V\left(1 - \frac{\sigma}{\omega_d}\sin\omega_d t - \cos\omega_d t\right)$

INDEX